# Be

# Tunisia

Front cover: a camel caravan crosses
the Sahara

Right: traditional architecture, Cap Bon

C000125705

# TOP 10 ATTRACTIONS

**Dougga** Africa's best-preserved Roman city *(page 44)*

**Hammamet** One of the most popular beach resorts still has the laid-back feel of a traditional fishing village *(page 50)*

**Zitouna Mosque** •
The finest mosque in Tunisia, it dominates the medina in Tunis *(page 31)*

**Kairouan** The holy city is the most important Islamic site in all North Africa *(page 60)*

**Chott el Jerid** On the shores of this vast salt lake, the verdant oasis towns of Douz, Tozeur and Nefta flourish among the desert dunes *(page 70)*

**Jerba** The island is noted for traditional pottery and carpets *(page 66)*

**El Jem** Its mighty amphitheatre was one of the largest in the Roman world *(page 63)*

**Hilltop villages** Known as *ksour*, these were the last outposts of the Berbers of southern Tunisia *(page 80)*

**Sidi Bou Said** A picture-postcard blue and white village near Tunis *(page 42)*

**Sousse** Famous for its beaches, *ribat* (monastery) and superb archaeological museum *(page 55)*

# CONTENTS

73

61

28

94

58

53

### Features

# INTRODUCTION

Tunisia is the smallest country in North Africa. It reaches a mere 200 km (125 miles) from the palm-fringed sands of its Mediterranean beaches to the sand-fringed palms clustered at its desert oases. Within its borders, however, there is a rich and varied culture waiting to be discovered.

A strategic location and fertile farmland have made Tunisia a much-coveted territory, captured and defended repeatedly through the ages by successive waves of invaders. The Phoenicians, Romans, Byzantines, Arabs and Ottomans left a legacy of ruined temples, forbidding fortresses, magnificent mosaics and ornate architecture for historically minded travellers to explore.

No less alluring are the exotic sights and sounds of the present-day country: the crowded souks of Tunis, crammed with colourful goods and redolent with the rich scents of leather, spices and jasmine; the hoarse bellow of a camel at the Thursday market in Douz, and the chatter of Arabic as flowing-robed nomads haggle over prices; the nimble fingers of a Jerban potter shaping an elegant urn from the pink island clay; and the gap-toothed grin of an elderly fisherman mending his nets beneath the kasbah walls in the old port at Bizerte. All these and more lie within easy reach of the popular holiday resorts lining the Mediterranean coast.

## Varied Geography

Squeezed between its giant neighbours Libya and Algeria, Tunisia runs only 750 km (465 miles) north to south, and at most 350 km (220 miles) east to west. However, its winding coastline is 1,200 km (745 miles) long and has some of the

Multicoloured fishing boats on the beach at Hammamet

finest beaches in the Mediterranean, while the varied landscapes of the interior range from the oak forests of the northern hills to the sand dunes of the Sahara Desert.

The northern part of the country is dominated by the fertile plain of the Medjerda Valley, which was once known as 'The Granary of Rome', and which is still the source of Tunisia's wheat harvest. To the north of the Medjerda are the thickly wooded chains of the Kroumirie and Mogod mountains, where forests of pine and cork oak overlook the attractive, rocky north coast, renowned for its pink coral reefs and remote, sandy beaches.

South of the valley is the Dorsale, an east-west range of hills that runs into the Cap Bon peninsula and divides the wetter north from the semi-arid steppe of central Tunisia. The central coast is known as the Sahel, where the famous beach resorts of Sousse and Monastir bask beside the warm,

Berber cave villages lie hidden in the hills near Medenine

shallow waters of the Gulf of Hammamet. Inland, the holy city of Kairouan and the Roman amphitheatre of El Djem bake in the dusty heat of the plains.

The huge salt lake of the Chott el Jerid almost cuts the country in two, and marks the northern edge of the desert. To the south are the shifting sands of the Grand Erg Oriental (Great Eastern Erg), a vast sea of dunes that extends far into the Sahara. Off the south coast lies the 'desert island' of Jerba, the 'Land of the Lotus Eaters' described by Herodotus and Homer, which is now a paradise for sun-worshipping tourists.

More than most North African countries, Tunisia has an environmental policy that seeks to reconcile developmental needs with environmental imperatives in order to protect natural elements, and aims to preserve the ecological balance, safeguard natural and human resources and control all forms of pollution.

## United under Islam

The population of Tunisia is over 10 million, concentrated in the north, especially around Tunis and Sousse. The people themselves are a mixture of Berber and Arab blood, but through the centuries the Berbers have been thoroughly assimilated into the dominant Arab culture. Only 2 percent of the population is now identifiably Berber, and the Berber language (which still flourishes in Algeria and Morocco) has almost died out, though traces of their former way of life survive in the *ksar* villages of the south. Today the main distinction is between rural and urban communities: 65 percent

of the population live in towns. In the Saharan oases you will
see black tribesmen descended from the original Sudanese
slaves who were transported to Tunisia by Arab slave traders,
a practice that did not die out completely until the middle of
the 19th century.

The conquering Arabs of the 7th century brought with
them the religion of prophet Mohammed and, although the
Berbers resisted strongly at first, Tunisia was eventually united under the banner of Islam.

Religion remains at the heart of Tunisian daily life. Like
all Muslims, most Tunisians adhere to the principles of the
religion known as The Five Pillars of Islam. These are: to declare that 'There is no God but Allah, and Mohammed is his
messenger'; to pray five times a day (at dawn, at midday, in
the afternoon, at sunset and after dark); to give alms to the

## The Place of Women in Tunisia

'It is unthinkable that half the population is removed from everyday life
and hidden away as if it were shameful,' declared president Habib Bourguiba on the subject of wearing the veil, which he described as an 'odi-
ous rag'. In August 1956, five months after independence, Tunisia's first
president introduced his Code du Statut Personnel (Personal Status
Code), which revolutionised the position of women.

It abolished polygamy, instituted official civil marriage and legal divorce
– which could be inititated by the woman – and reorganised the family on the basis of the equality of both spouses before the law. Bourguiba also encouraged women to go to work, and to participate in political
life: he gave them the vote in 1957. However, female emancipation takes
time; the reforms introduced nearly 50 years ago are still not universally effective. Marriage remains the only viable option for many Tunisian
women who, if they take a job, are still expected to perform all the traditional domestic tasks.

poor and towards the maintenance of the mosques; to fast between sunrise and sunset throughout the month of Ramadan; and to attempt to make the pilgrimage to Mecca at least once during their lifetime.

Along with the 'Five Pillars' go religious beliefs and obligations that characterise the devout Muslim: a conviction that all believers are equal before Allah, respect for the institution of marriage and the family, and the duty of hospitality and generosity towards strangers.

## A Warm Welcome

All this sits comfortably with the relatively recent growth of

Street scene: a mother and her children wait at a Tunis bus stop

tourism, which first started to affect Tunisia in the 1960s. Tunisians are friendly, and proud of their country and its history. In the country areas in particular, you will often find yourself the recipient of real, old-fashioned hospitality: you will be offered tea, and asked about your travels, your home and your family. People will take great pleasure in answering your own questions about the village, its history and traditions.

Too many tourists miss out on the best of Tunisia by sticking to the beach or hotel pool in the package-holiday resorts of Hammamet, Monastir and Jerba. Make the effort to explore a little further afield, and you will discover something of the true Tunisia that lies beyond the coast.

# A BRIEF HISTORY

Tunisia as a nation-state is a creation of the 20th century. This small country, strategically situated at the crossroads of the Mediterranean, has a long and complex history stretching back far into prehistory.

Primitive tools and weapons found near Gafsa in southern Tunisia have been dated to 6000BC, and are attributed to a society of nomadic hunters called the Capsian culture. These people probably migrated from western Asia, perhaps as long as 10,000 years ago, and it was their descendants who were encountered during the second millennium BC by the first Phoenician traders who ventured along the North African coast from the eastern Mediterranean.

Contemporary accounts describe them as light-skinned and speaking an unintelligible language. The Greeks called them *barbaros*, meaning 'not of our people' or 'uncivilised', and this persisted through the ages as 'Berber'. (The English word 'barbarian' comes from the same root.)

## Phoenician Pioneers

The Phoenicians were the first permanent settlers on the Tunisian coast, and they established trading posts at Sousse, Utica and Bizerte (12th century BC), before founding the city of Carthage (just northeast of present-day Tunis) in 814BC. Being brilliant navigators and traders, they spread throughout the Mediterranean world from their home cities of Tyre and Sidon on the Levantine coast (in what is now the Lebanon), and soon became masters of the seas.

Although it was the Phoenicians who invented the cursive form of writing on which all subsequent European alphabets were based, they left no written record of their achievements. Most of what we know about them comes from Greek and Roman accounts, which often include rumours of the Carthaginian custom of child sacrifice. Hundreds of funerary stones have been uncovered in the ruins of ancient Carthage, but controversy continues in academic circles as to their origins.

Dynastic rivalries in Tyre and Sidon allowed Carthage to gain more power, and when the Levantine cities fell to Cyrus the Great of Persia in the 6th century BC, Carthage became the undisputed centre of Punic (Phoenician) civilisation. From the eastern Mediterranean to the Atlantic, Punic settlements were established. Carthaginian captains took command of the Strait of Sicily, and challenged the Greeks for control of the trade routes.

Phoenician artefact at the National Museum of Carthage

## The Rise of Rome

Meanwhile, the fledgling Roman Republic had increased in strength to the point where it threatened to gain control of the strategic islands of Corsica and Sicily. The struggle for supremacy between Rome and Carthage led to the start of the First Punic War (264–241BC).

This was primarily a naval campaign. Before one of the many sea battles, the Roman admiral Claudius Pulcher consulted the sacred fowl that were kept aboard his flagship,

Roman grandeur: the Capitoline Temple in Dougga

hoping for a positive omen. The chickens were supposed to peck at their grain if he was to win, but they ignored the corn scattered on the deck. Claudius, a notorious hothead, tossed the sacred birds overboard to the applause of his crew, and charged into battle. He lost his entire fleet.

Rome may have lost that battle, but they won the war, having built a new fleet based on the design of a captured Carthaginian warship. Carthage was forced to pay huge war reparations, but the humiliating defeat rankled with such a proud people, and it wasn't long before they invaded Spain, prompting Rome to declare the start of the Second Punic War (218–201BC). It was this war that saw one of the most famous military campaigns in history.

Since Rome controlled the sea, the Carthaginians, led by a general named Hannibal, had little choice but to attack overland. Hannibal set out on his famous expedition from his Spanish beachhead at Sagunto, crossed the Alps with more than 30,000 men and around 30 elephants, and eventually clashed with the Roman army in 216BC. The battle, at Cannae in Apulia, southern Italy, was a devastating blow for the Romans, who suffered losses of over 50,000 men. They were not denied victory, though, for the Roman general Scipio finally crushed the Carthaginians on their home ground at Zama, forcing them to burn their fleet and surrender all territory except a small corner of eastern Tunisia.

Hannibal fled to Bithynia (today's Izmir), a part of the eastern Mediterranean that was not yet subject to Rome. When the King of Bithynia found himself at war with a neighbouring state, a client of Rome, he solicited the advice of the exiled Carthaginian general, whose tactical expertise took the Bithynians to victory. The Romans learned of Hannibal's role, and ordered that he be tracked down. Rather than give himself up to his old enemy, Hannibal took poison and died.

Carthage continued to trade, and grew rich again, exciting the jealousy of Roman merchants. The Third Punic War (149–146BC) saw the Romans besiege the city of Carthage for two years. When it finally fell to Scipio in 146 BC, the original population of around a quarter of a million people had been reduced to 50,000. The city was razed, the survivors sold into slavery, and the land ploughed with salt so that nothing would grow from the ruins. The proud Carthaginian Empire had been obliterated, and its territory was subsequently absorbed into the Roman province of Africa.

## Hannibal

A legend in his own time, Hannibal was both a master of military strategy and tactics and an outstanding leader of men. Many historians believe that, with sufficient resources, the Carthaginian could have put a stop to the expansion of Rome's power.

**Burnt to a cinder**

In 1858 a French archaeologist drilling a shaft on the site of Carthage came across a layer of cinders more than a metre (3ft) thick, containing fragments of stonework, twisted metal, molten glass and calcined human bones, and confirming that the old city had indeed been consumed by fire.

Only 100 years later, having vanquished his rival Pompey in North Africa, Julius Caesar decided that the blighted city should be rebuilt. He was assassinated before he could put his dream into effect, but his successor Augustus vigorously set about the reconstruction of Carthage. By the 2nd century AD it had become a flourishing Roman centre of 300,000 inhabitants, complete with a forum, temples, triumphal arches, theatres, baths and, after some time, churches.

Tunisia was under Roman rule for about 600 years in all, until barbarian hordes swept through Europe and into North Africa in the 5th century AD. By 439, an army of Germanic tribesmen, the Vandals, had occupied the province, pillaging Roman cities, smashing statues and laying waste to the countryside. Their leader, Genseric, was known as 'lord' of Carthage. When he died, the country collapsed in anarchy, allowing the Byzantine army of Emperor Justinian, under the general Belisarius, to take over in AD534.

Justinian ordered the restoration of the Roman towns and constructed defences to meet the threat of Berber tribes in the interior or any sea-borne invasion. An impressive amount of Byzantine building survives to this day. But Justinian's African empire lasted barely a century.

## Arab Conquest

United under the banner of Islam, Arab armies poured out of their homeland during the 7th century, and within a hundred years had created an empire that encompassed lands from Persia, through Egypt and North Africa, into Spain and part of France. Of the early Arab generals, none was bolder than Uqba ibn Nafi, who conquered the Maghreb (Arabic for 'the west'), a region that today includes Tunisia, Algeria and Morocco. His army reached Tunisia in AD670, travelling inland to avoid Byzantine strongholds along the coast. Ignoring the infidel city of Carthage, he established his own capital at Kairouan, saying: 'I shall build a town to be a citadel of Islam for all time.' From this base, he set off to the west, subduing all in his path until he reached the Atlantic coast of Morocco, calling on God to witness that only the ocean could prevent him going further.

Douiret was a stronghold of Berber resistance to the Arabs

The Arab Empire, which had begun as a simple religious community, was now a vast and far-flung kingdom. Dozens of different peoples speaking scores of languages lived within the Arab dominions and held tight to their ancient traditions. The Berbers, inhabitants of the lands north of the Sahara since prehistoric times, did not feel inclined to submit to Arab rule without a fight, and many tribes opposed the occupation.

Shortly after Uqba's invasion, a nomadic Berber tribe made a counter-thrust, led

The Great Mosque in Kairouan was built under the Aghlabids

by an influential queen known as Dihya al-Kahina (The Prophetess). Her forces recaptured much territory, and it took the Arabs five years to put down the revolt. After a final confrontation in the amphitheatre of El Djem, Dihya al-Kahina was executed and her head sent on a platter to the caliph in Damascus.

But Tunisia lay a long way from Damascus, and the local rulers, influenced by both the recalcitrant Berbers and the radical Islamic scholars of Kairouan, developed a strong independent streak. In AD797, the caliph appointed a provincial leader, Ibrahim ibn Aghlab, as governor of Tunis. Ibrahim declared himself *emir* (prince), and he and his descendants ruled Ifriqiya (Tunisia and eastern Algeria) for more than a century.

The Aghlabid era is generally looked upon as Tunisia's 'Golden Age'. The city of Tunis, which had been developed as an Arab port a century earlier, was expanded, and the Zitouna Mosque was erected, along with the Great Mosques of Kairouan, Sfax and Sousse, and the *ribats* (fortified monasteries) at Sousse and Monastir. Trade and agriculture flourished, and successful military campaigns captured Malta, Sicily and Sardinia, and even went as far as sacking St Peter's in Rome in AD846.

The Aghlabids were succeeded by the Fatimids, who conquered Egypt and moved their capital to Cairo. Tunisia slipped into anarchy, overrun by the hostile nomadic Arabs of the Beni Hilal tribe. Disorder and mayhem were quashed with the arrival of the Almohads, the fundamentalist rulers of Morocco, who captured Tunis in 1159, and who at their height ruled an empire stretching from their capital of Marrakech to Libya and Spain. They held Tunisia for 70 years, implementing an orderly government, religious discipline and a renewed prosperity. But it wasn't to last: the unity of their empire gave way when the local governors in Tunisia founded their own dynasty, the Hafsids, who ruled from 1228 to 1574.

With Tunis as their capital, the Hafsids fast grew in power and splendour. The city's first *medersas* (religious schools) and the picturesque souks of the perfumers (Souk Attarine) and cloth merchants (Souk des Etoffes) are just a small part of their architectural legacy. The great Sultan Abu Abdullah al-Mustansir (1249–77) assumed the title of *caliph*, and was acknowledged by Mecca as the Commander of the Faithful. In 1270 a crusade was undertaken against al-Mustansir, with France's heroic King Louis IX at the head of the army; but the crusade ended in failure, and Louis died in Tunis.

Two famous Turkish corsairs: Barbarossa and his brother Aruj

## Turkish Domination

Khayr ad-Din – better known as Barbarossa (Redbeard) – was a Turkish corsair from the Aegean island of Lesbos. With his brother Aruj and their pirate fleet he terrorised Spanish and Portuguese shipping from their base on the Tunisian island of Jerba. Barbarossa had grander ambitions, however, wanting an African dominion for himself. To this end he submitted to the Ottoman sultan in Istanbul in return for military support. He took Algiers in 1529, and was promptly named admiral of the Turkish fleet, then overcame the Hafsids to seize Tunis in 1534. But the following year he was driven out by King Charles V of Spain, who claimed the country for the Spanish Empire and reinstated the Hafsid Sultan el Hasan. But a sultanate dependent on Christian Spanish protection did not please the Ottoman Turks: in 1574, they dispatched a new fleet to North Africa, and by August Tunisia belonged to them.

## Pirates of the Barbary Coast

The Muslim corsairs roving the seas along the Barbary Coast (the North African coast from Libya to Morocco, named after the indigenous Berbers) were financed by wealthy backers in Tunis and Algiers in return for a percentage of their booty. The privateers attracted mercenaries from all over Europe, and their ships, called *galliots*, were powered by oars and were faster, less conspicuous and more manoeuvrable than contemporary sailing ships. A pirate *galliot* would race up to a merchantman or a coastal town, attack, take hostages and booty, and speed away again. Strict discipline was enforced at sea, and any man who was slack in his duties was summarily executed. When the pirates returned in triumph to Tunis, the whole town would explode with feasting and debauchery. Every man of the crew would be rich – even the galley-slaves who pulled the oars – once he had sold his portion of the loot. The merchants of Tunis bought all the stolen goods and later disposed of them at a good profit. Christian prisoners were sold into slavery, bringing good prices if they were craftsmen or had other special skills. Any nobles or wealthy merchants who were captured were quickly ransomed.

With the arrival of the Turks, Tunis became a notable medieval sea power. The corsairs, who were especially active in the Christian slave trade, became the terror of all shipping that was not Ottoman. During the 17th and 18th centuries Tunisian pirates made their country rich and powerful, and they were soon operating independently of the Turkish sultan. The bey of Tunis had originally been a simple local administartor, appointed every three years by the sultan in Is-

Ahmed Bey (1837–55) brought Tunisia into the modern world

tanbul. But from the early 18th century things changed: beys began to pass on the title to their descendants.

Hussein Bey (1705–40) founded the Husseinite dynasty, which continued to rule the country up to 1957. By the end of the 18th century, though nominally still a representative of Turkish imperial power, the bey was in effect a Tunisian king in everything but name. Tunisia, enriched by piracy, had achieved virtual autonomy.

Under Ahmed Bey (1837–55), the country made its first attempts to detach itself from a medieval society and join the developing world. Slavery was abolished and European aid was sought to build a modern army. New banks, factories and communications were set up, but Europe was already too far ahead. The pirate ships of the Barbary Coast met their match in swifter and better-armed European steamships. At the same time, the American navy, weary of paying 'protection money' to ensure the safety of its ships in the Mediterranean, attacked

Tunis and the other corsair bases. Barbary piracy was wiped out. Deprived of this important source of income, yet still trying to maintain his extravagant lifestyle, the bey plunged heavily into debt. France, Italy and Britain were the Tunisian government's principal creditors – and now these European powers began to eye North Africa as possible new territories for their growing empires.

## The French Protectorate

France had already seized Algeria in 1830, and soon set its sights on Tunisia. On the rather flimsy pretext that Tunisian tribesmen had made a raid into Algeria, the

Tunis 1905: avenue Jules Ferry (now avenue Habib Bourguiba)

French occupied Tunis and declared the country a protectorate, stealing a march on its rival Italy, which was already occupying neighbouring Libya. Under the Treaty of Bardo, signed on 12 May 1881, the bey was recognised as nominal ruler of Tunisia, but all the power was in the hands of the French, who appointed a resident general to run affairs.

The colonial experience was a disastrous one for the majority of rural Tunisians who were displaced from their land by French and Italian immigrants. However, the professional classes still managed to live comfortably: they learnt to speak French, sent their children to study in France and adopted many French customs. Despite being articulate and well-educated, though, the upper reaches of the administration were closed to them. The inevitable frustration prompted by this urban elite resulted in the birth of the country's first nationalist movements.

First came the Young Tunisians, a group of intellectuals modelled on the Young Turks, who began agitating for the overthrow of the Ottoman sultan in Istanbul. They gained little popular support until a bloody uprising in 1911 was cruelly suppressed by the French. The 'Jellaz Affair' stirred nationalist feeling among all levels of Tunisian society. Following these bloody incidents, the country was placed under a state of emergency and censorship was imposed on anti-colonialist press until 1921.

In 1920, the Destour Party was formed (*destour* meaning 'constitution' in Arabic); its objective was to work with the French towards greater Tunisian autonomy, but it ended in inertia and failure. A new shot of spirit was needed.

In 1927, a young Tunisian of exceptional ability arrived back in Tunis, with his new French wife, having studied law in Paris. Habib Bourguiba sympathised with the Destour Party at first, but soon he came to believe that there could be no progress without struggle, and forcefully expressed his views through newspaper articles. In 1934, he founded the Neo-Destour Party, which set out to gain massive popular support for self-determination. In that same year he was arrested, accused of being a political agitator, and sent to jail for two years. Following riots in Tunis in 1938, the French dissolved the party, and Bourguiba and his colleagues were interned in France.

When the Allies, headed by General Eisenhower, landed in North Africa towards the end of 1942, the Germans and Italians seized Tunisia as a vital base for the desert campaign being waged by Rommel. The area became the scene of fierce fighting for five months, until Commonwealth and American forces triumphed over German troops in May 1943.

## Towards Independence

By 1945, prospects for negotiations resulting in major concessions from France did not seem good, and Bourguiba left Tunisia to set up a Committee for the Liberation of the Maghreb in Cairo. By 1948, he had become president of the Neo-Destour Party and a noted public figure, travelling extensively to campaign for Tunisian independence. He found support from the Union Générale des Travailleurs Tunisiens (UGTT), Tunisia's first major trade union, under the direction of Ferhat Hached. Realising that they would have to negotiate with Bourguiba, the French invited him to Paris for talks, at which concessions were obtained and promises of increased autonomy were given. But the promises were not implemented, and groups of armed patriots began resorting to more militant tactics. Amid growing unrest, Ferhat Hached was assassinated by the pro-French Main Rouge

Habib Bourguiba and his wife Wasila on a visit to Kairouan

('Red Hand') movement. In 1952, the government was dissolved and Bourguiba thrown in prison.

Bourguiba's arrest inflamed already swollen passions, and bloody clashes became more frequent. A fierce resistance to concessions from Paris grew among the French settlers in the country, but in 1954 Pierre Mendès-France, the French premier, recognised Tunisia's right to self-government. The following year his successor, Edgar Fauré, met officially with Bourguiba to sign a protocol that granted Tunisia internal autonomy. Habib Bourguiba returned to Tunis in triumph, and on 20 March 1956, Tunisia gained full independence.

## Tunisia Today

The country was still nominally ruled by the bey up until 25 July 1957, when Tunisia was declared a republic with Bourguiba as its first president. The sweeping social reforms for which he was responsible included advances in education, the emancipation of women, legal restructuring and attempts at secularisation. His popularity was such that he was overwhelmingly re-elected to three further terms as president, and in 1975 the National Assembly named him president for life.

His future was not so easy, though, for economic troubles and increasing Islamic fundamentalism in the late 1970s and early 1980s led to widespread unrest. In November 1987, at the age of 84, Bourguiba was declared senile by doctors and forced to relinquish power. His prime minister, Zine al-Abidine Ben Ali, was named president the following day.

Ben Ali abolished the presidency for life and released thousands of political prisoners, including many Islamic activists. These were not slow to take advantage of this renewal of democracy. At the first signs of social agitation, Ben Ali slowed the process of liberalisation. Opposition parties based on religious convictions were prohibited by the National Pact of 1992. In October 2004 Ben Ali won another presidential election with, officially, an overwhelming majority. While offered all modern comforts under Ben Ali, his people are nevertheless kept under tight control with no say in politics. Tunisia is now effectively a one-party state with an autocratic president.

Tunisia today is regarded by the West as the most moderate and secular of Arab states, and despite its small size it plays an important role in international affairs. Tunis hosted the Arab League from 1979 to 1990, and the city has been the home of the Palestine Liberation Organisation's headquarters since 1982. The country also maintains close ties with both France and the USA, and has important trade links with western Europe, signing a free trade agreement with the EU in 1995. Above all, its highly successful tourist industry has established it as one of the most widely known Arab countries among Europeans.

Habib Bourguiba eventually died in 2000. His influence was felt in every corner of Tunisian life, and he is still very

**Ben Ali abolished presidency for life but has served four terms**

fondly regarded as the father of modern Tunisia. (It is hardly surprising that every town and city now has its avenue Habib Bourguiba.) A magnificent mausoleum and memorial mosque were erected in his hometown of Monastir.

Bourguiba's legacy is a more tolerant and forward-looking nation, with one of the highest standards of living in the developing world.

# Historical Highlights

**c.1200BC** Phoenicians establish trading posts on the North African coast.

**814BC** Phoenicians found the city of Carthage.

**264–241BC** First Punic War between Rome and Carthage.

**218–201BC** Second Punic War; Hannibal crosses the Alps.

**146BC** Third Punic War ends with the sack of Carthage.

**44BC–2nd century AD** Romans rebuild Carthage; the city flourishes.

**AD439** Carthage falls to Vandal invasion.

**671** Arab Conquest. Uqba ibn Nafi founds holy city of Kairouan.

**800–909** Aghlabid Dynasty and Tunisia's 'Golden Age.' Building of the Great Mosque of Kairouan.

**1159** The Almohads take Tunis.

**1535** Barbarossa captures Tunis for the Turks.

**1574** Tunisia becomes part of the Ottoman Empire.

**1837–55** Reign of Ahmed Bey, the first ruler open to Western influence.

**1881** Tunisia is made a French protectorate.

**1934** Habib Bourguiba founds the Neo-Destour Party.

**1942–3** Tunisia is the scene of fierce fighting: the Allies quash Rommel's desert campaign.

**1956** Tunisia is granted full independence.

**1957** Tunisia declared a republic; Habib Bourguiba is president.

**1987** Bourguiba replaced by Zine el-Abidine ben Ali.

**1989** First free elections since 1956. Zine el-Abidine ben Ali elected president without opposition.

**1990s** Islamic fundamentalism gains foothold, resulting in crackdown on all Muslim militants.

**2000** Death of Habib Bourguiba.

**2002** Al-Qaeda suicide attack in Jerba kills 21; tourism seriously affected. Major constitutional reform adopted by popular referendum.

**2008** Islamist militants and security forces clash in Tunis.

**2009** Kairouan is the Capital of Islamic Culture.

**2011** Ben Ali goes into exile after nationwide protests and an interim government is formed.

# WHERE TO GO

Tunisia is a compact country, and many interesting places lie within an easy day trip from the coastal resorts. One of the most popular excursions is to the cosmopolitan capital city of Tunis, and the nearby ruins of ancient Carthage.

## TUNIS

Tunis is a city with many faces. On the one hand, it's the modern capital of the Tunisian Republic, a city of tree-lined boulevards, modern buildings and bustling pavement cafés, which has a distinctly European flavour. On the other, it has a totally different character, determined by its medieval Arab *medina* (old town), an exotic maze of narrow, angled streets lined with tiny shops, grand mosques and impressive palaces.

You can easily spend two full days exploring Tunis and its surroundings (including historic Carthage, the ancient Punic capital), although a day and a half will be sufficient, if you're rather short of time.

The backbone of modern Tunis is the broad boulevard of **avenue Habib Bourguiba**, stretching between the medina and the Lake of Tunis. In the late afternoon and summer evenings, Tunisian families stroll along the shady central promenade, while young Tunisians meet their friends on one of the many café terraces that line the street. (Following the deposition of the elderly Bourguiba in 1987, the street was officially renamed avenue 7 Novembre, but even today everyone still refers to it by its old name.)

At the western end of the avenue, the place de l'Indépendance is dominated by the façade of the Catholic **Cathedral of St-**

*Ghorfas* (fortified houses that once held grain) in Medenine

**Vincent-de-Paul** (1882), a legacy of French colonialism. Facing it is the French Embassy and the beautifully restored Théâtre Municipal. Here the boulevard narrows to arcade-lined avenue de France, which leads to the gates of the medina.

## The Medina (Old Town)

The **medina** of Tunis is probably the easiest to navigate in all of North Africa. At all the main gates you'll find a large map with all the streets clearly named, and there are small orange signposts pointing the way to the principal sights. The souks have their share of the usual hustlers, so be wary of anyone offering to show you a view, a museum or a special exhibition. These invariably lead to carpet shops.

### A Tunisian Glossary

*The following are common Arabic and Berber words:*

| | | | |
|---|---|---|---|
| **aïn** | spring | **killim** | woven carpet with geometric design |
| **bab** | entrance, gate | | |
| **borj** | fort | | |
| **chott** | salt lake | **ksar** | fortified village |
| **dar** | house | **maqroudh** | semolina sweet-meats made with syrup and date paste |
| **erg** | region of sand dunes | | |
| **ghorfa** | fortified house | | |
| **haj** | pilgrimage (to Mecca) | **medersa** | religious school |
| | | **medina** | old town |
| **jebba,** | long-sleeved | **mergoum** | embroidered mat |
| **jellaba** | tunic | **ribat** | fortified monastery |
| **jebel** | mountain | **souk** | market street |
| **jemaa** | mosque | **tophet** | place of sacrifice |
| **kalaâ** | fortress | **zaouïa** | house of a religious order |
| **kasbah** | fortified citadel | | |

The free-standing archway of the **Bab el Bahr** – also called the **Porte de France** (built 1848) on the place de la Victoire – marks the main entrance to the medina. It was once continuous with the thick medina walls, and stood on the shore of the Lake of Tunis (the Arabic name translates as 'Sea Gate') before the French built their new town on reclaimed land. Walk

Stalls line the narrow alleys of the medina

through the Porte de France and then take the left-hand of the two narrow alleys facing you.

This is the **rue Jemaa ez Zitouna**, the medina's main street, and it is lined with colourful craft shops and souvenir stalls. As you merge with the crowds that shuffle slowly uphill, you will find yourself immersed in a world of heady sensations. Fragrant incense and exotic perfumes compete with the mouth-watering smell of roasting mutton and the aroma of freshly ground coffee. The tap-tap-tap of silversmiths' hammers and the scuff of sandalled feet on smooth paving stones almost drown out the muezzin's call to prayer from a minaret. The bright reds, blues and golds of flowing kaftans flash in the dappled interplay of sunshine and shade, and then the street disappears into a dark tunnel to emerge at the steps below the door to the Zitouna Mosque.

The focus of daily life in the medina for over one thousand years has been the **Zitouna Mosque** (Jemaa ez Zitouna, literally 'Mosque of the Olive Tree', Sat–Thur 8am–2.30pm, closed Fri). Founded in 732 on the site of a temple to Athena, the mosque has been enlarged and restored many times; the

The tranquil Zitouna Mosque

outer wall used stone taken from the ruins of Carthage. Visitors are allowed to climb the stairs to an arcade facing the central courtyard. From here, you can appreciate the tranquillity of the mosque, a stark contrast to the bustle of the streets outside. The prayer hall is to the left, through a horseshoe arch crowned with a white dome. The square minaret is a 19th-century addition.

The most interesting sections of the medina are clustered around the walls of the mosque. Centuries ago, these narrow streets were roofed over to provide quarters for the city's craftsmen. Members of high-class guilds such as the booksellers, jewellers and perfumers had the best locations, close to the mosque, whereas the noisier tradesmen, such as the metalworkers and saddlers, were housed some distance away so as not to disturb the scholars studying within. The unfortunate tanners, with their noxious smells, were banished even further afield to the far side of the city walls. Modern times, and the proliferation of souvenir shops catering to the tourist trade, have brought a breakdown of this strict segregation in the main souks (market streets), but a few of the old souks are still dominated by a single trade.

When you come out of the mosque, turn left and left again into the **Souk el Attarine** (Perfumers' Souk), which is situated along the north wall. Only a few genuine scent-makers remain, for their expensive creations have been displaced by cheaper modern toiletries. The little shops are stacked with hundreds of tiny bottles filled with priceless essential oils – rose, jasmine, sandalwood, lily of the valley, lavender, orange-flower, vanilla, cinnamon and clove – and extracts of civet, musk, ambergris and castor. You can choose a ready-made scent, or have one blended to suit your fancy. The unusual, many-branched candles hanging in the perfumers' shops are carried at the head of the procession that leads a Tunisian bride to her new home.

First left off Souk el Attarine, running along the west wall of the mosque, is one of the quietest souks, called the **Souk des Étoffes** (Drapers). Colourful cascades of cloth, kaftans and blankets muffle the spirited haggling of the shopkeepers. Souk des Etoffes ends at a crossroads at the southwest corner of the mosque. On the right, **Souk des Tapis** (Carpet Market, also called Souk el Leffa) is a concentration of rug and carpet sell-

## The Perfumer's Art

The art of scent-making was regarded by the Arabs as the noblest of trades, and in every city the perfumers' souk (Souk el Attarine) was given the place of honour nearest to the mosque (*attar* is Arabic for 'perfume'). Perfumery is a highly skilled profession and the Tunis scent-makers' reputation was the best.

A fine perfume may contain over 100 ingredients, blended in precise proportions – the recipes of famous scents are still jealously guarded secrets. The raw materials include essential oils extracted from flowers, fruits and spices – jasmine, lavender, lemon, nutmeg; aromatic woods like sandalwood; and animal secretions such as ambergris (from sperm whales), musk (from musk deer) and castor (from the beaver). The scent-maker strives to create a perfume that complements the natural scent of the wearer.

ers, where earnest salesmen unfurl their wares for your approval. It costs nothing to look. On the same side, a warren of tiny streets and alleys crowded with goldsmiths' and silversmiths' shops is the **Souk des Orfèvres**. The ringing of hammers issues from a dozen doorways, and shop windows glitter and shine with gold, coral, pearls and a host of precious stones.

A continuation of the Souk el Leffa, the **Souk de la Laine** (Wool Market) still contains some traditional tailors and weavers working on their hand looms, but the more affluent goldsmiths have begun to encroach into this area. Opening off on the right, the **Souk des Femmes** (Women's Souk) is where the women of Tunis come to buy the white or cream fabric they use to make their veils.

Take a right at the other end of the Souk el Leffa to find the **Souk el Berka**, the original site of the Tunis slave market, once stocked with Christian victims of Barbary Coast piracy and black Africans brought up through the south of Tunisia. The market was closed down by Ahmed Bey in 1841 to try to appease the European powers, despite the substantial taxes that the trade brought the government.

*Chechias* (tasselled hats) are still handmade in the souk

The **Souk des Chéchias**, a vaulted market situated between the **Souk el Bey** and rue Sidi ben Arous, is one of the most attractive spots in the medina. Each outlet off the tall, shadowy souk is a shop-cum-workshop with a wooden counter for sales and a group of intent craftsmen at work on *chechias*, the tasselled felt hats once worn throughout North Africa and the Middle East, and still favoured by many Tunisian men.

The Souk des Chéchias opens out on to the unmistakable pink-marble façade of the **Mosque and Tomb of Hammouda Pasha** (built in 1655). The story behind this colourful building reveals a bit of Tunisian history. When Turkish governors came to Tunis on the orders of the Ottoman sultan, they brought with them a slightly different form of Islam from that commonly adhered to in Tunisia. The Tunisians lived according to the Malikite rite, while the Turkish conquerors observed the Hanifite. Aware of this difference, Tunisia's third bey, Hammouda Pasha el Mouradi, decided to give his mosque a Turkish-style octagonal minaret with a gallery, rather than the square type common to the Maghreb, so that all would know that his mosque was of the Hanifite rite.

The octagonal minaret of the mosque of Hammouda Pasha

To the southeast of the Zitouna Mosque, along the **Souk des Librairies** (booksellers) are three stunning 18th-century *medersas*, where students from all over the country came to study: the **Medersa of the Palm Tree**, the **Bachia Medersa** and the **Slimania Medersa** (Mon–Sat 9.30am–4.30pm) on the corner. Opposite at No. 30 is a famous *hammam* (bathhouse) for men, the **Hammam Kachachine**. Further along, after the Mosque des Teinturiers, you will come across

## Sweet delights

The Souk el-Balat, near the Zitouna Mosque, is the Tunis street in which to buy *maqroudhs*, sweet cakes stuffed with figs, dates or almonds.

the **Dar ben Abdallah** (follow the small orange signs on the walls). This 18th-century palace houses the city's **Museum of Folklore and Popular Arts** (Mon–Sat 9.30am–4.30pm). The magnificently decorated central courtyard is flanked by four rooms, which are home to tableaux of 19th-century Tunisian life, including men having tea, a bride preparing for her wedding, women sewing and a grandmother teaching young girls about baby care.

### The Bardo

The **Bardo National Museum** (daily mid-Apr–mid-Sept 9am–5pm, mid-Sept–mid-Apr 9.30am–4.30pm) can be found in a 19th-century Beyical Palace in the western suburbs of Tunis. It is home to many of Tunisia's greatest archaeological treasures and includes relics from every period of the country's rich history, from Carthaginian times to the Islamic period. Among the exhibits are artefacts that may have been related to Punic rituals of child sacrifice rumoured to have been carried out at Carthage, Roman statuary and a fine baptismal font from the early days of Christianity.

The museum's main attraction is its superb collection of Roman mosaics on the first and second floors. These colourful images provide a fascinating record of daily life in Roman times, with scenes of farming, hunting and fishing, as well as grander themes depicting mythological events and tributes to the gods. The mosaics range in age from the 2nd century BC to the 7th century AD and come from all over Tunisia, with some fine examples from Sousse, Dougga and El Jem.

The most famous image is in Room XV, showing the poet Virgil flanked by two Muses – Clio, Muse of History, on the left, and Melpomene, Muse of Tragedy, holding a mask on the right. Among the other outstanding items are Perseus rescuing Andromeda from a sea monster and an enormous 4th-century AD floor mosaic, which illustrates 23 types of boats, with their names, floating on a sea full of fish. Finally, don't miss the depiction of Ulysses, in which the hero is tied to the mast of his ship to prevent him from answering the Sirens' song, on his way to the island of the nymph Calypso. His crew row on with their ears plugged.

The Bardo Museum occupies a palace that is almost as fascinating as the Roman mosaics it displays. Built in the middle of the 19th century, it was intended to represent the arts and crafts of all the provinces of Tunisia, and is a curious blend of traditional Moorish architecture, with slender columns, arcaded courtyards and faïence tiling, and European classicism, with gilded colonnades and sweeping marble staircases.

One of the Bardo Museum's many superb Roman mosaics

# EXCURSIONS FROM TUNIS

Easy excursions from Tunis include the ancient city of Carthage, the pretty village of Sidi Bou Saïd and, in the region known as the Tell (from the Arabic word for 'mountain'), the Roman sites of Thuburbo Majus and Dougga.

## Carthage

**Carthage** means 'New Town' in the Phoenician language, and when the city was founded in 814BC, that's just what it was –

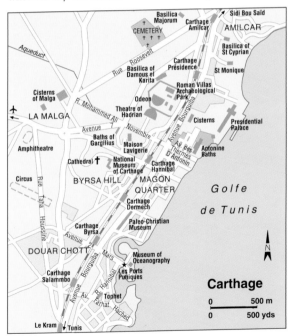

a new trading-post in a newly emerging maritime empire. Now, of course, it is the oldest city in Tunisia – at least, what little remains. Sacked by the Romans in 146BC, but later rebuilt, this once-great city fell into ruin following the founding of Tunis by the Arabs during the 8th century.

## Kasbah captives

On the way to Carthage, La Goulette is the port of Tunis. The dungeons of its kasbah, built in 1535 by Charles V of Spain, were used as cells for the captives taken by the Barbary Coast pirates.

The ruins of Carthage (Apr–mid-Sept 8am–7pm; mid-Sept–Mar 8.30am–5pm) lie 18km (11 miles) northeast of Tunis city centre, surrounded by an upscale suburb of villas and gardens. The site can be easily reached from Tunis on the frequent TGM electric train service *(see page 130)*. The ruins are spread out over quite a large area, and to see them all will take the best part of the day and involve a lot of walking.

If you leave the train at Carthage-Salammbo, a short walk from the station brings you to the Sanctuary of the **Tophet** (place of sacrifice), where for centuries the Carthaginians are rumoured to have sacrificed thousands of their first-born sons to the gods Tanit and Baal Hammon. One theory is that after the unfortunate victims were strangled, they were burned on an altar and the sacrificial remains buried in urns marked by engraved stone slabs called *stelae*, many of which are on display in the Bardo Museum. Nearby are the **Punic Ports** that once so impressed Rome. The circular one was the naval harbour, which was linked by a small channel to the rectangular trade harbour. A model in the small museum near the naval harbour gives a clear idea of what the area looked like at the time.

The ancient city was centred on the Hill of Byrsa, a site now occupied by the **National Museum of Carthage** (*Musée National de Carthage*; Apr–mid-Sept 8am–7pm; mid-Sept–Mar 8.30am–5pm). It is most easily reached by getting off the

The Cathédrale St-Louis now houses a cultural centre

train at either the Carthage-Dermech or Carthage-Hannibal station, then walking to the top of the hill. The museum contains an unparalleled collection of Carthaginian artefacts, from all periods. Exhibits include Punic and Roman sarcophagi, amphorae, Phoenician stelae and Greek and Roman statuary. Beside the museum is an excavation revealing the walls and foundations of Punic houses five or six storeys high, complete with water cisterns and drainage channels lined with pink stucco.

Next door, the Cathedral of St Louis was built in 1890 on the spot where the King of France, St-Louis, died in 1270 during the 13th crusade. It now houses the **Acropolium** (daily 9am–6pm; tel: 71 733 866, www.acropolium. com.tn), a cultural centre which stages an international festival of classical music every October.

A number of other ruins lie near the three railway stations (Carthage-Dermech, Carthage-Hannibal and Carthage-Présidence), including the impressive **Baths of Antoninus Pius** *(Thermes d'Antonin)*. Dating from the 2nd century AD, these were among the largest in the Roman Empire, covering an area of 3½ hectares (9 acres), and demonstrate the importance of Carthage as a Roman city. Only the foundations remain of this immense pleasure palace with hundreds of rooms: *frigidaria* (cool rooms), *tepidaria* (warm rooms) and *caldaria* (steam rooms); rooms with pools and fountains, mosaics and frescoes; rooms for dining and massage; rooms for worship and exercise – this was the social club and leisure centre of a rich commercial city. It also contained a *schola* (for the children of the wealthy – the Roman equivalent of a public school) and stores for fuel. A diagram chiselled into a slab of marble on a small observation platform explains the various sections of the baths.

A short walk uphill from the baths leads to the **Roman Villas** *(Villas Romaines)*, a group of ruins including the **odeon** and numerous hillside villas. One restored villa houses a small museum, giving a hint of what life was like here in ancient times. Much remains the same as then – the panorama of gentle green hills and vivid blue sea, a praying mantis motionless on a leaf, lizards clambering over the rocks. (One obvious addition to the scene is the heavily guarded modern villa which you can see down below, and which is the Presidential Palace.)

## Dido and Aeneas

Legend has it that the city of Carthage was founded by Dido, the sister of Pygmalion, King of Tyre. When her brother murdered her husband for his money, she fled with her followers to North Africa. There, a local chieftain called Iarbus agreed to sell her as much land as could be covered with the hide of a bull. The cunning Dido cut the hide into thin slivers which, when tied together, encircled the Hill of Byrsa. Here she laid the foundations of Carthage.

The poet Virgil allowed Dido to fall in love with his hero, Aeneas, when he arrived in Carthage after the fall of Troy (even though he would have had to have been 500 years old to have done so). When, at Jupiter's command, Aeneas abandoned Dido to found Rome, she committed suicide.

At a café in Sidi Bou Saïd

Downhill from the odeon, the **Roman Theatre** (*Théâtre d'Hadrien*) is almost entirely a 20th-century restoration. Evening performances of music and drama are staged here during the Carthage International Festival (see page 99). To the southwest lie the **Baths of Gargilius** (*Thermes de Gargilius*) and, further west, the **Cisterns of Malga**, which were formerly fed by aqueduct from the Zaghouan spring (see page 43).

## Sidi Bou Saïd

The picture-postcard village of **Sidi Bou Saïd** tumbles down a steep slope between its hilltop lighthouse and the sea in a cascade of sugar-cube houses with blue-painted doors and shutters. The village is famous for its unspoilt beauty and for the panoramic view from the top of the hill (go all the way up to the lighthouse). It is named after a 13th-century holy man who built his mosque and tomb here on the site of an earlier Arab *ribat* (fortified monastery) and lighthouse. Fanciful legend has it that it was in fact St Louis, who took refuge here after the sack of Carthage.

About a hundred years ago Sidi Bou Saïd became an exclusive retreat for well-off locals, artists and expatriates, and remains so to this day, though its peaceful cobbled streets are invaded daily by coach trips. In 1912, Rodolphe d'Erlanger, a wealthy French-American baron, built a sumptuous villa here, known as the **Dar Ennejma Ezzahra** (Tue–Sun 9am–1pm and 2–5pm). It is now the **Centre for Arab and Mediterranean Music**, housing a beautiful collection of musical instruments and an interesting archive. To have an idea of what the interiors of Sidi Bou Saïd's fine mansions look like, visit **Dar al Annabi** (daily 9am–6.30pm) in the cobbled street going up to the main square. This fine old house with 55 rooms is partially inhabited by the family, and partially a folklore museum.

To experience 'Sidi Bou' – as it is affectionately called locally – at its best, stay overnight in the romantic Dar Said hotel *(see page 139)* in the centre. The village's two famous cafés – the picturesque **Café des Nattes** and the **Café Sidi Chaabane** – have marvellous views of the sea.

## Thuburbo Majus

This Roman town, about 60km (37 miles) south of Tunis, acquired its distinctly un-Roman name from the Berber settlement that predated it. The ruins (daily 8.30am–5.30pm, 8am–7pm in summer) are spread across an undulating plain, and are frequented by local coin sellers and 'guides' who pester you to buy (invariably fake) goods. The centrepiece is the **Capitoline Temple**, dating from AD169–192, the majestic columns of which overlook the Forum. It was once home to a massive statue of Jupiter, whose head and foot are now in the Bardo Museum *(see page 36)*. From the temple steps you can see the rest of the site – the row of columns ahead and to the right marks the **Palaestra of the Petronii**, an exercise area adjacent to the Summer Baths. To its left are the **Winter Baths**, with a fine portico and columns of coloured marble from Chemtou in northwestern Tunisia.

### Water source

The Zaghouan spring, in the Tell, was harnessed by the Romans in the 1st century AD and provided water by aqueduct to the city of Carthage.

Dougga, one of the best preserved Roman sites in North Africa

## Dougga

The Roman city of Thugga (today called **Dougga**), lying some 100km (62 miles) southwest of Tunis, is one of the biggest and best preserved Roman sites in Africa (daily 8.30am–5.30pm, 8am–7pm in summer). Enthusiasts will find enough for a full days' exploration – there is a hotel at the nearby town of Tebboursouk if you want to stay overnight. If you have only an hour or two to spare, head for the main attractions listed below.

Dougga, constructed 600m (1,970ft) above the plain, was a thriving town for several hundred years before the Romans arrived in the 2nd century AD, but it was under them that it grew and prospered. The car park is next to the impressively complete **Roman Theatre**, with seats for 3,500 and elegant Corinthian columns overlooking the raised stage. The road beyond leads to the splendid portico of the **Capitoline Temple**, overlooking the **Square of the Winds**, where the paving is carved with a compass rose and the names of the twelve winds.

Downhill from the Capitol is the sprawling ruin of the **Baths of Licinius**, which have a well-preserved central hall, bathing pools, service tunnels and a hypocaust (under-floor heating) system. Below the baths, a narrow road (note the ruts which have been worn by cart wheels) winds down to the **House of the Trefoil**. This building, with its central court-yard lined with small booths and a trefoil-shaped dining room, was a brothel. Next door is the **Cyclops Baths**, notable for a semi-circular latrine in a fine state of preservation.

At the foot of the hill is Dougga's oddest and most mysterious monument. The **Mausoleum of Ateban** is a Libyco-Punic structure of the 3rd century BC, a unique blend of Libyan, Egyptian, Persian and Greek architectural styles, and one of the few surviving pre-Roman monuments to be found in Tunisia.

## THE NORTH COAST

The northern coast of Tunisia lies at the narrowest part of the Mediterranean – Sicily is only 140km (87 miles) away to the east. The main sea route from East to West passes through this strait, and the region's history has been shaped by seafarers since the earliest times. A good road leads north from Tunis towards the port of Bizerte, 70km (43 miles) distant. About halfway, a minor turning on the right leads to the ruins of Utica.

**Utica** was established around 1100BC as a staging post, roughly halfway between their home port of Tyre, now in Lebanon, and their entrepôt at Cádiz, in Spain. The sea once came right to Utica's doorstep, but over time the silt deposited by the nearby Medjerda River has left the ruined city (daily 8.30am–5.30pm, until 7pm in summer) stranded 10km (6 miles) inland. A museum (same opening hours) preserves the relics found in its Punic tombs, and remains of Roman villas and streets near the museum inspire visions of Utica in its heyday.

## Bizerte

You enter Bizerte across a modern bridge which spans a canal cut during the 1890s to link the saltwater Lac de Bizerte with the Mediterranean. The first channel here was dug by the Phoenicians, allowing access to this fine natural harbour, which has been used successively by the Romans, Byzantines, Arabs, Turks and French. Because of its strategic importance, it has been much fought over in the 2,000 years since it was constructed, most recently in the 1960s. Following Tunisian independence in 1956, the French continued to occupy their military base at Bizerte until a showdown with Tunisian forces in 1961, when over 1,300 local people lost their lives.

**The massive kasbah and Old Port of Bizerte**

After the French withdrew in 1963, Bizerte was transformed from a busy military and naval port to an industrial port and tourist town, modern in most respects but still retaining vestiges of its fascinating past. Today the **Vieux Port** (Old Port) is the city's most alluring quarter – a tranquil harbour filled with brightly painted fishing boats and lined by whitewashed old houses. The harbour entrance is guarded by the massive **kasbah** on one side, and the smaller **Fort Sidi el Hani** on the other. From the southeast bastion you can walk on top of the kasbah's impressive walls, which boast a wonderful café and great views over the sea and the old town. Fort Sidi el Hani houses a small **Oceanographic Museum**.

The hilltop **Fort d'Espagne** (Spanish Fort) above the town is a legacy of Bizerte's pirate past, when the Turkish corsairs would frustrate their pursuers by taking cover within its impregnable

> **Migration path**
>
> Lake Ichkeul, near Bizerte, is one of only two UNESCO Wetland World Heritage sites (the other is the Everglades in Florida). It's a vital stopping-point for birds migrating between Europe and Africa, and every year welcomes at least 150,000 overwintering wildfowl.

walls. At the head of the port, the octagonal minaret of the **Great Mosque** is another echo of the Turkish past.

Stretching north from the entrance to the Old Port is the **Corniche**, a long, narrow ribbon of golden sand lined with reliable hotels and a number of worthwhile seafood restaurants.

At the tip of the long, sandy peninsula to the east of Bizerte, **Ghar el Melh** is another 17th-century pirate port, complete with a number of Turkish fortresses and mosques. The journey to the nearby *koubba* (dome) of **Sidi Aalu el Mekki** passes alongside a fine beach, and there's yet another beautiful strip of sand at **Raf-Raf**.

## Coral Coast

To the west of Bizerte the main road keeps well inland, while the coast is wild, beautiful and almost untouched – a series of sandy beaches separated by rocky headlands, and backed by thick scrub and forests of oak, eucalyptus and juniper. The few villages that are located here once earned a living from the offshore coral, which has been harvested by divers for centuries. The coral is now protected, though, and diving is restricted.

The roads to **Cap Serrat** are not very good, but the swimming, fishing and snorkelling are excellent. Further west at **Sidi**

**Mechrig**, the stunning beach is overlooked by the ruins of a Roman bathhouse, and at **Cap Negro** you can see the remains of a French coral-fishing station dating from the 16th century. Further along the Bizerte–Tabarka highway, the mining town of **Sejnane** is known for its unusual, primitive pottery – intriguing little statuettes with red and black glazed motifs, part of a pagan Berber tradition which is over 1,000 years old.

## Tabarka

The little port of **Tabarka**, protected by its offshore island, is slowly but surely developing into a resort town. Founded by the Phoenicians in 800BC, it was originally a trading post, and its harbour was later used by the Romans for exporting the exotic red and yellow Numidian marble, which was quarried at **Chemtou**, 90km (56 miles) to the south. During the 16th century it was frequented by the pirate Barbarossa *(see page 19)*, who bought the freedom of fellow buccaneer Dragut by handing over the Isle of Tabarka to Charles V of

### Cork and Coral

The cork in your bottle of Tunisian wine began life as the bark of a tree – the cork oak *(Quercus suber)* – which is native to the western Mediterranean, and grows in abundance in the hills around Aïn Draham, south of Tabarka. The cork is harvested by prising off the thick, spongy bark around the trunk of the tree; the bark eventually grows back, and can be harvested again in 8 to 10 years.

Traditionally, the most popular souvenir in Tabarka has always been jewellery made from the precious coral which grows in the warm seas off northern Tunisia. Its colour can be yellow, purple or red, but most sought-after is the rose-pink variety for which Tunisia is famous. Coral has been gathered from these waters for centuries for use in the jewellery trade, to the extent that it is now endangered and protected.

Spain. Charles in turn gave it to a Genoese family, who were responsible for the fort which now crowns its highest point. The government's plans to turn Tabarka into a new Sousse are well under way. However, although it is growing fast, with the building of an airport, a new marina and several large hotels along the beach, it remains a laid-back resort.

Les Aiguilles near Tabarka

The main street, predictably called avenue Bourguiba, leads to a promenade next to the causeway, which now connects the island to the town. The promenade runs as far as a picturesque rock formation called **Les Aiguilles** (The Needles), a series of curiously eroded sandstone pinnacles and fins. Uphill from the main square is **La Basilique** (The Basilica), a Roman cistern that was converted to a church in the 19th century. Its garden is used for concerts during the summer Tabarka festival.

On the road to **Aïn Draham** is a cork museum, housed within a cork factory. This small museum is surprisingly interesting, with its displays about the local product *(see opposite)*.

Roughly 50km (31 miles) offshore lies the minute volcanic archipelago of **La Galite** – home to a colony of Mediterranean monk seals, an endangered species. The islands are a nature reserve, and can only be visited on a daytrip organised through Loisirs diving centre in Tabarka's fishing port.

The countryside in the area around Tabarka is covered in lush forests of pine, eucalyptus and cork oak; it is a landscape that feels more European than African. Roughly 24km (15 miles) to the south lies the quaint hill resort of **Aïn Draham**,

**Rich mosaics**

The underground Roman villas of Bulla Regia are named after the dazzling mosaics that adorn them: House of the Hunt, House of the Fish, House of Amphitrite, etc.

the 'silver spring', where the white houses with their red tile roofs look European, having been built by the French in an attempt to re-create the atmosphere of an Alpine village. Situated on a plateau some 800m (2,500ft) above sea level, in the heart of the Khroumira Forest and with the 1,200-m (4,000-ft) Jebel M'tir as a backdrop, the town is very popular with both foreign and Tunisian tourists, who come here for the combination of cool mountain air, bracing forest walks and nearby hot springs.

Even further to the south (60km/37 miles from Tabarka), the ruins of the Roman city of **Bulla Regia** (daily 8.30am– 5.30pm, 8am–7pm in summer) are well worth visiting. Here you have the opportunity to explore a collection of unique **underground villas**, many with superbly preserved *in situ* mosaic floors that constitute some of the best Roman mosaics to be seen outside the Bardo Museum.

## CAP BON PENINSULA

The Cap Bon peninsula is a blunt thumb of land protruding into the Mediterranean, separating the Gulf of Tunis to the north from the Gulf of Hammamet to the south. It is a fertile region of farms, vineyards and citrus groves, and is home to some of the most popular beach resorts in Tunisia.

### Hammamet

The stretch of golden sand between Hammamet and Nabeul is one of the most beautiful in the country, with warm, shallow, turquoise water and a lush green backdrop of palms, jasmine bushes and orange trees. **Hammamet**, which is located at the southern end, was a quiet fishing village until it was 'discovered' during the 1920s by a Romanian millionaire, George Sebastian. He started the ball rolling by building himself a luxury villa near the beach. (American architect Frank Lloyd Wright called it 'the most beautiful house I know'.) Sebastian's original mansion has now been converted into Hammamet's **International Cultural Centre** (Feb–Sept 8am–6pm, Oct–Jan 8am–5pm) where concerts, plays, lectures and exhibitions are held during the summer months.

The village has now become a full-blown resort town, with more than 100 hotels strung out along the bay. Most of the hotels near the centre are in low-rise buildings that have seen better days. The up-market tourism has moved south to Hammamet Yasmine, a new extension of the town, with over 40 four- and five-star hotels, shopping malls and even a recently built medina or 'old town'.

Looking down on Hammamet's town beach from the kasbah

Hammamet itself is clean and pretty, with good shopping and white houses neatly arrayed along its well-swept streets. Various restaurants, shops and cafés provide diversion for casual strollers. At the southern end, next to the beach, is the tiny **medina**, with the high walls of the **kasbah** in its northwest corner. It was garrisoned originally by Muslim soldiers and

Nabeul, famous for its pottery

later by the French Foreign Legion, and good views of the town and beach are available from its ramparts. Nestling in its protective shadow are the narrow alleyways of the compact medina, where you can browse among the souvenir shops, and perhaps find your way down to the old Sea Gate.

## Nabeul

Nabeul may be the administrative capital of the Cap Bon region, but it is really known as the **pottery** capital of Tunisia. Hundreds of workshops produce a wide range of glazed and unglazed ware, from functional pots and bowls to coloured **ceramic tiles**, a Nabeul speciality. The designs are handed down by Andalusian refugees who arrived here from Spain in the 17th century, and include stylised flowers or cypress trees surrounded by a patterned border, all in bold blues, greens and yellows.

A stroll through the streets reveals other crafts, including **stone carving**, gold and silver **embroidery** and **perfumes** made from the local citrus and jasmine blossoms. Be sure to visit the fixed-price **Artisanat** handicraft shops (93 avenue Habib Thameur and 144 avenue Farhet Hached) to get an idea of prices before you start haggling in the market. The Friday market is now a major attraction, drawing busloads of tourist to its many souvenir stalls.

The modern **Regional Museum** (Apr–Sept Tue–Sun 9am–1pm and 3–7pm; Oct–Mar 9.30am–4.30pm) has some fine mosaics and Carthaginian statuettes from excavations in the Cap Bon region. **Dar Zmen** (just off avenue Farhet

Hached) is a small private museum in a lovely 19th-century house with period jewellery and furnishings.

## Around the Cape

Many interesting places are situated within easy reach of the beach resorts at Nabeul and Hammamet. A good road leads north to the end of the peninsula, and back down its west coast, taking in most of the places of note.

The beautiful beaches continue north to the town of **Kélibia**, where the fishing harbour is dominated by an impressive fortress (daily 9am– 5pm, until 8pm in summer); there are fine views from the top of the 6th-century Byzantine ramparts. Stop here for a seafood lunch by the harbour, or at the rocky coves of **El Mansoura** to the north, and try a glass of the local white wine called Muscat Sec de Kélibia *(see page 107)*, which is light, refreshing and medium-dry.

A typical Cap Bon villa

The remains of the 5th-century BC Punic town at **Kerkouane** (daily 9am– 4pm, until 6pm in summer) are generally regarded as the best preserved of any Carthaginian settlement. The houses are famous for their neat little hip-baths, lined in pink stucco inlaid with white marble chips. The village of **El Haouaria**, right at the tip of the penin-

A falconer in one of El Haouaria's ancient quarries

sula, has the twin attractions of Carthaginian quarries (daily 9am–5pm, 8am–7pm in summer) and a falconry festival in mid-May. Falconry is a traditional means of hunting here: birds are taken from their cliff nests in spring and used to catch quail, partridge and hares in the early summer, before being released to freedom.

Nearby **Sidi Daoud** offers the spectacle of the *Matanza*, the annual tuna harvest, when local fishermen trap the migrating tuna in huge nets which stretch out from the shore. It takes place between May and July, in a ceremony that dates back hundreds of years.

A stunning coast road winds down the hills to **Korbous**, which has been famous since Roman times for its baths and hot springs. A number of hotels and spas are crammed into a narrow ravine beside the sea, where you can take a thermal cure, or just drink your health with a glass or two of the sulphurous mineral waters.

# THE SAHEL

The central coast of Tunisia is known as the Sahel (Arabic for 'coast' or 'margin') and centres on the cities of Sousse and Monastir. The region attracts thousands of tourists annually to its fine beaches, good hotels and historic sites, and even the surrounding countryside – an alluring patchwork of fields of grain, olive groves and wandering flocks of sheep – is an attraction in its own right. The area is also known for crafts, and the inhabitants of the scattered villages are specialists in embroidery, jewellery-making and cloth. Two sites are within easy reach of the coast: the holy city of Kairouan and the magnificent Roman amphitheatre at El Jem.

## Sousse

The capital of the Sahel is **Sousse**, Tunisia's third-largest city after Tunis and Sfax. Although it's a major port and a busy commercial and industrial centre, the workings of the city don't impinge on the relaxed atmosphere of the medina or waterfront. The golden sands stretch for miles north of town, lined with resorts, to the marina of Port el Kantaoui.

Held successively by the Carthaginians, Romans, Vandals and Byzantines, the city finally succumbed to the redoubtable Uqba ibn Nafi, the 7th-century Arab conqueror of the Maghreb *(see page 17)*. The citizens resisted his siege for two months, but when Sousse eventually fell, Uqba's forces plundered it all the more savagely. Almost all trace of earlier civilisation was wiped out, so that today Sousse has a fine collection of Islamic monuments, but few Roman and Punic remains.

**Avenue Habib Bourguiba**, the main boulevard, stretches from the beach to place Farhet Hached next to the medina, and is lined by shops, cafés, offices, hotels and cinemas. Just inside the entrance to the medina is the 9th-century **Great Mosque** (Sat–Thur 8am–2.30pm, Fri 8am–12.30pm

A monastery built like a fortress: the *ribat* in Sousse

in summer, daily 8am–2.30pm in winter). From the outside, the mosque looks like a fortress, with round corner towers and crenellated battlements. Inside, the courtyard is paved with bright marble and surrounded by a harmonious arcade; the double pillars on the far side mark the main entrance to the prayer hall (entry is forbidden to non-Muslims). You may notice that there is no minaret – the *muezzin* who calls the faithful to prayer uses the tower of the neighbouring *ribat*.

The **ribat** (daily 8am–6pm, until 7pm in summer) is an 8th-century fortified monastery, which was once home to a medieval community of devout Muslim warriors who observed a knightly code of conduct – rather like an Islamic equivalent of the Christian Knights Templar of the Crusades. Piety and bravery became their watchwords. An arched gate gives access to the courtyard, lined with cells where the warriors slept. Stairs on the south wall lead to the small prayer hall, and the claustrophobic spiral staircase which climbs to the top of the lookout tower. The panorama from here is well worth the climb.

Rue d'Angleterre leads through the souks to the far side of the medina, where you can climb up to the right to the **kasbah** and adjoining Khalaf Tower (which is now occupied by a lighthouse). The kasbah is home to the **Sousse Archaeological Museum** (Tue–Sun 9am–noon, and 2–6pm in winter; 8am–noon, 3–7pm in summer), where you can admire an excellent collection of Roman mosaics. Just inside the first courtyard, on the right, is a striking head of Medusa. The room on the far side has more spectacular mosaics: in the corner to the left of the door is a semi-circular pool showing the sea god Neptune, his hair crawling with lobsters and crabs and seawater gushing from his mouth, surrounded by sea creatures.

A passage leads to other rooms with some of the museum's finest mosaics, including a dining room floor (obviously commissioned by a Roman with a sense of humour) decorated with discarded lobster claws, chicken bones, shells, fruit stalks and fish bones. Another dining room floor shows four gladiators and a host of wild beasts, plus gladiators fighting leopards (the inscription tells us that the gladiators were awarded a prize of 5,000 *denarii* for their skill).

West of the *ribat* is **Dar Essid** (daily 10am–7pm in winter; 10am–1pm, 3–6pm in summer), the beautiful house of the famous Essid Sousse family, who still occupy part of the building. The rooms are filled with household objects and beautiful objets d'art, and there is a fine view over the medina from the café on the roof.

## Catacombs

Some of the mosaics in the Archaeological Museum were found in the **catacombs** to the southwest of the town (Tue–Sun 9am–noon, 2–6pm in summer; 8am–noon, 3–7pm in winter), where Christians were buried from the 2nd to the 4th centuries.

In the new town on rue du 2 Mars 1932, near Cinema Nejma, is the **Musée de l'Olivier** (daily 9am–7pm, Fri 9am–noon). This lovely museum explains all about olive trees, a staple of the Sahel region, with a tasting at the end.

Nearby **Port al-Kantaoui**, 9km (5½ miles) north of Sousse, is one of the country's most popular resorts with a wide choice of good hotels, a big marina, amusement parks and even a small zoo (daily 9am–7pm).

## Monastir

The town of **Monastir** has a long history similar to that of Sousse, and retains its 9th-century *ribat* (fortified monastery) and Great Mosque. Unlike Sousse, Monastir has been overwhelmed by the tourist trade, so feels more like a new town than a historic port. It is a pleasant resort with a sheltered beach, a marina and several beachfront hotels.

Monastir, with its sheltered sandy beach, is a popular resort

The imposing **ribat** (daily 8.30am–5.30pm, 8am–7pm in summer) dominates both the harbour and the town. It was built in 796 by Harthema ibn Ayun, who served in the army of Harun ar Rashid, Caliph of Baghdad. Additions and renovations over the centuries have created a complex of crenellated walls

### Film set

At the foot of the *ribat* in Monastir are the studios and headquarters of IMF (International Monastir Films). This region was the location for the shooting of the 13-part TV series *Jesus of Nazareth* and the feature film *Raiders of the Lost Ark*.

and turrets, with open courtyards and spartan cells. The former prayer hall is home to a small **Museum of Islamic Art** (closed Mon), which offers displays of woodwork, embroidery, glassware, parchments and papyrus documents, and an astrolabe from 927, used for taking star measurements. The airy top of the *nador*, or lookout tower, offers a panoramic view over the town. Next to the *ribat* is the plain but venerable **Great Mosque**, built from the 9th to 11th centuries. Near the tourist office, on rue de l'Indépendance, is the small **Museum of Traditional Costume** (Tue–Sat 9am–1pm, 3–7pm; 9am–4pm in winter).

Among Tunisians, Monastir is best known as the birthplace of Habib Bourguiba, the man who won independence for his country in 1956 *(see page 25)*. His kitsch golden statue stands in the square near the Gouvernorat. The **Bourguiba Mosque** (closed to non-Muslims) at the edge of the medina, was built in 1963 in the family's honour. Its features and styles have been borrowed from all periods of Tunisian architecture. An imposing avenue leads from the park outside the *ribat* to the ornate multi-million-dinar **Bourguiba Mausoleum** (Mon–Thur 2–4.30pm, Fri–Sat 9am–4.30pm, until 6pm in summer), where the former president, his family and his first wife are buried.

## Kairouan

The holy city of **Kairouan** is the most important Islamic site in all North Africa. Its name, derived from *qayrawan*, means 'caravan': it was an important staging-post on the ancient camel caravan routes. This was the place chosen in 670 by Uqba ibn Nafi to be the base for the Arab conquest of the Maghreb, where he vowed to build 'a citadel of Islam for all time'. During the 9th century, Tunisia's 'Golden Age' *(see page 18)*, the Aghlabid Dynasty made Kairouan the capital of the entire Maghreb. The city evolved into one of the great commercial, religious and intellectual centres of Islam, but it was sacked by the Beni Hilal in 1057. It is still revered as Islam's fourth holiest city, after Mecca, Medina and Jerusalem, and is referred to as 'the city of 50 mosques'.

The Mosque of the Barber is famous for its tilework

Kairouan lies about 60km (37 miles) from the coast, in the middle of a semi-arid plain given over to olive trees and sheep. The tourist information office here is on place des Martyrs, opposite Bab ach-Chouhada, but the ticket office (at the Syndicat d'Initiative), selling tickets for entry to all the main Islamic sites, is next to the Aghlabid Pools, on rue Ibn al Aghlab.

The **Aghlabid Pools** (daily 8am–6.30pm in summer;

8.30am–6pm in winter) are enormous circular cisterns filled with limpid water. They were constructed by the city's Aghlabid governors and were fed by water from the hills to the west of Kairouan, delivered here by a 35-km (22-mile) long aqueduct.

West along the main road is the **Zaouïa of Sidi Sahab al Balaoui** (Mosque of the Barber), notable for its magnificent tile decoration. Al Balaoui was one of Prophet Mohammed's companions, so his final resting place here is a sacred site.

Colonnade surrounding the Great Mosque's courtyard

The street across the highway from the Aghlabid Pools leads towards the medina; turn left after the kasbah walls and walk for five minutes to arrive at the Great Mosque. The city's most famous and venerable building, the **Great Mosque** (Jemaa Sidi Uqba, Sat–Thur 8am–2pm, Fri 8am–noon) looks more like a fortress with its high walls and strong, easily defended gates. The first mosque on this site was built by Uqba ibn Nafi in 671; the Great Mosque in its present form dates from the 9th century. Visitors are allowed to inspect the **courtyard**, paved in marble and surrounded by a colonnade and, through open doors, admire the gleaming tiles of the *mihrab* (prayer niche) and the rich marble and porphyry columns in the prayer room, which non-Muslims are not permitted to enter.

In the courtyard, look for the seven wellheads, their edges worn and notched from a thousand years of hauling bucket ropes. The stocky, square **minaret** is the oldest in North Africa; notice how the lower courses of masonry consist of

In the Kairouan medina

stone salvaged from Roman ruins. Take a stroll around the mosque after your visit to the courtyard, avoiding the carpet sellers if you can. The **Bab Lalla Rihana**, in the far wall, is the prettiest of the many portals.

The city walls beyond the kasbah lead to Bab Tunis (Gate of Tunis), the main entrance to Kairouan's **medina**. The main street through the centre of town is lined with *souks* festooned with Kairouan **carpets**, which are renowned throughout Tunisia. The city gives its name to a classic design with a broad border and a central motif based on the diamond. You can often glimpse women making the carpets on primitive looms, while street-corner stalls are piled up with gaily coloured skeins of wool – the carpet-weavers' raw material.

Lying in the heart of the medina is the **Bir Barouta** (Well of Barouta), concealed within a small, inconspicuous building near the souks. The water is lifted from the well by a mechanism driven by a blindfolded camel, which tramps in circles all day. This camel-powered pump has been in operation for almost three centuries. To the east of the well, the **Mosque of the Three Gates** (closed to non-Muslims) is notable for the verses from the Koran carved on its superb sculpted façade.

It is impossible to leave Kairouan without sampling at least one of the local sweets called **maqroudh**. There are many patisseries in the medina which sell these famous, bite-sized pieces of honey-soaked pastry filled with date paste.

## Sbeïtla (Sufetula)

Tunisia offers few sights more evocative of past glory than the temples of Roman **Sufetula**, rising majestically above a rubble-strewn plain, their ancient stone glowing golden in the morning sunshine. This fascinating site (daily 8am–5.30pm; 7am–7pm in summer) lies near the modern town of Sbeïtla, some 120km (75 miles) southeast of Kairouan. Very little is known about its history, but it is thought to have been built by the Romans around the time of Christ, and was then later taken by the Byzantines, who built several churches here.

The most obvious remains are the three **Capitoline temples**, which tower above the forum. According to traditional Roman practice, the central temple was dedicated to Jupiter and those on either side to Juno and Minerva. All three retain the niche in the back wall where the statues of the gods once stood.

The other main attraction at Sbeïtla is the Byzantine **Basilica of Vitalis**, which contains a beautiful baptismal font intricately decorated with mosaics and inscribed in Latin.

## El Jem

Halfway between Sousse and Sfax, **El Jem** is surrounded by a plain planted with millions of olive trees. Back in the 2nd century AD this was

Sufetula's temple columns

the site of the Roman city of Thysdrus, which grew wealthy on the bounty provided by these trees, selling their harvest of oil to the merchants of Rome. It's population was probably around 100,000, which made it the second city in size after Carthage.

Approaching El Jem by road, there can be little doubt as to the town's main attraction, for the **Roman amphitheatre** (daily 8am–5.30pm; 7am–7pm in summer) rises majestically above the low houses of the modern city. From whichever direction you approach, it is an extremely impressive sight. As one of the largest amphitheatres in the Roman world – it could seat 30,000 – this great colosseum, built during the 3rd century AD, has witnessed many a gory spectacle.

After the decline of Thysdrus, it was used throughout the centuries as a fortress by assorted brigands. In 1695, the Turkish bey bombarded the walls in an attempt to oust anti-government rebels holed up within. His work, destructive as it was at the time, benefits the visitor today, by exposing the

## We Who are About to Die...

Gladiatorial contests were very popular throughout the Roman Empire, as witnessed by the immense size of amphitheatres such as the one at El Jem. Gladiators were usually slaves or criminals, but those who won often became professionals. On the day of the contest, the gladiators paraded through the amphitheatre, and gave their famous salute to the presiding magistrate: *Ave! Morituri te salutant!* ('Hail! We who are about to die salute you!'). At the end of a bout, when one of the gladiators was badly wounded, he would raise his forefinger to appeal to the clemency of the crowd – if they waved their handkerchiefs, he would live; but if they pointed their thumbs down (as if plunging a sword into an opponent), crying *Iugula! Iugula!* ('Slay him!'), his end had come.

The mighty amphitheatre at El Jem could accommodate 30,000

intricate details of the building's construction – stairways, arches, vaults, buttresses and underground chambers.

Thysdrus was a lively and prosperous town, almost four times as large as present-day El Jem. At the edge of town on the road to Sfax, evidence of its wealth can still be seen in the striking mosaics on display in the small **museum** (daily 8am–7pm summer, 8am–5.30pm winter). Seashells and birds, peacocks, lions and tigers are all beautifully portrayed in scenes filled with bright colours. A large mosaic of the young Dionysus, dressed in a leopard skin and mounted on a tigress, is especially impressive.

Situated roughly 65km (40 miles) south of El Jem is **Sfax**, Tunisia's second-largest city (after Tunis) and an important industrial and commercial centre. There is a lively medina here, with fortress-like walls and an interesting archaeological museum. A ferry to the charming and peaceful **Kerken-nah Islands** departs from Sfax port.

## JERBA

As you drive off the little car ferry from Jorf, or cross the causeway from El Kantara, you will probably be struck by the extreme flatness of **Jerba**. Most of the island presents a dry and sandy landscape, covered with ancient olive trees, fruit trees, date palms and grasses. The villages are made up of clusters of little whitewashed, sugar-cube houses, each one topped by a hemispherical dome, while the irrigated fields are dotted with straw-hatted men and women and camels slowly pulling the plough.

**A white mosque stands in the arid fields of Jerba**

Jerba owes its peculiarities to its location. Located deep in the southern part of Tunisia, not far from the border of Libya, the island rests like a huge sandbank in the warm, shallow waters off the coast. There is less than 200mm (8in) of rainfall a year; the earth is parched, the dates grown here are of poor quality, fit only for camel fodder, and the crops survive thanks only to irrigation via the hundreds of wells and cisterns that pock the landscape. Nonetheless, the hot, dry weather and white sandy beaches make Jerba a paradise for the sun-worshipping tourists who flock year-round to the hotels of the north coast.

Jerba, along with Majorca and Menorca, claims to be the island of the Lotus Eaters described in Homer's *Odyssey*, where Odysseus' men ate the 'fruit of forgetfulness'. Legend apart, the first settlers on Jerba were probably Jewish exiles fleeing the destruction of Jerusalem in the 6th century BC; their descendants survive in the villages of Hara Kebira and Hara Seghira. The Phoenicians and Romans colonised the island, and built a causeway to link it to the mainland (just to the east of the modern causeway). It was taken by the Arabs in 655 and fought over by the Sicilians, Normans and Hafsids throughout the Middle Ages. In the 16th century it was employed as a base for the notorious Barbary pirates Barbarossa *(see page 19)* and Dragut Ali. It was from here that they launched their successful campaign to expel the Spanish from Algiers. Jerba finally became part of Tunisia during the Ottoman period.

**Distinctive design**

The architecture of Jerba is distinctive. Houses, surrounded by a formidable cactus hedge, are small fortresses of cubes and domes, with high, tiny windows and buttressed walls. The design, unique to Jerba, reflects the island's vulnerable past, and also helps air to circulate in summer.

## Houmt Souk

Houmt Souk is the 'capital' of the island, with airline offices, banks, car-hire firms, hotels, restaurants, shops and travel agencies, but even so it is little more than a large village. The town is centred on the **souks**, a maze of tiny alleys and whitewashed squares, where stalls are piled high with locally produced crafts – pottery, blankets, coral and jewellery.

At the edge of town, on the road to the hotel zone, you'll find the **Museum of Popular Arts and Traditions** (*Musée des Arts et Traditions Populaires*; Sat–Thur 9.30am–4.30pm;

8am–noon, 3–7pm in summer). This 18th-century *zaouïa* of Sidi Zitouni, set in a pretty garden, has been converted to hold exhibits which detail the lives of Jerba's people. The first room shows the traditional dress worn in different parts of the island, and the costumes used for important events such as weddings or circumcisions. The antique jewellery, religious manuscripts, pottery, joinery and wood carving on display are testaments to the skills of local craftsmen.

The 15th-century Borj el Kebir

Down by the sea is the 15th-century fortress, called **Borj al Kebir** (Great Fort, Sat–Thur 8am–7pm in summer, 9.30–4.30pm in winter). Built on the site of a 13th-century fort erected by the Sicilian Roger de Luria (which in turn sat on top of a Roman structure), it was occupied in its time by Spaniards, Hafsids, Turks and, during the 16th century, by the pirates Barbarossa and Dragut Ali.

In a notorious massacre in 1560, Dragut and his men captured the fort from the Knights of Malta, and ruthlessly put to the sword every one of the defenders. In memory of his victory, Dragut built a tower with the skulls and bones of the dead, a grisly monument that survived until 1848, in which year the expatriate community persuaded the bey to have it removed. A concrete obelisk in the middle of the parking lot beside the fort marks the site where it stood.

## Other Island Sights

To the east of Houmt Souk, the island's best beaches – **Sidi Mahares**, **Sidi Garous** and **La Seguia** – stretch for 20km (12 miles), interrupted only by the rocks of **Ras Taguerness**. This rocky headland, marked by a tall lighthouse, is Jerba's best snorkelling and spearfishing site. Just outside Ras Taguerness, on the El Kantara road, is the **Djerba Explore** (daily 9am–6pm, until 8pm in summer). This large complex includes a crocodile farm, a Folkloric Museum and the delightful **Lalla Hadria Museum** with a good collection of Islamic art.

About 8km (5 miles) south of Houmt Souk is the island's oldest place of worship, the synagogue of **El Ghriba** (Sun–Fri 7.30am–6pm). Head for the village of Er Riadh (formerly Hara Seghira, or 'little ghetto') and follow the signs to El Ghriba. The present synagogue was built in the 1920s, and according to local myth it occupies the spot where a holy stone fell to earth in 600BC; it is a place of pilgrimage for Jews from all over North Africa. A guide will show you the inner sanctum, the oldest part of the synagogue (the foundations may date from the 5th century BC), and allow you a glimpse of one of the world's oldest Torahs. You must take off your shoes and cover your head before entering.

**Guellala**, on the southern side of the island, is the centre of Jerba's pottery trade. The village has over 300 kilns and the main street is lined with potters' workshops and factories making all kinds of pots, ornaments, utensils and a lot of cheap tourist tat.

Guellala is home to most of the island's Berbers, who speak their own language and adhere to the strict Ibadite Muslim sect. South of

### Terrorist outrage

On 11 April 2002, a tanker carrying gas bottles exploded in front of the synagogue of El Ghriba. The suicide attack, for which al-Qaeda claimed responsibility, killed 21, including 14 German tourists.

the village is the 15th-century **Guellala Mosque**, a great place to watch the sunset. Situated 2km (1.2 miles) north is the **Guellala Heritage Museum** (daily 8am–6pm, until 1pm in summer), with tableaux explaining the old ways of Jerba.

**Midoun**, Jerba's second-biggest community, is basically a market town, hosting a lively open-air souk every Friday. The other weekly attraction is the traditional Berber 'wedding', held every Tuesday in summer for the benefit of tourists.

## SOUTHERN TUNISIA

Tunisia is cut in half by a natural depression that runs inland from Gabès to beyond the Algerian border. This trough, which was once an arm of the Mediterranean Sea, cradles a string of huge salt lakes called *chott*, forming a natural barrier to north–south travel. It also marks the boundary between the semi-arid steppes of central Tunisia and the true Sahara desert of the south.

The largest of these salt lakes, the **Chott el Jerid**, is also the largest in the whole of the Sahara, covering a staggering area of some 5,200 sq km (over 2,000 sq miles). Lying to the west and south of the *chott* is the Grand Erg Oriental, a vast ocean of shifting sand dunes, which are untamed and uninhabited with the exception of only a few isolated oases.

Dunes of the Grand Erg Oriental

The oasis towns of Tozeur, Nefta, Kebili and Douz can all be reached by good roads, either on an organised excursion or by hire car. Tozeur has its own airport, with direct flights from Tunis, Jerba and Paris.

## Gafsa

Travellers who are heading for the Chott el Jerid from Tunis, Sousse or Kairouan must first pass through the mining town of **Gafsa**, situated at a gap in the mountains, where all the roads south (except the coastal highway) converge. Set in the middle of Tunisia's phosphate-mining region, Gafsa is basically a working city of small businessmen, bureaucrats and

mine workers, rebuilt after World War II on the site of the Roman town of Capsa. There's not much to see here apart from the **Roman Pools** (*Piscines Romaines*), a pair of large stone baths filled with sparkling green water. These pools are fed by a hot spring which bubbles up between the ancient stone slabs, and then overflows into the neighbouring *hammam* (Turkish bath).

Near the mining town of **Metlaoui**, on the road from Gafsa to Tozeur, is the spectacular **Selja Gorge**. A railway runs through the gorge to the town of Redeyef, and daily in the summer months (July–September) a tourist train called the **Lézard Rouge** (Red Lizard) takes visitors on scenic trips through the ravine. The train was a gift to the bey of Tunis from the French, and its 19th-century carriages have been lovingly restored.

If you have time for a side trip, the remote oases of **Chebika**, **Tamerza** and **Midès** are some of the most scenic areas in Tunisia, with deep rock ravines and natural springs cascading from the rock faces. Only Tamerza, with its luxury Tamerza Palace Hotel overlooking the old oasis village, is accessible by public transport from Redeyef. If you want to go any farther, a four-wheel-drive vehicle is recommended.

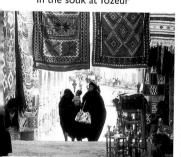

In the souk at Tozeur

## Tozeur and Nefta

The oasis town of **Tozeur** on the northern shore of the Chott el Jerid marks the limit of Roman colonisation in Africa. Its name is derived from the Roman settlement of Thusuros and many a Roman legion stopped at its cool springs on their way from Gabès to Nefta. The town is now the commercial centre of the Jerid region and is growing quickly – there's a sizeable airport where tourists arrive several times a week, and even an Arabian Nights theme park, Dar Cheraït. Cars and lorries (trucks) rattle along its sandy streets, while television antennae poke up from the ochre-coloured houses. Beyond this façade of modern prosperity, however, Tozeur still pursues its ancient traditions.

Traditional brick designs on a house in Tozeur

The houses in the **medina** display the local talent for decorative bricklaying, with geometric designs laid out in the traditional flat bricks of sand and clay. Souvenir shops display highly colourful carpets and rugs bearing stylised human and animal figures. Such patterns are unique to the region and quite unusual for a Muslim town, as Islam forbids the portrayal of man or beasts in any form. Veiled women scuff down the sandy streets to the bustling produce market (by the post office), while villagers who live out of town bargain with shopkeepers for the famous **deglat annour**. These delicious, plump, sweet dates (their name means 'fingers of light', because their flesh is almost translucent) are grown in the neighbouring palmery and then sold on the branch, or by the kilo neatly packed in little wooden boxes.

During the afternoon heat, you can make your escape to the cooler surroundings of Tozeur's extensive **palmery**, which is watered by streams that spring hot from the earth at Ras al Aïoun and ripple through a labyrinth of channels amid a forest of over 200,000 palm trees. The irrigation system was devised by the mathematician Ibn Chabbat in the 13th century, to guarantee that the local landowners all received their equal share of water. Here you can stroll among the shady gardens, or take a guided tour in one of the *calèches* (horse-drawn carriages) that tout for business around the entrance to the palmery.

## The Oasis – a Desert Paradise

To the people of the desert, an oasis – a 'plot of paradise in the midst of an inferno' – is more than just a watering place. It takes ingenuity and painstaking, meticulous labour to make the desert bloom. Each rivulet of precious water is coaxed and diverted into the bottom land. The soil is tilled and fertilised, and eventually a palmery (palm grove), essential for shade, is created. Soon the oasis-dweller's meagre diet of dates and camel's milk is augmented with grain, figs, apricots and a few root vegetables grown among the palms. All wastage, including camel dung, is ploughed back into the soil, and every square metre of shaded earth is used for cultivation. The village houses are built on higher land, exposed to the merciless sun. Finally, the palmery matures into a true garden paradise with a full range of fruit, vegetables, animal fodder and flowers.

The palm tree is the heart and soul of the oasis, and every part of it is used. The trunks provide bridges across the irrigation channels, and are used as roof beams in houses; the fibres that grow around its base make stuffing for saddles; the fronds are woven into mats and baskets; the heavy base of the leaf stalk is used as a beater by the washerwomen; and the sap is fermented to make the palm wine called *laghmi*.

The road from Tozeur to **Nefta** follows the crest of a low ridge, with the vast Chott el Jerid shimmering in the south. The intense heat and brilliant light create the illusion that the lake is full of water, but it's just a mirage: the lake only has water in it after very heavy rains – a rare occurrence in this arid region.

Nefta's verdant 'basket'

From the high ground that holds Nefta's buildings, you can look down into a bowl-shaped depression, once carpeted in palm trees and watered by innumerable springs. The famous **Corbeille** (Basket) of Nefta, a collection of lush and fragrant gardens – each owned by a different family – is slowly drying up – water is now pumped in and there are talks of a new project to bring more water in.

It's still a surprise to see the fertile abundance in the middle of so desolate a landscape, but this centuries-old multi-tiered agricultural operation somehow still functions: the lush green palms produce dates and provide shade for pomegranate trees below, which in turn shelter the orange trees. Beneath them grow onions, broad beans, peppers, barley and all manner of other fruits and vegetables. An elaborate system of irrigation channels brings water from the springs.

Many famous Muslim mystics, such as the Moroccan-born Sidi Bou Ali, practised meditation in Nefta, and the town has been a place of pilgrimage for Sufi Mulsims since the 9th century, earning it the title of 'Kairouan of the Desert'. Be warned that on religious holidays the town is particularly busy, and accommodation may be hard to find.

## Kebili and Douz

A good road leads southeast from Tozeur, and follows a causeway traversing the endless salt flats of the **Chott el Jerid**. The causeway runs dead straight for nearly 40km (25 miles) across a blinding, blue-white expanse of crusted salt, stained here and there with pink and green, the monotony relieved only by a few souvenir sellers and cafés at the roadside. The hot air sometimes creates strange optical illusions, and oncoming traffic gradually materialises out of a shimmering haze. As you approach the southern shore, drifts of blowing sand begin to encroach on the tarmac, and you realise that you have arrived at the edge of the Sahara Desert.

The edge of the Sahara: the salt flats of the Chott el Jerid

The first town you come to, 96km (60 miles) from Tozeur, is the dusty military camp of **Kebili**. Two picturesque old desert strongholds have been converted to hotel-restaurants, where you can dine among the ghosts of the Foreign Legion. Until the mid-19th century, Kebili was a notorious market for slaves brought from the south of the Sahara. Walking the dusty roads between the houses, you are likely to brush shoulders with the descendants of the Sudanese brought here during the 1,000-year trade.

Further on from Kebili, barriers made of palm fronds

fight a losing battle to prevent the fringing dunes of the
Grand Erg Oriental drifting
across the highway. The Nefzaoua, the region around
Douz, takes its name from a
semi-nomadic tribe of the Sahara. An avenue of fragrant
eucalyptus trees marks the
approach to **Douz**, the self-
styled 'Gateway to the Sahara' and a major centre for
camel trips and Land Rover

The Thursday market in Douz

excursions into the desert. (These treks follow the rocky, cor-
rugated track west from Douz, along the edge of the *chott*,
to the isolated oases of Zaafrane, Nouaïl, Touiba and Es
Sabria.) Due south of Douz, there is nothing but sand dunes
all the way to the Libyan border, 350km (220 miles) away.

The town is at its busiest on Thursday, when the semi-
nomadic tribesmen from surrounding oases come to trade at
the market. The market square is crammed with men in
brown *burnouses* (hooded cloaks) and white head cloths,
haggling over sacks of wool, bundles of camel fodder, piles
of beans and bunches of dates. Cafés are crowded, the tiny
local bakery turns out dozens upon dozens of delicious fresh
loaves, and everyone joins in the spirit of the usual weekly
festivities. Just a few minutes walk from the market square,
you will find the **camel market**, where buyers and sellers
haggle animatedly over the long-suffering beasts.

The **Musée du Sahara** (Museum of the Sahara; Tue–Sun
9.30am–4.30pm, 7–11am and 4–7pm in summer) in the town
centre gives a fascinating insight into the lives and traditions
of the Saharan nomads. Near the museum is a natural hot
spring (daily 6am–noon and 3–7pm) where you can either

bathe in the larger pool or in your own smaller private one. Douz's plantation of date palms is a peaceful place. The only sounds are the song of the bulbuls, the murmur of the turtle-doves and the fluttering of the sand-grouse, come to wet their feathers in the irrigation canals. The only traffic is the occasional donkey, drawing a cart filled with sand-covered palms from the Grand Erg Oriental.

Once a year (in Nov/Dec – dates vary according to Ramadan), Douz comes alive with the **Festival of the Sahara**, seven days of camel fights, shooting contests, greyhound races and traditional music and dance. Poets test their powers of improvisation in a *joute poétique* (poetry 'jousting match') and horsemen stage a *fantasia*, a mock battle-charge in which mounted tribesmen thunder down on the audience, spurred on by rifle shots and war cries, only to turn and retreat at the last moment.

The only traffic in Douz's palmery is an occasional donkey-cart

## Gabès

The road east from Kebili to Gabès crosses a dry and dusty plain that separates the salt lake of Chott el Fejaj and the Jebel Tebaga mountains. The jagged peaks of the mountain range are a sight of desolate beauty. At the foot of the mountains grow thorny desert bushes, which provide sustenance for the camels of the Nefzaoua, the semi-nomadic people who give this region its name. They live most of the year in this inhospitable area, taking refuge in the oases only when the summer heat becomes unbearable.

### Desert rose

Around Douz, amid the landscape of dunes and half-buried palm trees, there lies a mineral known as 'desert rose' – pink gypsum sculpted by erosion that you will find for sale in all the bazaars. Young boys may be seen digging tirelessly for the rose-shaped sculptures as if for gold.

At **El Hamma** there are hot sulphur baths which were once used by the Romans. If you care to try their malodorous waters, stone seats have been provided for your convenience.

**Gabès** is known as the 'Gateway to the South' because all highway traffic from north to south must pass through it. It is a large industrial town, dealing in phosphates, sulphuric acid and fertilisers, with some valuable oilfields just offshore. Although hotels, restaurants and a resort complex make the new town seem much the same as any other along the Tunisian coast, Gabès actually has the added attraction of a huge **palmery** right beside the sea.

The Gabès oasis, though not as large as the palmeries of Tozeur or Nefta, is large enough to contain a dozen separate villages in its shady depths, with a serpentine road winding through the palms and linking them together. André Gide was overwhelmed by the place: 'Gardens profuse with blooms, alive with bees, from which fragrance arose so insistently that they well-nigh replaced both food and intoxicating liquor.'

The coastal climate is too cool and moist to produce top-quality dates here; the Gabès palm trees are grown primarily for shade, allowing crops and fruit trees to be cultivated in the oasis gardens. The palm trunks are used for construction, while the dates provide animal fodder. The classic way to tour this forest of around 300,000 palms is by *calèche* (horse-drawn carriage); you can hire one at the tourist office in the centre of town. Most *calèche* tours head up to the village of Chenini (not to be confused with the spectacular hilltop Chenini, located south of Tataouine), where you can shop for handicrafts.

## THE KSOUR REGION

This region of southern Tunisia is perhaps the most intriguing of all: a beautiful landscape of craggy hills, scattered

An abandoned Berber *ksour* near Metameur

palms and white-domed *koubbas* at its edges giving way to the sandy dunes of the Grand Erg Oriental or the stony desert plain. At first it seems remote and only sparsely populated, but closer inspection reveals numerous foritified Berber villages, known as *ksour*, crowning hills and ridges, their mud architecture blending in to the terrain.

## Matmata

In the hills 40km (25 miles) to the south of Gabès lies **Matmata**, one of the most unusual villages in Tunisia. If you have seen the films *The English Patient* or *Star Wars*, then you have seen Matmata – the cave scenes and the archaeological digs in *The English Patient* and the scene in which Luke Skywalker goes back to the underground house where he grew up were filmed here. Matmata is a troglodyte village, where the locals have created subterranean homes by excavating chambers in the soft earth.

Most of their **cave houses** – in all there are more than 100 dwellings of this kind – follow the same basic design: a circular pit about 10m (33ft) across, with a sloping tunnel leading from the floor to ground level. This sunken 'courtyard' has a number of rooms leading off, used variously as bedchambers, animal pens and storerooms. The larger houses may have two or three courtyards linked by tunnels. These unusual dwellings are very practical: the insulation provided by the earth keeps the rooms cool in summer and warm in winter. The tradition of living underground goes back a long way – the Greek historian Herodotus records the existence of troglodytes in this region in the 4th century BC.

The people of Matmata are Berbers, and they work hard to glean a livelihood from the dry soil. Olive trees, figs, barley and a few stunted palms grow in the shady ravines that cleave the hillsides. The discovery of Matmata by the out-

The unique troglodyte houses of Matmata

side world has added a new element to the tenuous local economy – souvenir shops, restaurants and camel rides have taken over as the primary source of income. Most villagers now live above ground and charge a fee for looking inside their former homes.

In 1961, New Matmata (Nouvelle Matmata) was built 15km (9 miles) from the original village on the orders of President Habib Bourguiba, who considered that underground caves were not fit accommodation for his citizens. The population of 3,000 was rehoused in the new town but, understanding tourism better than the late president, the locals maintain the subterranean settlement for the benefit of visitors.

Several **hotels** have been set up in disused cave dwellings. The rooms are small and primitive, with few amenities other than rickety beds and a bare light bulb, but a night spent in one of these underground hotels is an experience simply not to be missed.

From the Hotel Les Berbères a new tarmac road leads west to the villages of Tamezret, Taoujou and Zeraoua through scenery full of unexpected vistas – the pink and blue Jebel Tebaga in the distance, pockets of cultivation in steep ravines, and white *koubbas* in relief against the dun-coloured hills. **Tamezret**, 10km (6 miles) away, is a compact village of above-ground stone houses clustered around the mosque. You can enjoy the view from the hilltop café while sipping almond tea.

## Medenine and the *Ksar* Villages

The mountains stretching south from Matmata were one of Tunisia's last strongholds of Berber culture. When hostile Arab tribes swept across North Africa in the 11th century, sacking villages and destroying farms to make pasture for their camels, the indigenous Berbers took to the hills and sought refuge in fortified villages. In time many returned to the plains and were assimilated into Tunisian Arab culture, but a few remained in their mountain strongholds, keeping alive the language and traditions of their ancestors. By the 19th century, however, spoken Berber had survived only in a handful of villages, and Berber culture had as good as disappeared. Today, the unique architecture of the fortified *ksar* villages in the hills to the west of Medenine stands as a monument to a past way of life.

### Kalaâ, Ghorfas and Ksour

When the Berbers first fled to the mountains they built crude hilltop forts, called *kalaâ*, on the crags above their villages, as protection from the marauding Arabs. The *kalaâ* of Douiret is particularly impressive, perched on top of a 700-m (2,300-ft) high peak.

A *ghorfa* is a Berber granary – a long rectangular room topped by a barrel-vaulted roof. The vault was made by piling earth-filled sacks into the right shape, bending olive branches over the top, and adding a roof of stone, mortar and clay; the sacks were removed when the roof had set. Very often *ghorfas* were constructed in rows, one on top of another, and honeycomb-like complexes of three, four or more storeys were not unusual. For protection, *ghorfas* were built around a rectangular courtyard to form a fortified communal granary called a *ksar* (plural *ksour*). In times of peace, the villagers would gather at the *ksar* to pray and socialise, as well as trade at the weekly market. When danger threatened, they would all take refuge within the protection of its fortress-like outer walls.

Roughly 75km (47 miles) south of Gabès, the town of **Medenine** was once a major grain depot, and its complex of 35 *ksour*, up to six storeys in height, held in the region of 8,000 *ghorfas* (fortified houses that once held the grain). Today there are only a few dozen *ghorfas* remaining, grouped around three courtyards, one of which has been converted into a shopping centre for tourists. On the outskirts of town in the village of **Metameur**, a picturesque *ksar* has been converted into a recommended hotel *(see page 137)*.

**Toujane**, 22km (14 miles) north, is quite a large village, but almost invisible from a distance. Like the caves in the naturally cratered landscape around Matmata, the flat-roofed stone village is camouflaged against the rock strata. You will spot washing drying on a line or a woman's bright clothes long before you discern the outline of a building.

Chenini is one of the more accessible of the *ksour*

To visit the *ksar* villages without a four-wheel-drive vehicle, you will have to drive south to **Tataouine** first, where a number of tarmac roads head into the hills. **Chenini** is the nearest and most popular with tour buses, an attractive village dramatically set high up in a rocky valley. A tiny white mosque sits on the pass above the village, but the rest of the buildings seem almost to blend into the rock. Constructed from the local stone and built along the natural rock strata, they were well camouflaged against marauding Arabs as they approached from the valleys below. The 'back rooms' are hollowed out of the soft rock and shielded from view by a row of *ghorfas* facing inwards. Chenini is still inhabited, but many of the villagers now live in the newer houses lower down the valley.

Close by, **Douiret** can be reached by an unsurfaced road from Chenini, or on a tarmac road which leaves the highway about 8km (5 miles) south of Tataouine. The well restored village makes an impressive sight, with a ruined *kalaâ* (fortress) perched atop a 700-m (2,300-ft) peak and two terraces of houses spread out below around the white-washed mosque. Many of the *ghorfas* have been kept in good repair, and you can also see an underground oil press near the mosque.

If you go back to the road to Chenini, a right fork leads to **Ghoumrassen**, a market town which holds a lively market in its modern quarter on Friday. The town is famous in Tunisia for its doughnuts – *ftair* – which can be bought in one of the many patisseries on the main street (*ftair* can also be found in towns all over the country, in shops belonging to Ghoumrassen emigrants). The town is set in a steep-sided valley, and rows of cave houses have been carved into the cliffs and spurs of the upper slopes. From here, a road branches left to the smaller village of **Guermessa**, where a narrow, rocky path climbs to the *kalaâ*, perched above town.

Most of the *ksour* southeast of Tataouine are less impressive, and differ only in their varying levels of decay. The exception is **Ksar Ouled Soltane**, one of the best-preserved *ksour* in Tunisia. As usual, the outside wall is blank and featureless; but through the gatehouse two rings of *ghorfas*, in perfect condition, rise to four storeys high. At the very end of the village, the hill suddenly drops to a plain, offering breathtaking views.

# WHAT TO DO

## SHOPPING

The best places to track down authentic crafts are the souks of Tunis, Sousse, Kairouan and Houmt Souk on Jerba. Elsewhere, many of the wares that fill the souks are not of a very high quality and made purely to serve the tourist trade.

Shops are generally open daily from 8am to 12.30pm and 2.30 to 6pm, though they may close on Friday, the Muslim holy day. The souks are at their liveliest in the morning and particularly in the late afternoon. Country towns have a weekly general market, a lively spectacle worth visiting whether you intend buying anything or not.

### Bargaining

In a place where many products are handmade, each item has its own unique value depending on the quality of the work-manship. Bargaining is a way of determining an appropriate price, not simply a way for the shopkeeper to make more money. To ensure the best price, you should get to know the market by browsing in several shops. When you find something you want to buy, ask the shopkeeper how much it costs, and then offer around half of what you're prepared to pay. Keep haggling until you settle on a mutually acceptable price. If the item is expensive – a carpet, say, or a leather jacket – the process might involve several glasses of mint tea and a good half-hour of your time.

### Golden rules

There are two golden rules you should obey when bargaining: never begin to haggle for an item that you do not genuinely intend to buy, and never offer a price that you are not actually prepared to pay.

Wooden puppets of Saracens are popular souvenirs

In the resorts on the coast, many traders are aware that some tourists feel uncomfortable with bargaining, and will quote you their 'best price' straight away if you ask them to. This is the minimum they are prepared to accept, and you will be wasting your time if you try to force them any lower.

If you prefer not to bargain, you can visit one of the 18 state-run SOCOPA shops, which sell a wide range of local handicrafts at fixed prices. (There are SOCOPA stores in all the major cities and tourist centres: enquire at the tourist office about the nearest one.) The quality of craftsmanship is high and the prices are good. They are a good place to educate yourself on prices before venturing into the souks; but remember that the souks offer greater variety and slightly lower prices.

Many shops will ship your purchases home if they are too bulky for you to take on the plane.

## What to Buy

**Pottery and ceramics.** Tunisia's main pottery-producing areas are Nabeul and Guellala, on Jerba, but their wares are available all around the country. Nabeul is famed for its Andalusian-style ceramics, such as bowls, vases and decorative panels, with intricate designs in blue, yellow and green on a white background. Guellala produces terracotta ware *(chawat)*, ranging from small bowls to huge amphorae (two-handled jars). It also produces traditional green and yellow kitchenware; the colours are said to represent a palm tree.

The Sejnane pottery from Northern Tunisia, between Bizerte and Tabarka, is very distinctive and follows a tradition that dates back to neolithic times. The bowls and animal figurines are hand moulded and then fired on an open fire. They are available from Bizerte market or the shop **Hanout** at 52 rue Jemaa ez Zitouna in Tunis.

**Carpets.** Tunisian carpets are not as high in quality as their more famous counterparts from Turkey and Iran; they will never be family heirlooms, but they are attractive and competitively priced. Carpet making is controlled by the ONA *(Office National de l'Artisanat)*, and all carpets have to be stamped on the back with one of three grades – *Deuxième Choix* (second choice), *Premier Choix* (first choice) or *Qualité Supérieure* (superior quality), according to the number of knots per square metre. There are two basic patterns:

## Deliberately Imperfect

All Tunisian carpets are handmade but some, the most expensive, are produced by knotting strands of wool while others, known as *mergoums*, are woven. Traditionally manufactured on looms by the Berber women of southern Tunisia, *mergoums* are adorned with geometrical motifs in bright colours on a plain background. The pattern is never perfectly symmetrical because, according to popular belief, too great a beauty incites envy and attracts the evil eye. Often the weaver leaves a section unfinished, or introduces a slightly different detail or colour. Most of a *mergoum's* motifs represent stylised natural phenomena (often symbols of fertility such as the snake or the tortoise) or talismans used to repel evil spirits: rhombuses, eyes, crosses, hands and knives.

bright, multicoloured designs on a blue or red background; and *allouchas*, made from undyed wool, with geometric designs in cream, beige, brown and black. The best shops for buying carpets are in Kairouan and Tunis, where shopkeepers will invite you to watch their carpetmakers at work.

**Mergoums** are carpets that are made by weaving as opposed to knotting, with colourful geometric patterns on a solid background (usually yellow-brown); they are traditionally woven by the southern Tunisian Berbers, in the bright reds and purples of the shawls worn by Berber women. *Mergoums* are sold mainly in the south, in Gafsa, Tozeur, Gabès and Jerba.

Traditional carpet weaving in Kairouan

**Jewellery.** Tunisia's jewellery was traditionally produced by the country's Jewish community; the best places to buy gold and silver are still in the old Jewish areas of Jerba and Tunis. Popular designs include a fish motif and the Hand of Fatimah, both of which are believed to ward off evil spirits. More difficult to find is traditional Berber silver – chunky bracelets, earrings and brooches, inset with semi-precious stones; try the shops in El Jem or Tozeur. In Tabarka you will find coral jewellery, but remember that coral is an endangered species: you should think twice about buying it.

**Leather goods.** These include *babouches* (Tunisian slippers), handbags, belts, purses, wallets, trousers, skirts and jackets. Price and quality both vary widely – a lot of the goods on offer in the popular tourist resorts can be shoddy, so check the standard of craftsmanship carefully before you buy. For better-quality leather products, try the shops in Tunis.

Beating plates and pots from brass in the Tunis medina

**Woodwork and metalwork.** The olive-growing region of the Sahel produces attractive items made from carved olive wood – bowls, chess sets, jewellery boxes and backgammon boards. Tunisian brassware is often low quality, but personalised teapots, plates, coffeepots and trays make attractive souvenirs. Rather more original are the ornate filigree bird cages from Sidi Bou Saïd.

## SPORTS AND OTHER ACTIVITIES

### Watersports

With more than 1,000 km (620 miles) of coastline, and some of the finest beaches in the Mediterranean, Tunisia is truly a paradise for watersports enthusiasts. The perfect white sands and the warm, shallow waters of Hammamet, Nabeul, Tunis, Sousse, Monastir and Jerba are just right for safe, sheltered **swimming**, ideal for children. In addition, most of the resort hotels have their own heated swimming pools.

The shallow, sheltered waters also mean that Tunisia's beaches are the ideal place to learn **windsurfing** – there are boards for hire and instructors on all the main beaches.

Other activities offered to enthusiasts on the beach include **parasailing**, **dinghy sailing**, **jet-skiing** and **water-skiing**. The beaches at Sousse, Port el Kantaoui, Monastir, Jerba, Hammamet and Nabeul are the best equipped.

Tunisia's rocky north coast is good **snorkelling** territory, and if you feel the urge to go deeper, **scuba-diving** instruction is available at Tabarka, Port el Kantaoui and Monastir. Contact FAST (*Fédération des Activités Subaquatiques de Tunisie*, BP 46, Cité el Mahrajène, Tunis; tel: 71 281 140, www.fast.org.tn) for more details. Scuba divers might want to explore the coast of Cap Bon, especially at Kelibia and Sidi Daoud, which is noted for its rich underwater life.

## Sea Angling

If you fish, feel free to cast a line from the rocks anywhere you like; a licence is not necessary for angling in Tunisia. For deep-sea fishing, boats can be hired from the marinas at Port el Kantaoui and Monastir. Among the fish found inshore are mullet, bream and sea bass, while offshore anglers can expect tunny, dorado and shark. Ask in the fishing ports whether you can accompany the local fishermen, either to watch them at work or to help them with the catch.

### Spearfishing

A permit from the Directeur de la Pêche et l'Aquaculture is required for underwater spearfishing. A travel agent can obtain this for you and explain the formalities, or you can get more information from the Centre Nautique de Tunisie (22 rue de Médine, 1001 Tunis, tel: 71 282 209).

## Desert Safaris

Any travel agent will have details of organised **four-wheel-drive tours** around southern Tunisia, ranging from two-day excursions to Matmata and the *ksar* villages to ten-day 'safaris' deep into the desert, with accommodation in Bedouin tents. Tours can be booked on the spot in Ham-

Parasailing is just one of the recreations on offer in Sousse

mamet, Sousse, Gabès, Jerba and Douz, but longer trips should be arranged in advance. Some adventure holiday companies in the UK offer all-inclusive safaris. Contact the ONTT (Office National du Tourisme Tunisien), *see page 128* for details.

## Sand Yachts and Hot Air Balloons
You can try out the exciting sport of sand-yachting on the salt flats of the Chott el Jerid. The 'yacht' is a three-wheeled vehicle fitted with a mast and sail, and it can attain a speed of over 50 kph (30 mph) in the strong desert winds. Contact the ONTT for details. In Douz the Pégase company (tel: 75 470 793) offers rides in a **hot air balloon** or **light aircraft** over the desert.

## Horse-Riding and Camel Treks
Fine Arab horses and ponies can be hired for a canter along the beaches at Gammarth, Sousse, Jerba and Hammamet, at reasonable prices. More serious riding can be arranged

through your hotel or the local tourist office.

You can try the delights of **camel riding** along most of the tourist beaches, and at the oasis communities of Tozeur and Douz. The latter also offer guided, multi-day camel treks into the desert, travelling from well to well and camping in nomad tents. For full details contact the ONTT (see page 128).

Camel trek into the desert

## Hunting

The hunting season for wild boar, hare, fox and mongoose is September to March, in the hills of Cap Bon, and in the forests around Tabarka and Aïn Draham. Licences and import permits for firearms must be organised through a travel agent well in advance. Further details from the ONTT or www.argotraveltunisia.com.

## Golf

The first golf course in Tunisia the Carthage Golf Club was built at La Soukra, near Tunis, in 1924, and is still welcoming visitors. There are nine other courses: the championship courses at Port el Kantaoui, which hosts the Tunisian Open every April; a course at Tabarka, surrounded by oak and pine woods; two challenging courses at Hammamet, two in Monastir, one at Midoun in Jerba, and the newest one in Tozeur. Equipment and caddies can be hired, and advance reservations are recommended. Some package tour companies also offer **golfing holidays** in Tunisia; for details contact a travel agent or www.golftunisia.com.

## Bird-Watching

During spring and autumn millions of migratory birds pass through Tunisia on their way to and from their summer nesting grounds in Europe, making use of the short sea crossing between Cap Bon and Sicily. The most impressive species are the **birds of prey**, which include sparrowhawks, peregrine falcons, buzzards, eagles and kites. Peregrines nest on the crags at the cape, and there is a falconry festival at nearby El Haouaria *(see page 54).*

Good places to see **wading birds**, especially flamingo, avocet and spoonbill, are the lagoons (known as *sebkhet*) and salt-marshes that fringe the eastern coast. The Kerkenna Islands, off the coast near Sfax, are the place to spot orioles and stone curlews. Lac Ichkeul National Park, near Bizerte, is North Africa's most important waterfowl site, providing a wintering ground for many varieties of wader, duck and goose. The best time to visit is between October and February, when rafts of wigeon, pochard and coot cover the water's surface as far as the eye can see. Rare birds on the lake include white-headed duck, little bittern and the spectacular purple gallinule.

# ENTERTAINMENT

You will always be able to find plenty to do in Tunisia, and for added entertainment most of the resort hotels put on shows for their guests.

## Nightlife

Most resort hotels have their own bars, nightclubs and discos, and some will also arrange tours to small night-spots in nearby towns. In addition they may arrange a *soirée folklorique* (folklore evening) each week, at which a typical Tunisian dinner is accompanied by local folk music, snake charmers, dancing and maybe a belly dancer as well.

Outside the resorts, Tunis is the only place that offers European-style bars or clubs, most of them in the streets around avenue Bourguiba. There is also a lively café society in the coastal suburbs of Sidi Bou Saïd and La Marsa. Nightlife in the smaller towns consists of a stroll along the main avenue, followed by animated conversation in one of the various cafés.

Nightlife everywhere perks up during Ramadan *(see page 97)*, when Muslims do not eat or drink during the hours of daylight. For four weeks, the evening is a time for feasting and celebrations that last well into the small hours.

Hammamet has an International Cultural Centre, where dramatic and musical events are held in the opulent grounds

The Carthage International Festival at the Roman theatre

of a luxurious former private estate *(see page 51)*. Displays of traditional Tunisian music and dance are regularly staged in the romantic setting of Hammamet's medieval kasbah, and at the *ribats* (fortified monasteries) of Sousse and Monastir.

## Folklore

One of the shows that is regularly staged for tourists is a traditional wedding – a Tunisian bride dressed for her wedding is a splendid sight. Her costume is made of variegated silks and cloth of gold and silver, all of which are set off by a king's ransom in jewellery – rings, bangles, earrings, head-dresses, necklaces, brooches, belts and sashes – and her hands and feet are decorated with henna patterned in intricate, lacy designs.

Real weddings are traditionally held in the summer, when relatives who have gone to work abroad come home for a holiday. Processions of merrymakers in cars and trucks wind through the town on a wedding day, honking on horns, banging on drums and playing the pipes. Celebrations may last for as long as a week, and visitors are more than welcome to join in the festivities – in Tunisia, weddings are public events at which everyone is encouraged to join in, whether they are acquainted with the happy couple or not.

## Festivals

Tunisia's major national festivals are all religious in nature. The dates they fall on are determined by the lunar calendar, with the result that each time they fall about 11 days earlier than the previous year *(see page 126)*.

For the month of **Ramadan**, all Muslims must abstain from eating, drinking, smoking and sex during the hours of daylight; exceptions are made for travellers, children, pregnant women and warriors engaged in a *jihad* (holy war). As soon as the sun sets, however, that all changes, and the evenings are given over to eating, drinking and revelry – street entertainment is often staged in the form of travelling storytellers, musicians and puppet shows. The end of Ramadan is marked by the feast of **Aïd es Seghir**, which is a national holiday. **Aïd el Kebir** (or **Aïd el Idha**) is a commemoration of Abraham's test of faith, when God commanded him to sacrifice his son Isaac. It is a time for family reunions, at which most families will slaughter a sheep in tribute to Abraham's trial. The feast of **Mouloud**, which marks the birthday of the Prophet Mohammed, is accompanied by special prayers and ceremonies. In particular it is a major festival for the holy city of Kairouan.

There are many other festivals during the year, including harvest festivals and arts festivals *(see opposite)*.

## TUNISIA FOR CHILDREN

Tunisia makes an excellent destination for a family holiday. The sandy beaches and sheltered shallow waters along the east coast offer a safe playground for children of all ages, while the resorts offer all kinds of facilities to entertain the younger ones, including beach games, paddling pools, camel rides, video games, table tennis, volleyball courts, miniature golf, sand-castle contests, discos for children under 16, and sometimes a weekly snake-charmer show.

Take the family for a ride in a *calèche* in the Gabès palmery

Most of the better hotels offer child-minding services, so that parents can enjoy an evening all to themselves.

# Calendar of Festivals

Tunisia stages numerous traditional festivals, as well as festivals of the arts. Check the exact dates with the tourist office.

**February** Modern Poetry Festival in Tozeur.

**March–April** Festival of the *Ksour* around Tataouine: reconstructions of Bedouin and Berber life. Orange Blossom Festival in Menzel Bouzelfa, Cap Bon. International Spring Festival at Kairouan: folklore, poetry, music, film, etc. Octopus festival in Kerbennah Islands.

**May** Jewish pilgrimage to the Ghriba synagogue at Jerba. Matanza of the Tuna in Sidi Daoud, Cap Bon.

**June** Falcon Festival at El Haouaria, Cap Bon. Dougga International Festival: classical drama in the Roman amphitheatre.

**July** Yasmine Hammamet Festival: cultural events. Thoroughbred Horse Festival, Meknassy (Sidi Bouzid).

**July–August** Carthage International Festival: drama, music, film and dance in the Roman theatre. Tabarka Jazz Festival. Festival of Ulysses at Houmt-Souk, Jerba: local folk music and dance. Sousse International Festival: music, drama, dance, etc. El Jem International Festival of Symphonic Music. Monastir International Festival: drama, ballet, film and music in the *ribat*. Testour International Festival of Arab and Traditional Music: musical groups from Tunisia, the Maghreb, the Middle East and Spain. International Festival of Dougga. International Festival of Symphonic Music at El Jem.

**August** Hammamet Festival: concerts and drama at the International Cultural Centre. Festival of the Sirens at Kerkenna: celebration of the sea and traditional weddings. Aoussou Festival at Sousse: music and folklore.

**September** Wine Festival at Grombalia, Cap Bon. International Rai Music Festival in Tabarka.

**October** Film Festival of Carthage (biennial). *Octobre Musical*: classical music in the Acropolium, Carthage.

**November** Oasis Festival in Tozeur: Jerid folklore, camel races, fantasias.

**December** Olive Tree Festival, celebrating the harvest in Kalaa Kebira. Sahara Festival Douz: camel races, fantasias, sand hockey and poetry; www.douz.org.

# EATING OUT

The dishes that make up a traditional Tunisian dinner reflect the culinary influences of the different peoples who have occupied the country in centuries past – couscous from the original Berbers, olives and olive oil from the Romans, coffee and spices from the Arabs, and honey-soaked pastries from the Turks. The French introduced restaurants and the idea of separate courses (eating out was not part of traditional Tunisian culture). In fact, the best way that you can sample true Tunisian cuisine is as a guest in a Tunisian home; but only a lucky few will receive such an invitation.

## Where to Eat

You can choose from a range of eating places. The basic café-restaurant called a *gargotte* is aimed primarily at local people, perhaps with a few tables set out on the pavement. It serves cheap, solid fare such as couscous, meatballs, soup, salad and bread, at very low prices. Even cheaper is the *rôtisserie*, a Tunisian-style fast-food stall, where you can fill up for a few dinars; they serve mostly fried food, which you eat standing at the counter. In the tourist resorts, European-style fast-food restaurants sell the usual burgers, chips (fries) and pizzas.

There are French-style cafés and patisseries in the larger cities and tourist towns, where you can enjoy a croissant, cake or pastry washed down with coffee, mint tea or fruit juice. Bistro-style restaurants often offer a mix of Tunisian, French and Italian classic dishes, while in Tunis and the more upmarket resorts there are a few top-quality contemporary Tunisian or French restaurants. Prices are often higher near a waterfront, or if the restaurant has a panoramic view. Along the coast, fish restaurants that take advantage of the Mediterranean's abundant seafood are perhaps the best of all the eating options.

Relaxing with a mint tea and a waterpipe in a medina café

Away from the cities and resorts there are very few restaurants, and, if you are travelling off the beaten track, it's most probable that you'll end up eating at your hotel. Women travelling alone should be aware that once you get away from the tourist resorts, cafés become a strictly male preserve, and a woman on her own is very likely to attract a lot of unwanted attention.

## Meal Times

**Breakfast**. In the resort hotels, breakfast is usually a self-service buffet; in smaller hotels you will be given a pot of coffee, fruit juice and a basket of croissants, pastries, bread, butter and jam. Breakfast is generally served between 7 and 9.30am. As a change from the hotel, you might like to join the locals in the patisserie and enjoy a coffee and croissant, or perhaps a traditional doughnut-like fritter, known as a *ftair*, at a sidewalk table.

**Lunch and dinner**. Lunch is eaten between noon and 3pm, while dinner is served between about 7 and 9pm. In areas away from Tunis and the tourist resorts, you are unlikely to find anywhere still serving food after 9.30 in the evening.

The standard Tunisian dinner offered at tourist restaurants consists of *chorba* (soup) followed by *brik* (stuffed crispy pancake) and then a main course of couscous, before finishing off with a dessert of fresh fruit or *maqroudh* (sweetmeats). All Tunisian meals are accompanied by a small dish of oily, red-coloured chilli sauce called *harissa* (be careful – it is very hot) and bread, which is always fresh and crusty.

French tradition: bread is served with all meals

The majority of Tunisians now enjoy French-style baguettes, but you can still find the round, flat, unleavened loaves common throughout the Arab world. It is not unusual for Tunisians to eat without cutlery, using their fingers and a piece of bread to scoop up food. If you wish to do the same, be very sure to use your right hand only – the left is reserved for ritual ablutions.

## Classic Tunisian Dishes

**Appetisers**. The most common starter is *chorba*, an oily, peppery soup thickened with pasta. Also very popular is *salade méchouia*, which is a delicious cold dish of roasted, skinless sweet peppers, tomatoes and onions, all garnished with chunks of tuna and hard-boiled egg.

For a uniquely Tunisian dish, try the *brik à l'œuf*, a pastry envelope containing an egg, sealed and fried in olive oil until crisp, and eaten with your fingers. This requires skill. You will fre-

---

### Casse-croûte

A popular sandwich is the *casse-croûte*, a baguette filled with a mixture of potatoes, boiled or fried, tomato, egg, tuna, lettuce and little black olives, the whole thing seasoned with spicy *harissa*.

---

quently also find *brik* served with other fillings, such as vegetables and seafood. *Doigts de Fatima* ('Fatima's fingers') are rolled-up *briks* stuffed with chicken, tuna, egg and cheese. A *salade tunisienne* (Tunisian salad) is usually a finely chopped mixture of cucumber, green pepper, tomato and onion, dressed with oil and vinegar and then flavoured with fresh coriander. Meat grills are popular as a main course: *merguez* are tasty spicy lamb sausages, *brochettes* are small cubes of lamb on skewers and *kefta* are meatballs of minced lamb on a skewer, all grilled on a charcoal grill.

However, the most typical main course of all is, of course, **couscous**. Of Berber origin and found all over North Africa, it consists of a heap of semolina grains that have been steamed over a stew of vegetables and meat or fish. Every housewife and chef has his or her own private recipe. The meat is usually chicken or lamb, and the vegetables are carrot, chick peas, squash and courgette (zuccini), all flavoured with herbs and spices. The stock is coloured red with tomato purée or, if it is a fish broth, yellow with saffron. If you prefer, it's always possible to ask for your couscous '*sans viande*' (without meat), although vegetarians should be aware that the vegetables have probably been cooked in meat stock.

Tunisians also eat all kinds of meat stews. *Kamounia* is a chicken, lamb or beef casserole, cooked long and slow and

A favourite starter, the *brik* can have a variety of stuffings

strongly flavoured with cumin. You will have to visit one of the better restaurants to find it. *Mirmiz* is a stew containing lamb and broad beans in a spicy sauce. *Koucha fil Kolla* is a lamb casserole sprinkled with rosemary and spices, baked in its own juices in a sealed clay pot. The pot is ceremonially broken open at your table. *Doulma* is a dish with Turkish origins: green peppers or marrow (squash), stuffed with meat, parsley, onion and egg.

Dishes based on eggs are popular: *ojja* consists of small pieces of meat or fish (or occasionally brains) cooked in a sauce of tomatoes, hot peppers, garlic, mint, coriander and caraway, and scrambled with eggs to make a tasty and unusual dish. A *chakchouka* is a kind of ratatouille of sweet peppers, chick peas, onions and eggs, seasoned with lemon.

In Tunisia, a *tajine* is not the slow-cooked stew found in Morocco but more like a chunky omelette based on a vegetable-and-egg mixture cooked in an earthenware casserole – similar to a quiche, but without the pastry. They are often flavoured with spinach or cheese.

**Fish and seafood**. The waters off Tunisia provide a rich harvest of fish. Red mullet *(rouget)*, sea bream *(daurade)*, sardines, tuna *(thon)*, grouper *(mérou)* and sea bass *(loup de mer)* head the list. Fish can be used in *ojja* or couscous, but is more often grilled or poached and served alone as a main course.

Tunisian waters also yield a wonderful selection of seafood *(fruits de mer)*, particularly octopus *(poulpe)*, squid *(calamar)* and prawns *(crevettes)*. A popular starter is *brik aux fruits de mer*, a *brik* filled with prawns and flaked fish in a sauce of cream and white wine.

**Desserts**. Fresh fruit – melons, watermelons, tangerines, peaches, figs, dates and apricots – is often served to round off a meal, but when it comes to desserts, the Tunisians have a very sweet tooth. A classic sweet is *baklawa*, which is alternating layers of thin pastry and ground nuts soaked with honey. The holy city of Kairouan is famous for *maqroudh*, little cakes of honey-soaked semolina pastry stuffed with date paste.

*Assida* is a sweet custard with hazelnuts, milk and eggs, decorated with pistachios, crushed hazelnuts and pine nuts, and served as a special treat on festive occasions. *Mesfouf* is a fine sweet version of couscous with cinnamon, nuts, dates and raisins, served as a dessert at celebrations such as wedding parties.

Dates, fresh or prepared, appear in many desserts

## Drinks

**Coffee** is available in French-style cafés, and is generally served strong and black *(café espresso)*. If you would like an espresso with milk added, ask for *crème espresso*. For a large, milky coffee, you should order *café au lait*. There's also *café turc* (Turkish style), black and sweet, served with the grounds in a tiny cup.

**Mint tea**, or *thé à la menthe*, is a delicious and refreshing drink which is made from an infusion of green tea with sprigs of fresh mint, sweetened with sugar. It is usually served in small tulip-shaped glasses. In the south of the country, the mint is sometimes replaced by almonds or verbena. Ordinary tea, *thé rouge*, is stewed for hours, and is served very strong and very sweet.

You should avoid drinking tap water, especially in the south. **Mineral water** *(eau minérale)* is available in all restaurants; still *(plate)* or sparkling *(gazeuse)*. In summer, cafés and patisseries offer sweet, refreshing lemonade, made from the whole lemon, including the peel.

Although Islam forbids the consumption of alcohol, wine, beer and spirits are available in hotels, bars and restaurants in tourist resorts. Tunisian **wines** are very palatable and well worth trying. The Phoenicians planted vineyards soon after they colonised Tunisia, so the country can claim more than 2,000 years of wine-production history. Nowadays, around 85 percent of the vineyards are on the Cap Bon peninsula.

The best Tunisian wines are strong and good quality, but can be hard to find, as some of them are exported. Some

## The Tea-Making Ceremony

In a Tunisian home, the honour of the friendly ritual of the tea-making ceremony usually falls to an important guest.

The curvy teapot of silver, pewter or blue enamel is rinsed with boiling water. Green tea and a sprig of mint are jammed into the pot and scalded with a small amount of boiling water, which is swished around and then poured away. Sugar is added, and the pot filled with boiling water from a copper kettle. It infuses for a few minutes, then the teapot is held high, a glass is filled, and the contents poured back into the pot. A second glass is filled and tasted for sweetness, more sugar is added if necessary and the tea, finally, is served.

of the best include the Sélian wines, Château St Augustin, and the excellent Jour et Nuit – the white a delicate mix of Chardonnay and Sauvignon grapes, and the red a more powerful Merlot-Syrah combination. Many old favourites, like the red Magon, the full-bodied Vieux Magon, Château Feriani and the dry Blanc de Blanc and Sidi Rais, are still good too.

Most Tunisian wine comes from the Cap Bon peninsula

Tunisia's best-known rosés are slightly sharp and need to be well chilled. The best are St Augustin Gris, Rosé Magon, Gris de Tunisie and Jour et Nuit Gris. Unique among Tunisian wines is Muscat Sec de Kélibia, a medium-dry, fruity white wine made with the muscat grape usually used for sweet wines.

Many French aperitifs and liqueurs are available in cafés and bars, but are somewhat more expensive than local products. *Thibarine* is a Tunisian date liqueur, while *boukha* is a dry fig brandy. In Jerba you may be offered the local firewater, *laghmi*, made with the fermented sap of the palm tree.

The only widely available Tunisian beer is a rather watery light lager called Celtia.

## To Help You Order …

| | |
|---|---|
| Do you have a set-price menu? | **Avez-vous un menu à prix fixe?** |
| I'd like… | **J'aimerais…** |
| The bill, please | **L'addition** (or **la note**) **s'il vous plait** |

# HANDY TRAVEL TIPS

## An A–Z Summary of Practical Information

# A

## ACCOMMODATION (logement; hôtel – see also CAMPING, YOUTH HOSTELS and the list of RECOMMENDED HOTELS)

**Resort hotels.** These are usually first class, well run and reasonably priced – especially if your room is included as part of a package tour. Single rooms can be expensive.

**Hotels.** All major towns have a good range of hotels, and it's usually possible to find both bargain and luxury accommodation. All hotels are rated by the National Tourist Office (ONTT; see page 128), ranging from one to four stars, plus a five-star luxury category. Rates should be quoted to you with breakfast, service and taxes included, and prices must by law be posted in each room, usually on the back of the door. (On arrival, be sure to check whether the quoted price is per person or per room.) Prices are considerably cheaper during the low season, between October and May.

**Pensions.** There are an increasing number of small, family-run establishments offering modest but comfortable accommodation.

**Marhalas.** The Touring Club of Tunisia and the Tunisian government have established *marhalas* (simple inns) in historic buildings. In Houmt Souk, Kairouan and Nefta, they are in converted *caravanserais;* in Matmata one is in a troglodyte dwelling; and in the far south several *ksour* (fortified villages) have been converted.

| Do you have a single/double room for tonight? | Avez-vous une chambre pour une/deux personne(s) pour cette nuit? |
|---|---|
| What's the rate per night? | Quel est le prix pour une nuit? |

## AIRPORTS (aéroports)

**Tunis-Carthage International Airport** (tel: 71 75 000) is 8km (5 miles) northeast of Tunis city centre. Facilities include a duty-free shop, currency exchange, travel agencies, car-hire (rental) desks, restaurant and coffee bar. Porters are available to help with luggage. Taxis can be picked up outside the terminal, and take about 15 minutes to reach the city centre. The No. 35 bus service runs from 6am to 9pm every ½ hour. The more luxurious TUT bus leaves every ¼ hour.

Charter airlines fly into **Monastir Airport** at Skanès (tel: 73 520 000), 8km/5 miles west of Monastir. It too offers good facilities. Package tourists will be met by a coach; independent travellers can take the No. 52 bus (departing on the hour, 30-minute journey) or the Metro (the station is just 200m from the terminal) to Monastir, Mahdia or Sousse. Trains run every 45 minutes between 5am and 10pm. A taxi to the town centre takes about 30 minutes.

## B

### BICYCLE AND MOPED HIRE *(location de bicyclettes/motos)*

Bicycles and mopeds can be hired by the hour or day in some resorts. A cash deposit (or credit card) is required, and a valid licence for anything larger than 50cc. Inspect the bike carefully before taking it, and check that the quoted rates for mopeds and motorbikes include tax and insurance.

### BUDGETING FOR YOUR TRIP

To give you an idea of what to expect, here's a list of prices in Tunisian dinars (D) and millimes (M). These can only be regarded as approximate, as inflation continues to push costs up.

**Airport transfer.** Taxi, Tunis Airport to city centre, 6D (8D at night); bus, 750M. Metro, Monastir Airport to Monastir, 1D.

**Bicycle and moped hire.** Bicycles 4D/hour, 15D/day. Mopeds 10D/hour, 40D/day.

**Buses.** Tunis city buses charge a flat fare of 500M. Inter-city coaches from Tunis to Sousse cost 8–10D; Tunis to Tabarka 9–12D; Tunis to Kairouan 9D.

**Camping.** In official sites, around 4–5D per person per night, plus 4–5D for a car, and 5D for a caravan.

**Car hire.** Renault Super 5 – 50D plus 350M per km for 1 day, and 420–500D for 7 days (unlimited km). Petrol costs 850M per litre.

**Excursions.** Day trip from Hammamet to Tunis, Carthage and Sidi Bou Saïd, 50D. Three-day Land Rover 'safari' around southern Tunisia from Sousse, 220–250D.

**Ferries.** Car ferry from Jorf to Jerba, 800M per car; from Sfax to Kerkennah Isles, 4.500D per car, 800M per person.

**Hotels.** *See* RECOMMENDED HOTELS, *page 134.*

**Meals and drinks.** Coffee 800M–25D; soft drinks 700M–1.500D; beer 1.500–2D; bottle of mineral water 1D. Meals, per head, excl. drink: lunch in café, 5–10D; lunch in waterfront restaurant, 25D; dinner in hotel, 20–25D; dinner in good restaurant, 30+D.

**Metro.** Tunis city centre to the Bardo Museum, 900M. The TGM train from the city centre to Sidi Bou Saïd costs 1D one way.

**Sightseeing.** Admission to most museums and archaeological sites is 1–2D; the Bardo, Carthage, El Djem and Kairouan cost 5–700D. There is a 1D surcharge for camera or video.

**Taxis.** The fare for a cross-town trip in Tunis is 3–4D.

**Trains.** From Tunis to Sousse, first class, 10D; Tunis to Gabès, first class, 20D. The *Lézard Rouge* tourist train costs 20D round trip from Metlaoui.

# C

## CAMPING (le camping)

To date, Tunisia has only a few official camping sites with electricity, water and shops. The most popular are at Hammam-Lif (20km/12 miles east of Tunis), Hammamet, Nabeul, Gabès and Zarzis. Elsewhere you can camp almost anywhere, except on the Sahel beaches. Always use discretion and good sense, and ask permission from the landowner or the local police. The ONTT (see

Tourist Information Offices) has current prices and information about recognised camping sites.

## CAR HIRE *(location de voitures – see also Driving)*

Renting a car is an ideal but expensive way of exploring Tunisia. There are numerous rental firms in the tourist resorts and main towns; local firms often charge less than the big international chains, but the cars may not be as good. Rates vary, and you should shop around – the best rates are usually found by booking and paying for a car before leaving home. Check that the quoted rate includes unlimited mileage, Collision Damage Waiver, Personal Accident Insurance and Value Added Tax (TVA in Tunisia).

Usually you must be over 21 to hire a car. You will need a full, valid driving licence, held for at least 12 months, a passport and a major credit card – cash deposits are prohibitively large.

| | |
|---|---|
| I'd like to hire a car now/tomorrow for one day/a week | **Je voudrais louer une voiture tout de suite/demain pour une journée/une semaine** |

## CLIMATE

Northern and central Tunisia enjoy a Mediterranean climate, with hot, dry summers and mild, rainy winters. The coastal resorts are hot and sunny from mid-May to mid-September, though at either end of the season the evenings can be chilly. The hills of the north coast are the wettest part of the country. The desert of southern Tunisia has little rainfall and summer temperatures of over 40°C (104°F). The sea tempers the coastal climate, and Jerba's maximum of around 30°C (86°F) is more comfortable.

The following chart shows the average daily maximum temperatures for each month in Tunis and Jerba, and the sea temperatures on Tunisian beaches:

| | | J | F | M | A | M | J | J | A | S | O | N | D |
|---|---|---|---|---|---|---|---|---|---|---|---|---|---|
| Tunis | °C | 11 | 12 | 13 | 16 | 19 | 24 | 26 | 26 | 26 | 20 | 16 | 12 |
| | °F | 52 | 54 | 55 | 61 | 66 | 75 | 79 | 79 | 79 | 68 | 61 | 54 |
| Jerba | °C | 11 | 13 | 16 | 19 | 21 | 24 | 27 | 28 | 26 | 23 | 16 | 14 |
| | °F | 52 | 55 | 61 | 66 | 69 | 75 | 81 | 82 | 79 | 75 | 61 | 52 |
| sea temp | °C | 14 | 13 | 14 | 16 | 18 | 21 | 24 | 26 | 26 | 24 | 17 | 11 |
| | °F | 57 | 55 | 57 | 61 | 64 | 69 | 75 | 79 | 79 | 75 | 63 | 52 |

## CLOTHING

From June to September lightweight cottons are best, but remember a jacket or sweater for the evenings. Remember also a long-sleeved shirt and sun hat to protect against the strong midday sunshine. At other times a light jacket and a raincoat or umbrella will be handy, plus a warm coat for cool desert nights.

Respectable clothing should be worn if you are away from the beach or hotel, especially in mosques and other Islamic monuments – long trousers or skirt and long-sleeved shirt or blouse are best.

## COMMUNICATIONS

(See also OPENING HOURS and TIME DIFFERENCES)

**Post.** Post offices *(la poste)* are marked by a yellow sign with the letters PTT. For stamps, go to the counter marked *timbres*. Stamps can also be bought at tobacconists' kiosks *(tabacs)* and hotel desks, and at tourist shops that sell postcards. Letters and cards to the UK take about four or five days to arrive.

| | |
|---|---|
| A stamp, please. | **Un timbre, s'il vous plaît.** |
| airmail | **par avion** |

**Telephones and internet.** Domestic and international calls can be made from public telephones in the main post office, from *Taxi-*

*phone* agencies or from call boxes on the street *(cabines)*, which take 100M, 500M, TD1 and TD5 coins. There are Publitel and Taxiphone offices almost everywhere.

To make a call, lift the receiver, insert your coins, and simply dial the number, which is always eight digits. Note that there are no longer any area codes; the first two digits, which now always begin with a 7, are treated as part of the number.

To make an international call, dial 00 and wait for a second tone, then dial the country code (UK: 44; USA and Canada: 1), and the full number including area code, minus the initial zero. To make a reverse-charge (collect) call, dial the international operator and ask to be connected to an operator in your home country.

There are still relatively few internet cafés, except in Tunis and the main resorts, where it should be no problem to find one.

## COMPLAINTS

Complaints should first be made to the management of the establishment involved. If this doesn't work, request the complaints book *(livre des réclamations)*; the law requires that all hotels, restaurants and official guides provide one. Usually, just demanding it will settle the matter; if not, then seek advice from the local branch of the ONTT (see TOURIST INFORMATION OFFICES).

## CRIME AND SAFETY (See also EMERGENCIES and POLICE)

Tunisia has a low crime rate. However, the usual precautions should still be taken when travelling: don't carry large amounts of cash; leave valuables in the hotel safe; and beware of pickpockets. Never leave bags or valuables on view in a parked car – take them with you or lock them in the boot (trunk). Any theft or loss must be reported immediately to the police in order to comply with your travel insurance. If your passport is lost or stolen, you should also inform your consulate.

In public, women should take care to dress conservatively and refrain from going out alone to avoid the possibility of harrassment.

## CUSTOMS (douane) AND ENTRY REQUIREMENTS

Citizens of the EU, USA, Canada and Japan need only a passport and return ticket for visits of up to 90 days; the passport must be valid for a minimum of three months after the date you arrive. You will have to fill in an immigration form before your flight lands: hand it to the immigration officer, with your passport, on arrival. He will stamp both copies and return one to you: keep this with you at all times, as it serves as your identity card when in Tunisia.

**Visas.** Citizens of Australia and South Africa can get a 90-days visa at the airport. Other nationalities need to apply before arrival at any Tunisian embassy. (Visa regulations change from time to time, and should be checked with your travel agent.)

**Duty-free allowance.** People over 18 years of age are allowed to take the following duty-free into Tunisia: 400 cigarettes or 50 cigars or 500g of tobacco; 2 litres of wine and 1 litre of spirits; 250 ml of perfume or 1 litre of toilet water.

**Currency restrictions.** You can take as much foreign currency as you like into or out of the country, but anything more than the equivalent of 500 dinars must be declared on entry. The amount of dinars you can re-convert on departure must not exceed 30 percent of the total of all your exchange receipts, up to a maximum of 100 dinars, so keep all currency exchange receipts. It is illegal to import or export Tunisian dinars.

| | |
|---|---|
| I've nothing to declare. | **Je n'ai rien à déclarer.** |
| It's for my personal use. | **C'est pour mon usage personnel.** |

## D

## DRIVING (See also CAR HIRE)

The minimum legal age for driving in Tunisia is 21 years old. Motorists planning to take their own vehicle into the country will need a full driving licence, an International Motor Insurance Certificate ('Green Card') and a Vehicle Registration Document. A nationality plate must be displayed near the rear number plate, and headlamp beams must be adjusted for driving on the right. A red warning triangle must be carried. Motorcycle riders and their passengers must wear crash helmets. Full details are available from automobile associations or your insurance company.

| (international) driving licence | **permis de conduire (international)** |
|---|---|
| car registration papers | **carte grise** |
| insurance certificate | **certificat d'assurance** |

**Driving conditions.** Drive on the right, pass on the left. Speed limits are 110kph (70mph) on the motorway, 100kph (60mph) on highways and 50kph (30mph) in towns and cities. Traffic joining a road from the right has priority, unless signs or markings indicate otherwise. Most importantly, this means that cars already on a roundabout must give way to those joining it (ie, the opposite of what happens in most other countries). One local quirk you should be prepared for is that drivers making a left turn on a two-lane road often cross to the wrong side of the road before turning. This can be rather disconcerting if you are travelling in the opposite direction.

Outside the cities, the main routes are generally good, with long, straight stretches and little traffic. Minor roads are often wide enough for one vehicle only, and you will have to move onto the gravel shoulder to pass oncoming traffic. Look out for pedestrians, donkey carts and mopeds, especially near towns, where the former two often wander across the road without any apparent concern for their own safety. They also make driving after dark particularly hazardous.

If you do plan to explore off the main routes, a reliable road map is essential. Many of the minor roads are unsurfaced, and should not be attempted without a four-wheel-drive vehicle and a local guide (hire cars are not insured for unsurfaced roads). Many of the minor roads in the south can be rendered impassable by flash floods.

**Petrol.** Petrol *(essence)* and diesel *(gazoile)* are easily obtained. There are plenty of service stations in and around towns, but they can be few and far between in the south, so always fill up at the beginning of the day when you are travelling in the more remote areas. Most cars take premium grade *(super)*; unleaded petrol *(sans-plomb)* is available only in the larger towns.

| Fill the tank, please. | **Le plein, s'il vous plaît.** |

**Parking.** Parking is rarely a problem, except in central Tunis, where illegally parked cars will be towed away. The best idea is to choose a hotel in Carthage or Sidi Bou Saïd where you can leave your car, and take the Metro into the city centre.

**Traffic police.** Motorcycle police patrol the main highways, and quite often set up checkpoints. You may be asked to produce your passport and registration or car-hire documents, but once the officer realises that you are a tourist, he will usually just wave you on. A policeman will sometimes wave you down to ask for a lift either for himself or for a friend.

**Breakdown.** In most towns there should be no problem finding a mechanic for minor repairs. Larger towns and cities have full repair shops and towing services. If you break down in the more remote parts of the country, you will probably have to rely on assistance from passing cars, or carry out repairs yourself. If you have a hire car, follow the procedure set by the hire company – there will usually be a 24-hour emergency telephone number that

| My car has broken down. | **Ma voiture est en panne.** |
| There's been an accident. | **Il y a eu un accident.** |

you can call. Anyone planning to travel off the main roads in the south of the country should be prepared: a four-wheel-drive vehicle, equipped for desert survival, is necessary, and you must inform the National Guard post in the nearest town of your proposed route and destination.

**Road signs.** Roads are generally well marked and most directional signs are in both French and Arabic. International pictographs are also used. You may come across some of the following signs in French:

| | |
|---|---|
| **Attention** | Caution |
| **Attention travaux** | Caution, road works |
| **Crue** | Liable to flood during rains |
| **Déviation** | Diversion (detour) |
| **Serrez à droite** | Keep to the right |
| **Défense de stationner** | No parking |
| **Virages** | Bends (curves) |

## E

## ELECTRICITY

200v/50Hz AC is standard. An adapter for two-pin sockets will be needed; American 110v appliances will also require a transformer.

| | |
|---|---|
| an adapter plug | **une prise de raccordement** |
| a battery | **une pile** |

## EMBASSIES AND CONSULATES

**British Embassy:** rue du Lac Windermere, Berges du Lac, tel: 71 108 700, www.britishembassy.gov.uk/tunisia.
**Canadian Embassy:** 3 rue du Sénégal, Tunis, tel: 71 104 000.

**US Embassy:** route de la Marsa, zone Nord-Est, 2045, Berges du Lac, tel: 71 107 000, http://tunis.usembassy.gov.

## EMERGENCIES (See also EMBASSIES and POLICE)

The national emergency telephone number is **197**; it helps if you are fluent in French or Arabic.

| | |
|---|---|
| **Police** | **197** |
| **Ambulance** | **190** |
| **Fire** | **198** |

## ETIQUETTE

It is customary to shake hands on meeting, and then to place your right hand briefly over your heart. If you are invited into a Tunisian home, remember to remove your shoes before entering. Most important of all is dress: away from the beach, you should dress modestly and avoid shorts and skimpy tops. Choose long trousers or a skirt reaching below the knee, with a long-sleeved top; women travelling alone will attract less attention if they wear a headscarf. (See also WOMEN TRAVELLERS.)

## G

## GUIDES AND TOURS

If you are on a package tour, a guide will be provided when you visit Roman ruins or the medina in Tunis. English-speaking guides can be hired independently in popular places such as the Bardo Museum and at major sites such as Dougga.

A number of unofficial 'guides' and hustlers often tout for business around the medina gates. They can be persistent. If you genuinely don't want their services, be firm and polite, and don't lose your temper. If you do decide to engage one, make sure you agree in advance *exactly* what you want to see and the price to be paid (generally about half the cost of an official guide). They will invariably try to take you to a shop, under various pretexts, since they can earn commission from the owner. If you don't want to buy anything, then politely insist on not going in.

## L

## LANGUAGE

The official language of Tunisia is Arabic, but a large proportion of the population is bilingual in Arabic and French; most signs and street names are in both languages. Although written Arabic is the same throughout the Arab world, the spoken dialect of Tunisian Arabic is quite distinctive, and travellers who have learned the Arabic of the Middle East will struggle to get by. In the main destinations many people speak some English, and almost all speak French.

Although Tunisians will always greet you in French or English, it is polite to learn a few basic phrases – local people will welcome any attempt you make:

*Some useful expressions in Arabic:*

| | |
|---|---|
| Good morning | **S'báh 'l khéyr** |
| Hello | **Aslámah** |
| Welcome/hello | **Marhaba beek** |
| Good night | **Tis 'báh 'ala khéyr** |
| Good afternoon | **Msá 'l khéyr** |
| Goodbye | **Beslémeh** |
| Please | **Min fádlak** |
| Thank you | **Bárakallahúfik, ayyishik** |

*Some useful expressions in French:*

| | |
|---|---|
| Does anyone here speak English? | **Y a-t-il quelqu'un ici qui parle anglais?** |
| What does this mean? | **Qu'est-ce que cela veut dire?** |

## LAUNDRY *(blanchissage)*

Even a modest one-star establishment will have a laundry service. Washing should be handed in before noon for return the following morning. Tunis has the only public laundry in the country.

## LOST PROPERTY *(objets trouvés)*

Ask for advice from your hotel receptionist or the local Tourist Information Office before contacting the police. For items left behind on public transport, ask your hotel receptionist to telephone the bus or train station or taxi company.

| | |
|---|---|
| I've lost my handbag/ wallet/passport. | **J'ai perdu mon sac à main /ma portefeuille/mon passeport.** |

## MAPS

Most of the necessary maps are on sale in Tunisia, but maps of Jerba are difficult to find. If you are planning to travel around a lot, you should equip yourself with a good map. The Michelin Algérie-Tunisia 958 is very good, and so is the Kummerly-Frey map of just Tunisia. Tourist information offices will be able to provide you with basic town plans. In Tunis, it's better to buy a good map in a stationer's.

## MEDIA

**Radio.** If you have a short-wave radio you will be able to pick up the BBC World Service and Voice of America. Otherwise, you can listen to local stations which offer a choice of traditional and pop music, or news, sport and current affairs in French or Arabic.

**Television.** You will find a TV supplied in the more expensive hotels. There are four Tunisian channels broadcasting in Arabic and

French. The better hotels also have satellite TV with the French channel TV5, as well as Sky, CNN, MTV and Superchannel.

**Newspapers.** Local French-language papers include *La Presse*, *L'Action* and *Le Temps*, all of which provide a rather thin diet of North African and international news and sports. The French dailies *Le Monde* and *Le Figaro*, and the American *International Herald Tribune* are also widely available on city newsstands. British newspapers can be found, a day or two after publication, on city centre newsstands in Tunis, and in the coastal resorts.

| | |
|---|---|
| Have you any English-language newspapers/magazines? | **Avez-vous des journaux/ des revues en anglais?** |

## MEDICAL CARE (See also EMERGENCIES)

There is no free health care for visitors to Tunisia – all medical services must be paid for. You should not leave home without adequate insurance, preferably including cover for an emergency flight home in the event of serious injury or illness. Your travel agent, bank, building society or insurance broker can provide a comprehensive policy which will cover not only medical costs, but also theft or loss of money and possessions, delayed or cancelled flights and so on.

**Vaccinations.** There are no compulsory immunisation requirements for entry into Tunisia, but inoculations against tetanus, polio, typhoid and hepatitis A are recommended.

**Health hazards.** The main health risks in Tunisia are stomach upsets and sunburn. Take a sun hat, sunglasses and plenty of high-factor sunscreen, and limit your sunbathing sessions to an hour or less until you begin to tan. Sunburn can seriously ruin your holiday.

Diarrhoea can be avoided by eating only freshly cooked food and drinking only bottled water and canned or bottled drinks (without ice). Avoid restaurants that look dirty, food from street stalls, undercooked meat, salads and fruit (except fruit you can peel yourself, such as bananas, oranges, melons etc), dairy products and tap water. The standards of hygiene in most tourist hotels and restaurants are usually adequate, but you can never be sure.

If you are unfortunate enough to catch a stomach bug, rest and take plenty of fluids to avoid dehydration – soft drinks will do, but a solution of four heaped teaspoons of sugar and a half teaspoon of salt in a litre (around 2 pints) of bottled water is best. Most cases go in three or four days; if symptoms persist, seek medical advice.

**Chemists/drugstores.** For minor ailments, ask advice from the local pharmacy *(pharmacie)*. These are usually open during normal shopping hours. After hours, at least one per town remains open all night, called the *pharmacie de service* or *pharmacie de nuit*. Its location is posted in the windows of all other pharmacies.

| | |
|---|---|
| Get a doctor, quickly! | **Un médecin, vite!** |

## MONEY

**Currency** *(La monnaie).* The unit of currency is the Tunisian dinar (D), divided into 1,000 millimes (M). Notes come in denominations of 5D, 10D, 20D and 30D, and coins in 5, 10, 20, 50, 100M, 500M and 5D. The dinar is a soft currency, and the exchange rate is controlled by the government, so there's no point shopping around for the best rate – they're all the same. (See also CUSTOMS & ENTRY REQUIREMENTS.)

**Banks and currency exchange** *(banque; change;* see also OPENING HOURS). The most efficient service is usually the STB *(Société Tunisienne des Banques).* The normal procedure is for the clerk to fill in the forms at the counter, then give you a receipt or token

| | |
|---|---|
| I want to change some pounds/dollars | **Je voudrais changer des livres sterling/dollars** |

which you take to the cashier *(la caisse)* where you pick up your cash. Since this involves queuing twice, changing money in a bank can be a time-consuming business. Most hotels, three-star and above, exchange money as well.

**Travellers cheques** *(chèques de voyages)*. These are accepted by most banks and hotels, though smaller establishments may refuse to cash them and will direct you elsewhere; Thomas Cook and American Express are the most widely accepted. You will need your passport, and occasionally the purchase receipts too; no commission is charged. You can exchange cash easily in hotels and tourist shops.

**Credit cards** *(cartes de crédit)*. Major credit and charge cards are accepted in the more expensive hotels (three-star and up) and restaurants in the larger cities, and by tourist shops and car-hire firms. If you are unsure whether an establishment will accept your card, ask first. Visa and Access/MasterCard can also be used in large branches of banks to obtain cash advances, though this can take time.

| Do you accept travellers cheques/this credit card? | **Acceptez-vous les chèques de voyage/cette carte de crédit?** |
|---|---|

O

## OPENING HOURS *(heures d'ouverture)*

**Archaeological sites.** Generally 8.30am–5.30pm Tue–Sun, sometimes longer in summer.

**Banks.** In winter, normally Mon–Thur 8am–noon and 2–4.30pm, Fri 8am–noon and 1–4.30pm; during Ramadan hours are 8am–2.30pm; and in July and August 7–11.30am only.

**Currency exchange offices.** 8am–8pm daily in popular resorts. Airport desks are open 24 hours, but may close between flight arrivals.

**Museums.** Generally open 9am–noon and 2–5pm. The majority close on Mondays.

**Post offices.** Hours in winter are generally Mon–Fri 8am–noon and 2–6pm, Sat 8am–noon; in summer Mon–Sat 8am–1pm. During Ramadan hours are Mon–Sat 8am–3pm. Main post offices are open longer for the sale of stamps and sending telegrams. In Tunis, Sfax, Houmt Souk and Sousse, these services are available 24 hours a day.

**Shops.** Generally 8am–12.30pm and 2.30–6pm; some close for short periods on Fridays, the Muslim day of rest.

## P

## PHOTOGRAPHY

Film is widely available, but can be expensive. Shops in major resorts process colour prints in 24 to 48 hours at reasonable prices, and some offer a 1-hour service. The use of flash or tripod is forbidden in some museums, so always check. Most museums and archaeological sites charge an extra fee for the use of a camera or video.

Whether in the resorts, the cities or the countryside, if you want to take photos of local people, ask first – many country people in particular object to having their picture taken.

| | |
|---|---|
| I'd like a film. | **Je voudrais un film.** |
| a black-and-white film | **un film noir et blanc** |
| a film for colour prints | **un film couleurs** |
| a colour-slide film | **un film pour diapositives** |

## POLICE *(la police* – see also EMERGENCIES)

Tunisia's civil police *(Sûreté Nationale)* wear blue-grey uniforms. There is a police station *(poste de police or gendarmerie)* in most towns. If you want to report a crime, it is a good idea to get a fluent French or Arabic speaker to help you – your hotel or the local tourist office may assist. In an emergency, dial 197. The *Sûreté* also man traffic checkpoints and patrol the highways (see DRIVING).

| | |
|---|---|
| Where's the nearest police station? | **Où est le commissariat de police le plus proche?** |
| I want to report a theft. | **Je veux signaler un vol.** |
| My ticket/purse/passport has been stolen. | **On a volé mon billet/ porte-feuille/passeport.** |

## PUBLIC HOLIDAYS *(jours fériés)*

Tunisia has two kinds of public holidays: secular holidays (same date each year), and religious holidays (which fall according to the lunar calendar). Many businesses close on these secular holidays:

| | | |
|---|---|---|
| 1 January | *Jour de l'An* | New Year's Day |
| 20 March | *Fête de l'Indépendance* | Independence Day |
| 21 March | *Fête de la Jeunesse* | Youth Day |
| 9 April | *Anniversaire des Martyrs* | Martyrs' Day |
| 1 May | *Fête du Travail* | Labour Day |
| 25 July | *Fête de la République* | Republic Day |
| 13 August | *Fête de la Femme* | Women's Day |
| 15 October | *Evacuation de Bizerte* | Evacuation of Bizerte |
| 7 November | *Fête de la Nouvelle Epoque* | New Era Day |

The religious holidays listed below are marked by two days off. Public transport may be reduced. The dates vary according to the lunar calendar and are often announced only days before the holiday. Check with your travel agent or the Tunisian Embassy for the dates:

| | |
|---|---|
| *Aïd el Kebir* or *Aïd el Adha* | 'Great Feast', commemorating the sacrifice of Abraham |
| *Ras el Am* | Muslim New Year |
| *Mouloud* | Birthday of the Prophet Mohammed |
| *Aïd es Seghir* or *Aïd el Fitr* | 'Little Feast', the end of the month of Ramadan |

Ramadan encompasses the four weeks before Aïd es Seghir, during which many businesses adopt special opening hours, closing at dusk as workers head home to break their fast.

## R

### RELIGION

Tunisia is a Muslim country, but is very tolerant of other faiths. Christians account for only 0.1 percent of the population, but there are Roman Catholic churches in most large towns and tourist resorts, and Anglican and Protestant churches in Tunis. Synagogues can be found in Tunis and Jerba. Details of local religious services are held by the local tourist office (see page 128).

## T

### TIME DIFFERENCES

Tunisia remains one hour ahead of GMT all year round, making it the same time as the UK in summer, and one hour ahead in winter. The table below shows the time difference in various cities when it's summer in the northern hemisphere.

| New York | London | **Tunisia** | Sydney | Los Angeles |
| --- | --- | --- | --- | --- |
| 7am | noon | **noon** | 9pm | 4am |

### TIPPING (pourboires)

It is customary to offer a tip for services rendered: 100–200 millimes is usual for café waiters, porters, petrol-pump attendants and guardians at monuments and museums; restaurant waiters expect 10–15 percent on top of any service charge. If a taxi driver uses his meter, then tip 10–15 percent of the fare; if you agree a price beforehand, nothing extra will be expected.

### TOILETS/RESTROOMS (toilettes; WC)

Public toilets are few and far between outside airports and major railway stations; if you need one in a hurry, try a café or restaurant.

## TOURIST INFORMATION OFFICES
*(office de tourisme; syndicat d'initiative)*

The Tunisian National Tourist Office (*Office National du Tourisme Tunisien* or ONTT) has its head office in Tunis, and branches in towns and resorts throughout the country. The staff can help with general inquiries, advise on local accommodation (no booking service) and provide maps and brochures. The official website of the Tunisian National Tourism Office is www.tourismtunisia.com. It offers information on sights, hotels, restaurants, culture, sports, festivals and shopping.

**Tunis** (head office): 1 avenue Mohamed V, tel: 71 341 077.
**Jerba** (Houmt Souk): blvd de l'Environnment, tel: 75 650 016.
**Hammamet:** avenue de la Republique, tel: 72 280 423.
**Kairouan:** place des Martyrs, tel: 77 231 897.
**Monastir:** place de l'Indépendance, tel: 73 461 960.
**Nabeul:** avenue Taieb M'Hiri, tel: 72 286 800, www.nabeul.net.
**Sousse:** 1 avenue Habib Bourguiba, tel: 73 225 157.
**Tozeur:** avenue Abou el Kacem Chebbi, tel: 76 454 503.

Tourist-office opening hours are generally Mon–Thur 8.30am–1pm and 3–5.45pm, Fri–Sat 8.30am–1.30pm (7.30am–1.30pm Jul–Aug), closed Sun. Most towns also have a *Syndicat d'Initiative*, a local information office. The ONTT maintains a number of overseas offices, from which you can obtain information before you go.

**Canada:** Tunisian Tourist Office, 1253 McGill College, Bureau #655, Montreal, Quebec H3 B2 Y5, tel: (514) 397 1182, email: tunisinfo@qc.aira.com.
**UK:** 77A Wigmore Street, London W1U 1QF, tel: 020 7224 5598, email: www.cometotunisia.co.uk.
**USA:** Tourist Section, Tunisian Embassy, 1515 Massachusetts Avenue NW, Washington DC 20005, tel: (202) 862 1850, email: ezzedine@ix.netcom.com.

## TRANSPORT

**Buses.** Tunisia is covered by a comprehensive bus network. Intercity coaches run by SNTRI *(Société Nationale de Transport Rural et Interurbain)* link Tunis with every major town in the country; regional companies link major towns with villages in the surrounding area. Tickets are cheap and can be bought at the bus station before departure. Timetable information is hard to find; try the local ONTT office or *Syndicat d'Initiative*, or ask a driver. Destinations are displayed in French as well as Arabic. Popular routes, with approximate journey times, are: Tunis–Sousse, 2 hours 15 minutes; Tunis–Kairouan, 2 hours 30 minutes; Tunis–Tabarka, 4 hours; Sousse–Sfax, 2 hours; Sfax–Tozeur, 5 hours 30 minutes.

| | |
|---|---|
| When's the next bus to...? | **Le bus pour... part quand, s'il vous plaît?** |
| single (one-way) | **un aller simple** |
| return (round trip) | **un aller-retour** |

Tunis has good city buses, and maps are posted in the terminals.

**Ferries.** There are two car-ferry services: Jorf to Ajim on the island of Jerba, departing every 30 minutes during the day, less often at night, crossing time 15 minutes; and Sfax to the Kerkennah Islands, four crossings a day in winter and eight in summer, journey time 1 hour 15 minutes.

*Louages.* A faster and slightly more comfortable alternative to the bus for shorter journeys between towns is the *louage*. This is a large estate car seating six passengers, which shuttles back and forth along a set route. There are no fixed departure times; the taxi departs as soon as all the seats are filled. To find a seat, you simply turn up at the 'terminal', usually a piece of waste ground on the edge of the town centre (the tourist office or your hotel will tell you where – there's usually a different location for different destinations), and ask the drivers. Fares are per person for a full car; ask other passengers (or your hotel receptionist) what the standard fare is.

| What's the fare to...? | Quel est le tarif pour...? |
| --- | --- |

**Metro.** Tunis's light rail network is the Metro. The most useful line is Line 4, linking place Barcelone in the centre (via Line 2, change at République) with the Bardo Museum. The Metro is linked (via Tunis Marine station at the foot of avenue Habib Bourguiba) with another railway, the TGM (Tunis–Goulette–Marsa), which runs every 15 minutes during the day to Carthage, Sidi Bou Saïd and La Marsa.

The Sahara Metro links Monastir and Sousse, with stops at Monastir International Airport and the Skanès hotel zone. Trains run hourly from 6am to 10pm.

**Taxis.** See also LOUAGES, above. Taxis can be hailed in the street, or picked up at a rank. Meters are used, and rates are low by European standards. All taxis levy a 50 percent surcharge for night travel (usually 10pm–6am Apr–Sep, 9pm–7am Oct–Mar), when you will probably have to negotiate a price, especially from the airport.

**Trains.** The national rail company, SNCFT (*Société Nationale des Chemins de Fer Tunisiens*, www.sncft.com.tn), maintains a limited but efficient rail network from Tunis north to Tabarka and south to Nabeul, Sousse, Sfax, Gabès, Gafsa and Tozeur. Mainline trains are comfortable and inexpensive (slightly slower but more comfortable than the bus). There are three classes: *grand confort* (luxury), first class and second class. Full timetables *(horaires)* are posted in main stations; buy tickets a day in advance (or you may have to pay double the fare; return tickets are cheaper) for a seat in an air-conditioned carriage *(voiture grand confort)*. From Tunis to Sousse takes about 2 hours; to Gabès, 7 hours.

From July to September, a special tourist train called the *Lézard Rouge* (Red Lizard; tel: 76 241 469) runs from Metlaoui through the spectacular Selja Gorge, hauling restored 19th-century carriages *(see page 72)*.

## TRAVELLERS WITH DISABILITIES

As yet there are very few facilities for disabled travellers in Tunisia. Getting around the city centres, especially the medinas, is difficult in a wheelchair, and most public transport is inaccessible. Some of the more modern beach hotels, however, do have wheelchair access. Ask your tour operator before booking. The national organisation for the disabled, AGIM (*Association Générale des Insuffisants Moteurs*, 1 rue des Bassatines, BP 233, Khaznadar, 2000 Bardo, Tunis; tel: 71 612 687) may be able to help with specific enquiries.

## TRAVELLING TO TUNISIA

### By Air

**Scheduled flights from the UK and Ireland:** The national airline, Tunis Air, www.tunisair.com, flies from London Heathrow to Tunis four times a week, with connecting services to Sfax, Jerba and Nefta-Tozeur. For details call your local Tunis Air office or representative. GB Airways, www.gbairways.com, flies five times a week from London Gatwick to Tunis. For details, contact British Airways. There are no direct flights from Ireland.

**From the USA and Canada:** There are no direct flights from North America to Tunisia; you will have to fly via London, Paris, Amsterdam, Frankfurt or Rome.

**Charter flights and package tours from the UK and Ireland:** (www.charterflights.co.uk) UK charter flights are available from Gatwick, Birmingham, Manchester, Glasgow and several other airports to Monastir. Charter flights from Ireland operate during the summer. These are either flight only (cheaper than a scheduled flight, but with more restrictions), or as part of a hotel or self-catering package holiday. Most companies offer a variety of excursions. An increasingly popular option is the adventure holiday, which combines a week in a coastal resort with a week-long Land Rover safari to the desert oases, Matmata and *ksour* villages of the south. For full details ask a travel agent.

## By Road and Sea

There are car ferries to Tunisia from Marseille (France), Valencia (Spain), Genoa, Salerno (Italy) and Tràpani and Palermo (Sicily). The shortest crossing is from Tràpani to Tunis (7–10 hours; www. lauro.it and www.tirrenia.it) with one crossing a week. Tickets must be bought well in advance, particularly in summer when it gets overbooked. Marseille–Tunis goes 1–6 times a week and takes 21–24 hours; www.ctn.com.tn. Other companies that run ferries from Italian ports to Tunisia are Grandi Navi Veloci, www.gnv.it, and Grimaldi Ferries, www.grimaldi-ferries.com. Timetables are also available from Viamare Travel: www.viamare.com.

### WATER

Although the tap water is said to be safe in most parts of Tunisia, you are advised to avoid it. Bottled mineral water is easily bought – *Safia* and *Aïn Oktor* (still) are the most popular brands; the latter has a strong mineral flavour. *Aïn Garci* is carbonated.

### WEIGHTS AND MEASURES (See also DRIVING)

The metric system – a French invention – is universally used.

| | | |
|---|---|---|
| 1 kilometre | = | 1093 yards or approx 0.6 mile |
| 1 kilogram | = | approx 2.2 lb |
| 1 litre | = | 1.75 pints |

### WOMEN TRAVELLERS

It is unfortunate, but true, that foreign women travelling in Tunisia are sometimes subject to harassment from local men. This can range from catcalls and whistles to rude comments and bottom-pinching. A woman accompanied by a man is less likely to attract unwanted attention, but is not immune.

The way you dress is all-important; shorts and a halter top are not a good idea (although this does not apply to resorts such as Hammamet and Monastir, where beachwear is the norm, nor to downtown Tunis, where Tunisian women dress in Western fashions). The best strategy is to dress modestly, in long trousers or preferably a long skirt, and a long-sleeved, loose-fitting top.

Avoid eye contact with local men and ignore any rude comments. Try not to lose your temper, and don't get into an argument: it's highly likely that you will not get the better of your antagoniser, and you will probably get little in the way of sympathy from passers-by.

Having said this, the majority of Tunisians are courteous and friendly, and will show you genuine hospitality. You just have to keep your wits about you and judge each encounter as it comes.

## Y

### YOUTH HOSTELS (auberge de jeunesse)

Tunisia has two dozen or so basic youth hostels (Auberges de Jeunesse) and youth centres (Maisons des Jeunes). You'll find the best ones are in Tunis, Nabeul, Aïn Draham, Gabès and Houmt Souk. If you're planning to make use of youth hostels during your stay, contact your national youth hostel association before departure to obtain an international membership card. Further information and a full list of hostels in Tunisia are available from the International Youth Hostel Federation (IYHF), Trevelyan House, Dimple Road, Matlock, Derbyshire, DE4 3YH, tel: 01629 592600, www.yha.org.uk. For bookings of youth hostels: www.hihostels.com. In Tunisia, the body responsible is the Association Tunisienne des Auberges et Tourisme de Jeunes, 8 rue d'Alger, BP 320, 1015 Tunis, tel: 71 353 277, www.atatj.org.

# Recommended Hotels

Our selection of hotels is based on the requirements of both group visitors and independent travellers, concentrating on locations that make useful base camps or stop-overs during a tour of Tunisia. If you're travelling independently, most establishments are signposted from the main road.

The official star-rating of each hotel *(see page 109)* is given after its name ('u/c' means 'unclassified'). As a basic guide, the symbols below indicate prices for a double room with bath, including breakfast, in high season:

| | |
|---|---|
| $$$$ | over 100D |
| $$$ | 50–100D |
| $$ | 30–50D |
| $ | below 30D |

## BIZERTE

**Bizerta Resort (\*\*\*\*) $$$$** *Route de la Corniche, tel: 72 436 966, email: hbizerta@gnet.tn.* The best place in town, with indoor and outdoor pools. Right on the sandy beach, 10 minutes' walk from the centre of town, the old port and the medina.

**Petit Mousse (\*\*) $$** *Route de la Corniche, tel: 72 432 185.* Small, friendly, family-run hotel overlooking the beach, 2km (1 mile) out of town along the Corniche, with an excellent restaurant *(see page 140)* and a garden pizzeria in summer. All rooms have a balcony with a sea view. Booking recommended.

## CAP BON

**Dar Hayet (\*\*\*\*) $$$** *33 rue Farhat Hached, Hammamet, tel: 72 283 399, email: dar.hayet@planet.tn.* An attractive blue-and-white hotel with balconied rooms, enjoying a superb position overlooking the beach, with good views of the medina and the coastline. Pleasant swimming pool and indoor and outdoor restaurants.

**Hasdrubal Thalassa & Spa (\*\*\*\*\*) $$$** *South end of Hammamet Yasmine, tel: 72 244 000, www.hasdrubal-hotel.com.* Hammamet's top resort hotel with all watersports facilities and extremely luxurious rooms and gardens.

**Les Jasmins (\*\*\*) $$** *Nabeul, tel: 72 285 343. Off avenue Hedi Nowia, www.hotellesjasmins.com.* An elegant *pension* situated in the middle of an olive grove, between jasmine and pine-trees, 2km (1 mile) from Nabeul on the Hammamet road. Well-known for its handicrafts (pottery, mats, embroidery and carpets); serene ambience.

**Résidence Romane (\*\*) $$** *Rue Assad ben Fourat, centre Hammamet, tel: 72 263 103, email: rommene.sami@gnet.tn.* Friendly family-run hotel with bright attractive rooms, all with clean ensuite bathrooms and balconies.

**Sindbad (\*\*\*\*\*) $$$$** *Avenue des Nations Unies, Hammamet, tel: 72 280 122.* This long-established, low-rise hotel is set in beautiful gardens adjacent to the beach about 1.5km (1 mile) from the medina. The comfortable, well-furnished rooms have either balcony or garden patio. Pool, restaurants. Very friendly staff.

## DOUGGA

**Thugga (\*\*) $$** *Route de Tunis, Teboursouk, tel: 78 466 647.* Comfortable and modern. Rooms on the old courtyard have traditional barrel-vaulted ceilings.

## JERBA

**Dar Dhiafa (\*\*\*\*) $$$$** *Erriadh, Jerba; tel: 75 671 166, www.hoteldardhiafa.com.* Small luxurious boutique hotel with 10 individually decorated rooms and 4 suites occupying several traditional houses in the village. The hotel also has two swimming pools, a hammam (Turkish bath) and a wonderful restaurant.

**Dar Faiza (\*\*\*) $$** *boulevard de l'Environnement, Houmt Souq, tel: 75 757 667, www.darfaizadarsalem.com.* Pleasant three-star family-friendly hotel at the edge of town with clean simple rooms in a lovely garden with a small pool.

**Dar Salem (***) $$** *Zone touristique outside Houmt Souq, tel: 75 757 667, www.darfaizadarsalem.com.* Situated on the beautiful beach of Sidi Mahrez, this delightful hotel has white-and-blue rooms with loggias overlooking either the sea or the lovely gardens. Facilities include a swimming pool and a Tunisian restaurant.

**Marhala (u/c) $** *Rue Moncef Bey, Houmt Souk, tel: 75 650 416.* An old *fondouk*, converted by the *Touring Club de Tunisie* into a basic hotel full of character. Rooms are set around an attractive courtyard with a well and an ancient rainwater cistern. Some rooms share bathroom facilities.

**Les Sables d'Or (u/c) $** *Houmt Souk, tel: 75 650 423.* A charming small hotel in an old house. Rooms surround a central courtyard. Each has its own shower but toilets (impeccably clean) are shared.

## KAIROUAN

**Continental (***) $$$$** *Rue Ibn al Aghlab, tel: 77 232 006.* Kairouan's biggest, smartest hotel, popular with groups. Handy location near the city centre and the tourist office. Very attractive pool.

**La Kasbah (***) $$$–$$$$** *Avenue Ibn el Jazzar, tel: 77 237 30, www.goldenyasmin.com.* The best hotel in town, built behind the facade of the old Kasbah. Delightful pool in the central courtyard, and spacious rooms.

**Splendid (***) $$** *Rue du 9 Avril, tel: 77 230 041.* Grand hotel with tiled decoration and airy rooms. Good restaurant.

## MAHDIA

**Le Phénix (***) $$–$$$** *Avenue Habib Bourguiba, Mahdia, tel: 73 690 101.* Contemporary-styled boutique hotel in the heart of town and near the beach, with spacious rooms, all with floor to ceiling windows and large balconies. Efficient service and a good Tunisian restaurant..

## MATMATA

**Diar el Barbar (****) $$$** *On the Douz Road, Matmata, tel: 75 240 074, www.diarelbarbar.com.* Built like a gigantic cave pit, this hotel offers luxurious mock cave dwellings and a fantastic swimming pool.

**Marhala (u/c) $** *tel: 75 240 015.* An underground hotel occupying one of the old cave houses *(see page 81)*. Probably the best of Matmata's troglodyte hotels, but far from luxurious. Rooms are tiny and basic, facilities shared; bar and restaurant.

## METAMEUR (NEAR MEDENINE)

**Les Ghorfas (u/c) $** *tel: 97 560 533.* Attractive hotel that was once the village *ksar* (a collection of earthen buildings surrounded by high walls). Rooms are small and basic, but comfortable.

## MONASTIR

**Monastir Beach (**) $** *Monastir Beach, tel: 73 464 766, email: monastirbeach@yahoo.com.* Clean, very basic rooms with great views of the beach and ocean.

**Yasmine (u/c) $$** *Route de la Falaise, 2km (1.2 miles) from Monastir, tel: 73 501 546.* Delightful family-run pension away from the crowds. Comfortable, spotless rooms and great breakfast.

## SFAX

**Thyna (***) $$** *37 rue Habib Maazoun; tel: 74 225 317* Modern hotel in the heart of Sfax, just a stone's throw from the entrance to the medina. Good value spacious rooms overlooking the elegant square.

## SOUSSE

**Hasdrubal Thalassa & Spa (\*\*\*\*) $$$** *BP N° 56, Port el Kantaoui, tel: 73 348 944, www.hasdrubal-hotel.com.* Four-star hotel overlooking Port El Kantaoui, with its cobbled streets, restaurants, cafés and marina. Beautiful gardens cascade down to the beach.

**Hotel Medina (\*\*\*) $$** *15 rue Othmane, medina Sousse; tel: 73 221 722.* Charming hotel opposite the Great mosque in the medina of Sousse, with friendly management, large clean rooms and a good Tunisian restaurant.

**Marhaba Club Hotel (\*\*\*) $$,** *Route Touristique, Sousse, tel: 73 242 180, www.marhabahotels.com.tn.* Part of a group of four resort hotels, this mid-range hotel is well situated on the beach, close to central Sousse. Amenities include an indoor and a huge outdoor pool, as well as fitness centre and sauna; good entertainment and nightlife.

**Sousse Azur (\*\*) $$$** *Rue Amilcar, tel: 73 227 760.* Small, friendly hotel off avenue Bourguiba in the town centre. Bright rooms with private bathrooms.

## TABARKA

**Les Aiguilles (\*\*) $–$$** *18 avenue Bourguiba, tel: 78 673 789, www.hotel.lesaiguilles@wanadoo.tn.* Small but comfortable hotel in the centre of town, with pleasant and airy rooms – some with balconies.

**Dar Ismail (\*\*\*\*\*) $$$$** *Zone Touristique, Tabarka; tel : 78 670 188; www.hoteldarismail.com.* Five-star hotel in Moorish design with spacious comfortable rooms, a great garden and large swimming pool.

**Les Mimosas (\*\*\*) $$$$** *Route Touristique, tel: 78 673 018, www.hotel-les-mimosas.com.* Large, comfy rooms with en suite bathrooms. Pool and terrace garden on hillside. Approached by a private driveway on the left just after the turn off to Aïn Draham.

## TOZEUR

**Dar Cheraït (\*\*\*\*\*) $$$$** *Route touristique, Tozeur, tel: 76 454 888, www.darcherait.com.* The most upmarket hotel with luxurious rooms and suites surrounding a large garden with lovely swimming pool. Next door to the museum complex.

**Résidence Karim (u/c) $** *150 avenue Aboul Kacem Chebbi, Tozeur, tel: 76 454 574.* Popular budget option with colourful tiled rooms set around tranquil courtyards filled with bougainvillea, and a lovely rooftop terrace.

## TUNIS

**Dar el Medina (\*\*\*\*) $$$** *64 rue Sidi ben Arous, Tunis medina, tel: 71 563 022, www.darelmedina.com.* Converted mansion of the Belahouen family, who lived here until 2003. The decor is a wonderful blend of traditional medina architecture and contemporary touches.

**Dar Said (\*\*\*) $$$** *Rue Toumi, Sidi Bou Saïd, tel: 71 729 666, www.darsaid.com.tn.* Picturesque 19th-century house in the heart of the village, set around patios with fountains and perfumed trees. Small swimming-pool in a peaceful garden overlooking the sea.

**Hotel de France (\*\*) $** *8 rue Mustapha M'Barek, Tunis Ville Nouvelle, tel: 71 326 244, email: hotelfrancetunis@yahoo.fr.* Old-fashioned colonial hotel with good-value, spotless, comfortable rooms.

**La Résidence (\*\*\*\*\*) $$$$** *Raoued Beach, La Marsa, tel: 71 910 101, www.theresidence-tunis.com.* One of the country's best hotels, with spacious rooms overlooking the sea, several pools, excellent restaurants and a very good thalasso spa.

**Villa Didon (\*\*\*\*\*) $$$$** *Next to the Cathedral on Byrsa Hill, Carthage, tel: 71 733 433, www.villadidon.com.* Futuristic ultramodern hotel offering just a few rooms with magnificent views over the site of Carthage, the sea and the whole white city of Tunis. Excellent service and very good restaurant.

## Recommended Restaurants

In the main tourist resorts there is often little to distinguish between restaurants apart from price; most have similar menus offering a few Tunisian dishes and French and/or Italian dishes. Generally, the further away from the beach, main square or main avenue a restaurant is located, the cheaper it will be. You can eat well for very little money if you go off the beaten track, especially in the medina.

Below is a list of restaurants recommended by Berlitz. Reservations are not usually necessary, but where a booking might be appropriate, we have included the restaurant's telephone number. As a basic guide, the following symbols indicate the price of a three-course meal for two, excluding drinks:

$$$   over 40D
$$    20–40D
$     below 20D

### BIZERTE

**Le Petit Mousse $$** *Route de la Corniche, tel: 72 432 185.* Excellent-value seafood restaurant in the hotel of the same name, with dining room and terrace. Dinner bookings recommended.

### CAP BON

**Chez Achour $$** *rue Ali Belhouane, Hammamet, tel: 72 280 140.* The best seafood restaurant in town, popular with local families for its delicious fish couscous.

**Le Corsaire $$** *Port, Yasmine Hammamet, tel: 72 240 323.* Up-market seafood restaurant in a boat moored in the glitzy marina, with delicious fish and seafood specialities. The deck is a great place to watch the world go by.

**Sidi el Maharsi $** *4–5km (2½–3 miles) outside Nabeul, on the Hammamet Road (open in summer, afternoon until late at night).* Very

pleasant terrace overlooking the sea and one of the most beautiful beaches in the region. A place to come for drinks after the beach.

## JERBA

**Princesse d'Haroun $$–$$$** *Harbour, Houmt Souk, tel: 75 650 488.* One of the best restaurants on the island, especially noted for its seafood – fresh lobster, octopus and squid. Bookings recommended.

**Le Moulin $$** *Zone Touristique, Jerba, tel: 75 758 336.* Popular for its simple but market-fresh and well-prepared Tunisian cuisine with a focus here too on fish and seafood, in a very relaxed atmosphere.

## KAIROUAN

**Le Roi du Couscous $–$$** *Avenue Ali Zouaow, tel: 77 231 337.* One of the best places in Kairouan to try a classic Tunisian dinner of *chorba, brik, maqroudh* and couscous. Reservations recommended.

**Sabra $** *Avenue de la République, tel: 77 235 095.* Popular, cheap restaurant with friendly service. Fill up on couscous for a few dinars.

## MATMATA

**Hotel Matmata $$** *tel: 75 240 066.* This is the only real restaurant in the village, and is consequently often packed with tour groups at lunchtime. Serves classic Tunisian dishes. Poolside café-bar.

## MONASTIR

**Le Chandelier $$** *Marina Monastir, tel: 73 462 232.* Cosy restaurant with excellent French and Tunisian food – fish is a speciality – served on a large terrace overlooking the yacht harbour.

## SOUSSE

**L'Escargot $$–$$$** *Route de la Corniche, tel: 73 224 779.* Sousse's best restaurant, offering quality French cuisine in chic surroundings.

**Le Petit Café Maure $** *Souk el Reba, Sousse.* This small blue cafe in the heart of the souk is the best place to take a rest, sipping a mint tea, or a coffee perfumed with orange blossom.

## TOZEUR

**Azzurra $** *Opposite the Museum of Dar Cheraït, Route Touristique, tel: 76 46 30 82.* Popular pizzeria with outdoor terrace, serving good pizzas, sandwiches and salads, perfect for a light lunch or dinner.

**Le Minaret $$** *Avenue Habib Bourguiba, tel: 23 52 42 03.* Delightful French-run restaurant serving an inventive Tunisian cuisine, excellent couscous and camel carpaccio, in a colourful dining room or on the terrace under a lovely palm tree.

## TUNIS

**Au Bon Vieux Temps (Ayyam Zaman) $$–$$$** *On the pedestrian street past Café des Nattes, Sidi Bou Saïd, tel: 71 744 733.* Charming restaurant with excellent food.

**Dar bel Hadj $$** *17 rue des Tamis, off rue Jemaa Zitouna, Tunis medina, tel: 71 200 894.* Tunisians love this traditional restaurant, set in a stunning old house with a beautiful courtyard. The Arab-Moorish concerts at night are especially popular. Book ahead for dinner.

**Dar el Jeld $$$** *5 rue Dar el Jeld, Tunis medina, tel: 71 560 916.* The country's best Tunisian restaurant, in a stunning house in the medina.

**Le Dôme $$$** *Tunisia Palace Hotel 13 avenue de France, tel: 71 242 700.* Centrally located restaurant with a splendid period dining room offering upmarket Tunisian and French cuisine. The rooftop terrace bar Ciel de Tunis has fabulous views over the medina.

**Restaurant Neptune $$–$$$** *waterfront in Quartier Magon, Carthage, tel: 71 73145.* Delightful Mediterranean fish restaurant with a large terrace overlooking a few Carthagean ruins and the sea, serving excellent fish and seafood.

# INDEX

**pocket guide**

# Tunisia

**Twelfth Edition 2009**
Reprinted 2011

**Written by** Neil Wilson
**Updated by** Sylvie Franquet
**Series Editor:** Tom Stainer

**Photography credits**
All photographs by Gregory Wrona/Apa
except those on pages 3 (Jerba), 11, 28, 32,
72, 77, 80, 82, 90, 91 and 105 from Berlitz
Archives; pages 12, 34, 53, 54, 58, 60, 65,
66, 68, 75, 76, 78, 88, 98 and 102 by Gary
John Norman/Apa; pages 21, 22 and 24 by
Alain Le Garsmeur; page 26 by TopFoto;
page 96 from the Tunisian National Tourist
Office.
**Cover picture:** Photolibrary

Every effort has been made to provide
accurate information in this publication,
but changes are inevitable. The publisher
cannot be responsible for any resulting
loss, inconvenience or injury.

### Contact us

At Berlitz we strive to keep our guides as
accurate and up to date as possible, but if you
find anything that has changed, or if you have
any suggestions on ways to improve this guide,
then we would be delighted to hear from you.

Berlitz Publishing, PO Box 7910,
London SE1 1WE, England.
email: berlitz@apaguide.co.uk
www.berlitzpublishing.com

# MCSE Test Success: SQL Server 7 Administration

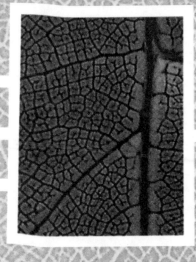

# MCSE Test Success™:
# SQL Server™ 7
# Administration

Michael Lee
Rick Sawtell

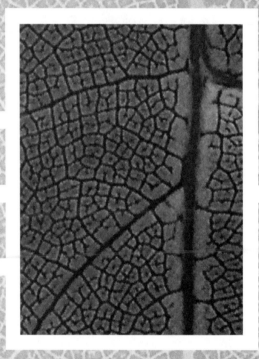

San Francisco • Paris • Düsseldorf • Soest • London

NETWORK PRESS®
SYBEX

Associate Publisher: Guy Hart-Davis
Contracts and Licensing Manager: Kristine O'Callaghan
Acquisitions & Developmental Editor: Brenda Frink
Editor: Kathy Grider-Carlyle
Project Editor: Bronwyn Shone Erickson
Technical Editor: Jim Cooper
Book Designer: Bill Gibson
Graphic Illustrator: Tony Jonick
Electronic Publishing Specialist: Nila Nichols
Project Team Leader: Shannon Murphy
Proofreaders: Blythe Woolston, Nancy Riddiough
Indexer: Matthew Spence
Cover Designer: Archer Design
Cover Photographer: FPG Int'l

Library of Congress Card Number: 99-61297
ISBN: 0-7821-2375-9

Manufactured in the United States of America

10 9 8 7 6 5 4 3 2

*To all those with the courage to embrace new things. May you always reach your goals.*

# Acknowledgments

**A**s usual, the professionalism of the Sybex staff has saved the day. Thanks to Bronwyn, Brenda, Kathy, Shannon, and Nila for giving this book the extra attention to make it a quality product that we can all be proud of. You are tops.

Thanks to Rick who is always consistent, accurate, and entertaining. You make every project that we work on together much easier to manage. Many thanks to my wife Raelynn, who sticks with me when deadlines arrive. You're my motivation. Finally, to Bob Taylor and Jon Hansen, the men to whom I owe my current career; thanks for the direction and support.

Michael Lee

Thanks goes to the wonderful group at Sybex, especially Brenda, Bronwyn, Kathy, Shannon, and Nila. Thank you for your patience on this project. I know it got pretty tight at times, but you always kept your cool and kept the project rolling along smoothly. You guys are the reason that Sybex puts out top-notch books, year after year.

I would like to say thanks to Mike Lee for bringing me in on this project and giving me the opportunity to add my input to this book. As always I have to thank my wife who has been wonderful and patient while I spent more time with my computer than her. It's time for us to get away and get reacquainted! Finally, a special thank you to Kenya (my cat) whose detailed knowledge of SQL Server administration has made my job that much easier.

Rick Sawtell

# Contents at a Glance

# Table of Contents

# Introduction

The Microsoft Certified Systems Engineer (MCSE) certification is *the* hottest ticket to career advancement in the computer industry today. Hundreds of thousands of corporations and organizations worldwide are choosing Microsoft products for their networks. This has created a tremendous need for qualified personnel and consultants to help implement and support these networks. MCSE certification and the recently introduced MCSE+Internet (or MCSE+I) certification are your way to show that you have the professional abilities these corporations and organizations need.

There's an old Army Reserve commercial in which a person can't get employed because he has no experience, and he can't get experience because he can't get employed—a classic "Catch-22" situation. Although certification is best used in conjunction with real-life experience, it can go a long way in making up for lack of experience.

The value of certification is undeniable. Many people get certified just to compete in the job marketplace. For example, if you were an employer and you had two candidates with the same experience—but one was also certified—which one would you hire? The fact is that even though the number of certified professionals has grown tremendously, the demand has grown at least as fast as, if not faster than, the number of certified people.

Whether you are just getting started or are ready to move ahead in the computer industry, the knowledge and skills you have are your most valuable assets. Microsoft, recognizing this, has developed its Microsoft Certified Professional (MCP) program to give you credentials that verify your ability to work with Microsoft products effectively and professionally. The Microsoft Certified Systems Engineer (MCSE) certification is the premier MCP credential, designed for professionals who support Microsoft networks.

Microsoft has recently announced a new certification called the Microsoft Certified Database Administrator (MCDBA). The MCDBA certification will have four core required tests, one of which is SQL Server 7 Administration. Currently the four required tests are SQL Server 7 Administration, SQL Server 7 Implementation, NT Server, and NT Server in the Enterprise. Electives include SQL Datawarehouse, IIS, TCP/IP, and others.

## Is This Book for You?

If you want to become certified as a Microsoft Certified Systems Engineer (MCSE), this book is for you. *Microsoft Certified Professional Magazine*'s recent surveys reveal the average MCSE is earning more than $65,000 (US) per year, while the average MCSE consultant is earning more than $95,000 per year. If you want to acquire the solid background you need to pass one of Microsoft's required client exams, take a step closer to your MCSE, and boost your career efforts, this book is for you.

## What Does This Book Cover?

Think of this book as your guide to the Microsoft SQL Server Administration exam. The book is broken into seven units. Each unit covers a major exam area. The units are further broken down into specific exam objectives (Official Microsoft Exam Objectives), which can be found on the Microsoft Web site at http://www.microsoft.com/train_cert. The final unit (Unit 7) is a sample exam with questions posed in a format similar to what you will see on the real test.

- Unit 1: Planning
  - Develop a security strategy.
  - Develop a SQL Server capacity plan.
  - Develop a data availability solution.
  - Develop a migration plan.
  - Develop a replication strategy.
- Unit 2: Installation and Configuration
  - Install SQL Server 7.
  - Configure SQL Server.
  - Install and configure the Full-Text Search service.

- Unit 3: Configuring and Managing Security

  - Assign SQL Server access to Windows NT accounts, SQL Server login accounts, and built-in administrator accounts.

  - Assign database access to Windows NT accounts, SQL Server login accounts, the Guest user account, and the DBO user account.

  - Create and assign SQL Server roles. Server roles include fixed server, fixed database, public, user-defined database, and application.

  - Grant to database users and roles the appropriate permissions to database objects and statements.

  - Audit server and database activity by using the SQL Server Profiler.

- Unit 4: Managing and Maintaining Data

  - Create and Manage databases.

  - Load data by using various methods. Methods include the INSERT statement, the SELECT INTO statement, bcp, Data Transformation Services (DTS), BULK INSERT, Host Data Replication (HDR), the Transfer Manager.

  - Back up system and user databases by performing a full backup, a transaction log backup, a differential backup, and a filegroup backup.

  - Manage replication.

  - Automate administrative tasks.

  - Enable access to remote data.

- Unit 5: Monitoring and Optimization

  - Monitor SQL Server performance by using Performance Monitor and Profiler.

  - Tune and optimize SQL Server memory and CPU usage.

  - Limit resources used by queries by using the Query Governor.

- Unit 6: Troubleshooting

  - Diagnose and resolve problems with upgrading from SQL Server 6.*x*.

  - Diagnose and resolve problems with backup and restore operations.

  - Diagnose and resolve replication problems.

  - Diagnose and resolve job or alert failures.

  - Diagnose and resolve distributed query problems.

  - Use the Client Configuration Utility to diagnose and resolve client connectivity problems.

  - Diagnose and resolve problems with access to SQL Server, databases, and database objects.

- Unit 7: The Exam: Sample Test

Throughout each unit, you will find concise reviews of exam-related topics. At the end of each unit you will have many fill-in-the-blank and True/False style questions to test your understanding of the concepts involved in each unit. You will then be presented with several exam style questions complete with reasoning for the answers given.

We have also provided a glossary of important SQL Server related terms. We suggest that you review the glossary before you take the exam.

## How Do You Become an MCSE, MCSE+I, or MCDBA?

Attaining MCSE, MCSE+I, or MCDBA status is a serious challenge. The exams cover a wide range of topics and require dedicated study and expertise. Many people who have achieved other computer industry credentials have had troubles with the MCSE. This difficulty, however, is why the MCSE certificates are so valuable. If achieving MCSE status were easy, the market would be quickly flooded by MCSEs, and the certification would quickly become meaningless. Microsoft, keenly aware of this fact, has taken steps to ensure that certification means its holder is truly knowledgeable and skilled.

## Exam Requirements

Successful candidates have to pass a minimum set of exams that measure technical proficiency and expertise:

- Candidates for the MCSE must pass four core requirements and two electives. SQL Server 7 Administration is one of the electives you can take.

- Candidates for the MCSE+Internet must pass seven core requirements and two electives. SQL Server 7 Administration is one of the electives you can take.

- Candidates for the MCDBA must pass four core requirements and one elective. SQL Server 7 Administration is one of the four required tests.

For a more detailed description of the Microsoft certification programs, go to http://www.microsoft.com/train_cert.

This book is a part of a series of Network Press MCSE Study Guides, published by Sybex, that cover all the core requirements of the MCSE and MCSE+I tracks as well as the electives you need.

## Where Do You Take the Exams?

You may take the exams at any of more than 1000 Authorized Prometric Testing Centers (APTCs) and VUE Testing Centers around the world. For the location of a testing center near you, call APTC at 800-755-EXAM (755-3926) or VUE at 888-837-8616. Outside the United States and Canada, contact your local Sylvan Prometric or VUE registration center.

To register for a Microsoft Certified Professional exam:

1. Determine the number of the exam you want to take.

2. Register with the registration center nearest to you. At this point, you will be asked for advance payment for the exam—as of April 1999, the exams are $100 each. Exams must be taken within one year of payment. You can schedule exams from one working day to six weeks

prior to the date of the exam. You can cancel or reschedule your exam with notice of at least two working days prior to the exam. Same-day registration is available in some locations, subject to space availability. Where same-day registration is available, you must register a minimum of two hours before test time.

You can also register for your exams online at http://www.sylvanprometric.com/ or http://www.vue.com/ms/

When you schedule the exam, you'll be provided with instructions regarding appointment and cancellation procedures, ID requirements, and information about the testing center location. In addition, you will receive a registration and payment confirmation letter from Sylvan Prometric or VUE.

Microsoft requires certification candidates to accept the terms of a Non-Disclosure Agreement (NDA) before taking certification exams.

## What Is Adaptive Testing?

At this writing (Spring 1999), Microsoft is in the process of converting all of its exams to a new format, called *adaptive testing*. This format is radically different from the conventional format previously used for Microsoft certification exams. If you have never taken an adaptive test, there are a few things you should know.

When new tests first come out they are usually the standard format, i.e., about 60 questions in 80 minutes. After enough people have taken the test an adaptive version of the test is created. Although the SQL Server 7 test started as the standard version, by the end of 1999 it will probably be adaptive.

Conventional tests and adaptive tests differ in that conventional tests are static, containing a fixed number of questions, while adaptive tests change, depending upon your answers to the questions presented. The number of questions presented in your adaptive test will depend on how long it takes the exam to figure out what your level of ability is (according to the statistical measurements upon which the exam questions are ranked).

To determine a test-taker's level of ability, the exam will present questions in increasing or decreasing orders of difficulty. By presenting sequences of questions with predetermined levels of difficulty, the exam is supposedly able to figure out your level of understanding.

For example, we have three test-takers, Herman, Sally, and Rashad. Herman doesn't know much about the subject, Sally is moderately informed, and Rashad is an expert. Herman answers his first question incorrectly, so the exam gives him a second, easier question. He misses that, so the exam gives him a few more easy questions, all of which he misses. Shortly thereafter, the exam ends, and he receives his failure report. Sally, meanwhile, answers her first question correctly, so the exam gives her a more difficult question, which she answers correctly. She then receives an even more difficult question, which she answers incorrectly, so the exam gives her a somewhat easier question, as it tries to gauge her level of understanding. After numerous questions, of varying levels of difficulty, Sally's exam ends, perhaps with a passing score, perhaps not. Her exam included far more questions than Herman's did, because her level of understanding needed to be more carefully tested to determine whether it was at a passing level. When Rashad takes his exam, he answers his first question correctly, so he's given a more difficult question, which he also answers correctly. He's given an even more difficult question, which he also answers correctly. He then is given a few more very difficult questions, all of which he answers correctly. Shortly thereafter, his exam ends. He passes. His exam was short, about as long as Herman's.

 Microsoft is also introducing more simulations into the exams. These simulations require that you complete a task or tasks on an element that looks just like the actual graphical interface of a Microsoft product. If you are familiar with the Microsoft product, you might find these questions to be a bit less abstract, and therefore slightly easier, than similar questions presented in purely text format. Some tests (such as the IIS test) have many simulation-type questions while others (such as the current SQL Server 7 Administration test) have few or none.

Microsoft moved to adaptive testing for several reasons:

- It saves time by focusing only on the questions needed to determine a test-taker's specific abilities. This way an exam that, in the conventional format, took 1 1/2 hours can be completed in less than half that time. The number of questions presented can be far fewer than the number required by a conventional exam.

- It protects the integrity of the exams. By exposing a smaller number of questions at any one time, it makes it more difficult for individuals to collect the questions in the exam pools with the intent of facilitating exam cramming.

- It saves Microsoft and/or the test delivery company money by cutting down on the amount of time it takes to deliver a test.

**WARNING** Unlike the previous test format, the adaptive format will not allow you to go back to see a question again. The exam goes forward only. Once you enter your answer, that's it; you cannot change it. Be very careful before entering your answer. There is no time limit for each individual question (only for the exam as a whole). As your exam may be shortened by correct answers (and lengthened by incorrect answers) there is no advantage to rushing through questions.

## Tips for Taking the Exam

The exam focuses on fundamental concepts relating to Microsoft SQL Server operation. It can also be quite specific regarding how SQL Server administrative tasks are performed. This exam is often perceived as one of the more difficult of the Microsoft Certified Professional tests. Careful study of this book, along with hands-on experience with the operating system, will be especially helpful in preparing you for the exam.

Here are some general tips for taking the exams successfully:

- Arrive early at the exam center so you can relax and review your study materials, particularly tables and lists of exam-related information.

- Read the questions carefully. Don't be tempted to jump to an early conclusion. Make sure you know *exactly* what the question is asking.

- Don't leave any unanswered questions on standard tests. They count against you. If you are taking an adaptive test, you cannot skip any questions so if you have to guess make sure the answer you have selected is your best guess.

- When answering multiple-choice questions you're not sure about, use a process of elimination to get rid of the obviously incorrect questions first. This will improve your odds if you need to make an educated guess.

- Because the hard questions will take up the most time, you may want to answer them quickly and mark them for later (on standard tests). You can move forward and backward through the exam on standard tests (unless the question specifically states that you cannot go back), and can see which items you have marked for later inspection.

- This test has some exhibits (pictures). It can be difficult, if not impossible, to view both the questions and the exhibit simulation on the 14- and 15-inch screens usually found at the testing centers. Call around to each center and see if they have 17-inch monitors available. If they don't, perhaps you can arrange to bring in your own. Failing this, some have found it useful to quickly draw the diagram on the scratch paper provided by the testing center and use the monitor to view just the question. You should always double check your answer when looking at an exhibit in case you check the wrong answer when going back and forth.

- One of the keys to correctly answering Microsoft test questions is figuring out just what it is that you are being asked. Most test questions are in the form of a story problem—cutting through the fluff and understanding the issue involved is most of the battle. You may want to look at the answer choices and "reverse-engineer" the question.

- Many of the Multiple Rating Items (MRI) questions that ask you "How well does this solution address the problem?" are very intimidating at first, because they are very long. Our strategy is to look at the solution and compare it against each desired outcome, keeping track of whether it works or doesn't. The available responses will sometimes consist of a count of the number of items that were successfully accomplished, which is the running total we have kept in our heads. Sometimes the question will end with a list of objectives, and you will be asked to specify whether they were fulfilled. We found these much easier, as we could look at the solution and see whether it fulfilled each individual objective.

- On simulations, do not change settings that are not directly related to the question. Also, assume default settings if the question does not specify or imply what they might be.

- This is not simply a test of your knowledge of Transaction SQL commands, but on how it is used to administer SQL Server 7 on Windows NT. You will need to know how to use the Transaction SQL language *and* the graphical utilities to perform your administrative tasks.

- A reminder: The adaptive format will NOT allow you to go back to see a question again. Be very careful before entering your answer. Because your exam may be shortened by correct answers (and lengthened by incorrect answers) there is no advantage to rushing through questions.

## How to Use This Book

This book can focus your effort when preparing for the SQL Server exam. To best benefit from this book, you might want to use the following study method:

1. Study a unit carefully, making sure you fully understand the information.

2. If there are areas you don't understand, you can deepen your knowledge with the *MCSE: SQL 7 Administration Study Guide*, or look at the SQL Server Books Online.

3. Answer the questions related to that unit.

4. Note which questions you did not understand and study those sections of the book again.

5. Study each unit in the same manner.

6. Before taking the exam, try the practice exam in the last unit of this book. It will give you an idea of what you can expect to see on the real thing.

7. Use resources available on the Internet to help supplement and update your training preparation. The best place to start is the Certification area on Microsoft's Web page, www.microsoft.com/mcp. When you are ready for more details about a particular test or objective list, the www.microsoft.com/train_cert Web site is another invaluable resource.

If you prefer to use this book in conjunction with classroom or online training, you have many options. Both Microsoft-authorized training and independent training are widely available. See Microsoft's Web sites (www.microsoft.com/mcp and www.microsoft.com/train_cert) for more information.

To learn all the material covered in this book, you will need to study regularly and with discipline. Try to set aside the same time every day to study, and select a comfortable and quiet place in which to do it. If you work hard, you will be surprised at how quickly you learn this material. Good luck.

## Contact Information

To find out more about Microsoft Education and Certification materials and programs, to register with Sylvan Prometric, or to get other useful information, check the following resources. (Outside the United States or Canada, contact your local Microsoft office or Sylvan Prometric or VUE testing center.)

**Microsoft Certified Professional Program — (800) 636-7544**  Call the MCPP number for information about the Microsoft Certified Professional program and exams and to order the latest Microsoft Roadmap to Education and Certification.

**Sylvan Prometric Testing Centers — (800) 755-EXAM**   To register to take a Microsoft Certified Professional exam at any of more than 1000 Sylvan Prometric testing centers around the world, or to order this Exam Study Guide, call the Sylvan Prometric testing center.

**VUE Testing Centers — (888) 837-8616**   To register to take a Microsoft Certified Professional exam at a VUE testing center, call the VUE registration center.

**Microsoft Certification Development Team — Web:**
`http://www.microsoft.com/Train_Cert/mcp/examinfo/certsd.htm`
Contact the Microsoft Certification Development Team through their Web site to volunteer for one or more exam development phases or to report a problem with an exam. Address written correspondence to: Certification Development Team; Microsoft Education and Certification; One Microsoft Way; Redmond, WA 98052.

**Microsoft TechNet Technical Information Network — (800) 344-2121**
Use this number to contact support professionals and system administrators. Outside the United States and Canada, call your local Microsoft subsidiary for information.

**Microsoft Related Training Resources**
`http://www.microsoft.com/train_cert/train/`
`http://www.cyberstateu.com/text/catalog/nt.htm`

## How to Contact the Authors

We welcome any of your comments, suggestions, and feedback.
You can e-mail Mike Lee at:
`Mlee@sabrepoint.org`

You can e-mail Rick Sawtell at:
`Quickening@email.msn.com`

## How to Contact the Publisher

Sybex welcomes reader feedback on all of their titles. Visit the Sybex Web site at www.sybex.com for book updates and additional certification information. You'll also find online forms to submit comments or suggestions regarding this or any other Sybex book.

# UNIT

# 1

Planning

# Test Objectives: Planning

- **Develop a security strategy.**

  - Assess whether to use Microsoft Windows NT accounts or Microsoft SQL Server logins.

  - Assess whether to leverage the Windows NT group structure.

  - Plan the use and structure of SQL Server roles. Server roles include fixed server, fixed database, and user-defined database.

  - Assess whether to map Windows NT groups directly into a database or to map them to a role.

  - Assess which Windows NT accounts will be used to run SQL Server services.

  - Plan an *n*-tier application security strategy, and decide whether to use application roles or other mid-tier security mechanisms such as Microsoft Transaction Server.

  - Plan the security requirements for linked databases.

- **Develop a SQL Server capacity plan.**

  - Plan the physical placement of files, including data files and transaction log files.

  - Plan the use of filegroups.

  - Plan for growth over time.

  - Plan the physical hardware system.

  - Assess communication requirements.

- **Develop a data availability solution.**

  - Choose the appropriate backup and restore strategy. Strategies include full database backup; full database backup and transaction log backup; differential database backup with full database backup and transaction log backup; and database files backup and transaction log backup.

  - Assess whether to use a standby server.

  - Assess whether to use clustering.

- **Develop a migration plan.**

  - Plan an upgrade from a previous version of SQL Server.

  - Plan the migration of data from other data sources.

- **Develop a replication strategy.**

  - Given a scenario, design the appropriate replication model. Replication models include single Publisher and multiple Subscribers; multiple Publishers and single Subscriber; multiple Publishers and multiple Subscribers; and remote Distributor.

  - Choose the replication type. Replication types include snapshot, transactional, and merge.

Exam objectives are subject to change at any time without prior notice and at Microsoft's sole discretion. Please visit Microsoft's Training & Certification Web site (www.microsoft.com/Train_Cert) for the most current exam objectives listing.

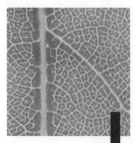

In this unit, we will look at the planning stages of a SQL Server installation. We will begin with a discussion of planning security and physical data storage. We will then look at network and fault tolerance needs. Finally, we will review the planning requirements for upgrading a SQL Server to version 7 and replicating data from a SQL Server 7 database.

This chapter covers only the planning phases of these tasks, not the implementation detail. Implementation information is covered in later chapters.

# Develop a Security Strategy

**M**icrosoft SQL Server 7 supports two different server authentication methods, SQL Server authentication and Windows NT authentication. SQL Server authentication requires that SQL Server maintain lists of server logins and authenticate these logins when users access SQL Server. With Windows NT authentication, SQL Server trusts that Windows NT has properly authenticated each user and SQL Server simply determines whether these users should be allowed access to the SQL Server.

In this section, we will discuss factors that play into which authentication methods you should choose and how they will be configured. We will also explore alternate security options such as using Microsoft Transaction Server as a security mechanism.

## Authentication Modes

SQL Server 7 can operate in one of two security modes. The default mode is a mixed mode where both SQL Server and Windows NT authenticated users are allowed. You may also select a Windows NT–only mode that does not permit SQL Server authenticated users.

Your network structure and your application security needs will be the primary factors that influence your decision regarding which security mode to implement. Using Windows NT authentication offers the following advantages:

- You have access to Windows NT and SQL Server with a single login.
- More security features such as password encryption, aging, auditing, etc. are available.
- Access to SQL Server is consolidated by using Windows NT groups. This eliminates the need to add individual users to SQL Server.

The inability of some types of clients to create trusted connections is the primary advantage of using a mixed authentication mode that allows both SQL Server and Windows NT authentication. It is also the primary disadvantage of using the Windows NT–only mode. Trusted connections cannot be created from clients such as:

- Unix-based
- Macintosh-based
- Internet

## Using Windows NT Groups

One of the new features of SQL Server 7 is the ability to configure SQL Server access and permissions directly to Windows NT groups. This feature eliminates the need to configure access and permissions at the user level, increasing the ability to leverage the Windows NT group structure.

For example, assume that a Windows NT user named Bill is a member of a Windows NT group called SQLUsers. If the SQLUsers group were permitted assess to the SQL Server and given access to the Pubs database, then Bill would be granted the appropriate access. His user name in the database would be Bill, even though that user name never had been explicitly added to the user account list for the Pubs database.

The primary advantages to using the Windows NT group structure are:

- Consolidating network and database access administration
- Simplifying access to SQL Server in a Windows NT authentication mode

The greatest disadvantage to using the Windows NT group structure is that the management of ownership and permissions can be complicated by this approach. Remember that in the previous example, the user name Bill is recognized by the database and Bill would own any objects that he created unless he specifically assigned ownership to another user, such as dbo. Special care must be taken to ensure that objects are created with the appropriate ownership.

Properly managing object ownership is critical to the security needs of the application. Whenever there is a change in ownership in the calling sequence of objects, permissions must be checked. It is much more stable to ensure that the dbo user owns all objects in the database.

## SQL Server Roles

SQL Server 7 supports a role-based security model. Rather than assigning permissions directly to a SQL User or Windows NT group, permissions can be assigned to roles, and roles can be associated with SQL Users or Windows NT groups. A user or group account will inherit all of the aggregated permissions allotted to the roles with which the account has been assigned. SQL Server 7 supports three different types of roles:

**Fixed server** These roles cannot be created or dropped. They are part of a standard installation and provide permissions to perform server-level functions such as creating databases, managing file structures, managing security administration, and providing full system administration.

**Fixed database** These roles cannot be dropped. They provide permissions for basic database administration functionality, as well as permissions to either grant or deny read or write activities in a database.

**User-defined database** These roles are created by the administrator to implement custom security management. Permissions to individual database objects are assigned to roles, and users or groups can be associated with these roles.

For basic administrative activities, you should consider the use of fixed roles. User-defined roles can significantly aid in the consolidation of your security administration activities. By assigning roles to users or NT groups, you can change the security requirements of your application at any time simply by modifying the permission structure of the role.

## Roles versus Windows NT Groups

As you can see from the previous discussion, Windows NT groups and SQL Server roles have extremely similar security effects. Both are used to aggregate users together for the ease of administration. In both cases, you can assign permissions to either a group or a role to control access to database objects.

The key difference between Windows NT groups and roles is that roles allow broader membership. Roles can include:

- Windows NT logins

- Windows NT groups

- SQL Server logins

Windows NT groups can contain only other Windows NT accounts, not SQL Server accounts. Although using Windows NT groups might be an effective approach when you are utilizing a Windows NT authentication mode, using roles might be more beneficial when you must support SQL Server authentication.

## Service Accounts

SQL Server 7 is actually a suite of Windows NT services. Four primary services make up the SQL Server 7 product. They are:

**MSSQLServer** The SQL Server engine. This service is required for all data services.

**SQLAgent** The SQL automation engine. This service supports the job scheduling, alert, and replication systems.

**MSDTC** The Microsoft Distributed Transaction Coordinator. This service provides for atomic transactions across multiple servers.

**SQLMail** The SQLMail service allows the SQL Server to interact with a MAPI-compliant mail system.

You have two options when assigning NT accounts to a service. You can use the local system account or a user account. You should use a user account instead of the local system account for the services. This will allow the SQL Server to interact with other SQL Servers on the network in a Windows NT authentication mode. Figure 1.1 illustrates the installation dialog that provides service account options.

**FIGURE 1.1**

Configuring service
accounts

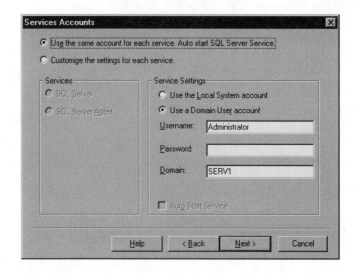

You can set the services to either a domain user account or a local user account. If you plan for your SQL Server to interact with other SQL Servers on the network via replication, e-mail, etc., you should use a single domain user account for all of the services.

Although the figure illustrates the Windows NT Administrator account as the service login account, you should use a different user account that is a member of the NT Administrators group.

## Other Security Options

Using Windows NT logins and groups or using SQL Server logins and roles can provide effective security implementation. However, you may not need the extensive security provided by these approaches, or you may desire to take an alternate approach.

Some of these alternative security approaches include:

- Using a single login

- Using a middle-tier security mechanism

- Using guest accounts

## Single Login

If security is not a significant issue, you can allow access to your SQL Server through a single login account. All permissions required to interact with the server can be assigned to this single login account. The largest drawback to this approach is that is does not create a very secure system, especially if some users need different access rights than other users.

## Middle-Tier Security

Using a middle-tier technology such as Microsoft Transaction Server is also a viable option for a secure application environment. Using this solution, you would create components in a language such as Visual Basic or Visual C++ and manage those components in a middle tier, assigning access permissions to Windows NT users who are allowed to access the components.

Using Microsoft Transaction Server, you can create roles in the middle tier and associate those roles with different middle-tier components. The component can then access the SQL Server under a single login, thereby shifting all of the authentication to the middle tier.

This solution is most appropriate when the following conditions exist:

- The application has constantly changing security requirements and user volatility.

- A distributed architecture is planned for the application for reasons other than security management.

- There is no need to perform extensive security logging or profiling at the SQL Server level.

## Guest Access

SQL Server 7 provides guest login access to the server as well as guest user access to database resources. If security is not an issue or if it is only a minor concern, then using guest access can eliminate many of the security-related administrative tasks.

# Develop a SQL Server Capacity Plan

**E**very SQL Server database has a primary data file and one or more transaction log files. Databases may also include secondary data files, allowing the administrator to effectively distribute the database throughout the data storage system. The placement of these files can be critical to performance as well as to future capacity planning.

In this section, we will evaluate some of the capacity planning options such as the use of files and filegroups, network requirements, and the physical hardware required to get the best performance out of your SQL Server.

## Database File Structure

When you initially create a database, you must first decide where to place the data and the transaction logs for the database. This critical decision can affect both the performance and recoverability of your database. You have some options for the arrangement of files:

- You can use a RAID solution for performance and fault tolerance.

- In a non-RAID environment, you can spread the database across multiple physical disks.

### Disk Planning without RAID

If you are not using a RAID solution, you should at least divide your databases across multiple physical disks. The transaction log files should not exist on the same physical disk as data files. Separating them aids in the recoverability of the database. Figure 1.2 illustrates a database divided across three physical disks: C, D, and E.

---

**F I G U R E  1.2**

Using multiple disks
without RAID

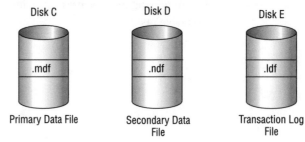

| Disk C | Disk D | Disk E |
|--------|--------|--------|
| .mdf | .ndf | .ldf |
| Primary Data File | Secondary Data File | Transaction Log File |

## Using Disk Striping with Parity

Using RAID disk striping with parity (RAID 5) allows fault tolerance in case of media failure. If a single disk in the stripe set fails, the parity information located on the other disks allows the stripe set to continue to be used. The failed media can then be regenerated when convenient. Figure 1.3 illustrates a striping with parity solution. In this case, both the data files and log files are striped across all physical disks in the stripe set.

**FIGURE 1.3**

Using disk striping with parity

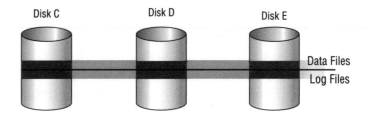

Although Windows NT supports disk striping with parity, it does not provide the best performance solution. A SQL Server system administrator should consider hardware-based solutions as superior.

## Advanced RAID Solutions

Disk striping with parity is a valuable fault-tolerant approach, but it has a performance drain for heavily modified data sources. Disk mirroring (RAID 1) is much more efficient in terms of CPU performance, but it requires more disk space. A commonly used solution is a combination of disk striping with parity for the database files and disk mirroring for the transaction logs. This approach is called RAID 5+1. When this approach is used, the database is fully recoverable if media is lost; however, CPU cycles and disk space are not wasted. Figure 1.4 illustrates this approach.

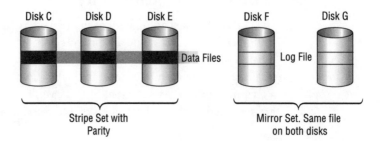

**FIGURE 1.4**

RAID 5+1
implementation

## Using Filegroups

A filegroup is a set of files that are treated as a unit for certain administrative purposes. These may include backups, object storage, etc. Filegroups are primarily used to support user-defined segmentation in very large databases. Files should be placed into filegroups so that they:

- Take advantage of I/O subsystem by spreading filegroups across multiple disks

- Group tables and indexes together on the same filegroup

- Enhance the performance of either the query execution or recoverability of a database

As an example of implementing a filegroup, you could create a filegroup and extend the database by adding multiple secondary data files, adding them to the filegroup. These files can be created on multiple physical disks. When you create an object such as a table or index, placing it on the filegroup separates it from other related objects also placed on the same filegroup. You can create multiple filegroups to organize very large databases.

Using Raid 5 can duplicate much of the query benefit that you can derive from using filegroups. It might still be beneficial, however, to use filegroups to support backups for very large databases.

## Database Growth

Databases can be expanded both manually and automatically. When increasing databases manually, you will use an ALTER DATABASE statement to either add a secondary data file or increase the size of an existing data file.

When automatic data file growth is used, you simply need to monitor the size of the files over time, ensuring that they do not approach the maximum file size stated when the database was created.

Planning for growth is more that making sure that you have enough disk space available. The database application can also experience growth in the number of users or network requirements. What is most important is that you always have adequate resources available for your application.

This may mean adding more memory to accommodate more users or data caching needs. It might mean adding more disk space to increase your data storage capacity. It might also mean increasing your network bandwidth to ensure the proper movement of data across your network. The key is to be flexible.

# Planning Server Hardware

The minimum hardware requirements for the Standard Edition of SQL Server 7 include:

- Intel Pentium 166MHz or Alpha processor.

- 32MB RAM.

- 65–180MB hard drive space.

- CD-ROM drive.

- Mouse or other pointing device.

- The computer should be connected to a network with a NIC or modem through a dial-up adapter.

Although these standards will be sufficient to install SQL Server, they should be considered minimums and should be increased depending on the goals of the application. For example:

1. Disk space should be increased to accommodate the needed data storage capacity as well as the Tempdb database.

2. Memory should be increased to accommodate needed data cache, procedure cache, user connection overhead, operating system and network needs, etc.

3. Processor capacity should be increased to accommodate additional server-side processing of data including OLAP and data warehousing functionality. If software-based RAID solutions are implemented, you will require additional processor capacity to calculate parity information.

### Software Requirements

SQL Server 7 is designed to reside primarily on a Windows NT Server; however, the Desktop Edition of SQL Server 7 installs on a Windows 95/98 desktop. In addition to the operating system, SQL Server also requires:

- Service Pack 4 or higher for Windows NT installations

- Network protocols for communicating with other computers

- Internet Explorer 4.1 Service Pack 1

For performance reasons, you should disable any Windows NT services and network protocols that are not being used. Remember that you should never use a server like a workstation.

# Develop a Data Availability Solution

It doesn't do much good to have a perfectly planned and implemented database solution unless you have access to that data when you really need it. Although RAID can help increase the fault tolerance of your server, there is no replacement for a good data recovery strategy.

In this section, we will look at the three primary approaches to data recovery and availability:

- Backups

- Standby servers

- Clustering

## Backup Strategy

If there is a theme to SQL Server backups, it is flexibility. You have four backup options available, namely:

- Full database backups

- Transaction log backups

- Differential backups

- File/filegroup backups

Each of these approaches has its own benefits and drawbacks. When backup methods are used together, they can be combined to support numerous backup strategies. The most common backup strategies are:

- Full database backups only
- Full database and transaction log backups
- Full database, differential, and transaction log backups
- File/filegroup and transaction log backups

## Database-Only Backups

Full database backups are used alone in two primary circumstances. First, when you have a small database with minimal data modifications and can accept the possibility of some data loss, you may only need to take periodic database backups.

For example, assume that you have a 100MB database that is not heavily modified. A day's worth of data modifications could be lost without causing a critical business situation. If you backed up the database every morning at 6:00 A.M. and a media failure occurred at noon, only 6 hours of work would be lost.

In a second scenario, this strategy can be used without any data loss. If the transaction log for the database is stored on a separate physical disk from the database, then a media failure for the database would not destroy the transaction log. If the transaction log is large enough to accommodate a day of transactions, then the previous scenario might work out a little differently.

1. When the media failure occurs at noon, a backup is made of the orphaned transaction log.

2. After the full database backup taken at 6:00 A.M. is restored, the orphaned log backup can be applied, eliminating data loss.

## Database and Transaction Log Backups

Most of the time, you will have a larger database and/or lower tolerance for data loss. To accommodate these needs, you might consider taking periodic transaction log backups between your full database backups. Just like a full database backup, the transaction log backup will truncate the inactive portion of the transaction log to prevent the log from filling.

Suppose that you have a 100GB database that has moderate modifications. The database is too large to back up every day; however, you have no tolerance for data loss. In this case, you might consider backing up the database once every 2–3 days and taking transaction logs backups periodically between these database backups. This procedure will truncate the transaction log and capture the transactions in a backup. To recover in this situation, you would:

1. Back up the orphaned log.

2. Restore the most recent full database backup.

3. Apply all of the transaction log backups taken since the last full database backup.

4. Apply the backup of the orphaned transaction log.

## Using Differential Backups

We use transaction log backups because databases are often too large to back up very frequently. The problem with transaction log backups is that because they store a set of transactions that must be issued back to the database, they can often be very time-consuming to apply. When you have a large database that is frequently modified, this problem is exaggerated.

The solution lies in the differential backup. A differential backup stores only those pages that have been modified since the last full database backup. This means that you don't have to back up the entire database every time; however, you don't have the restoration problems that can occur with large numbers of transaction log backups.

Suppose for example that you have a large database with frequent modifications. You might choose to do a full database backup over the weekend with a differential backup every night. Transaction log backups could be taken every hour during the day. This would enable you to periodically back up only the pages that had been modified and only have to apply transaction log backups for a single day of activity. The restore process would be:

1. Back up the orphaned transaction log.

2. Restore the last full database backup.

3. Restore the most recent differential backup. Because differential backups are cumulative, there is no need to restore all of the previous differential backups.

4. Restore any transaction log backups taken since the last differential backup.

5. Restore the orphaned log backup.

## File and Filegroup Backups

Sometimes database are so large that it would be impossible to back up the entire database in a production cycle. For example, suppose that you had a database that took 60 hours to completely back up. You could barely back up this database using the entire weekend! An alternative would be to use file or filegroup backup approaches.

When you back up a file or filegroup, you are backing up only the data that is stored on that file or filegroup. If you need to back up your entire database every week, you could put yourself on a rotating backup schedule with which you back up on a different file or filegroup every night. Because filegroups are more often used for this type of backup, let's look at an example scenario.

Suppose you have a very large database that is divided into five filegroups. Each filegroup contains a logical organization of tables and their indexes. You could back up the filegroups according to the schedule illustrated in Table 1.1

| **T A B L E   1.1** Possible Filegroup Backup Schedule | Filegroup/Transaction Log | Backup Schedule |
|---|---|---|
| | Filegroup A | Monday night |
| | *T Log | Tuesday noon |
| | *T Log | Tuesday 6:00 P.M. |
| | Filegroup B | Tuesday night |
| | * T Log | Wednesday noon |
| | * T Log | Wednesday 6:00 P.M. |
| | Filegroup C | Wednesday night |
| | * T Log | Thursday noon |
| | * T Log | Thursday 6:00 P.M. |

| **T A B L E 1.1** (cont.) | **Filegroup/Transaction Log** | **Backup Schedule** |
| --- | --- | --- |
| Possible Filegroup Backup Schedule | Filegroup D | Thursday night |
| | * T Log | Friday noon |
| | * T Log | Friday 6:00 P.M. |
| | Filegroup E | Friday night |
| | * T Log | Monday noon |
| | * T Log | Monday 6:00 P.M. |

Now suppose a media failure that affected filegroup C occurred only at 4:00 P.M. on Friday. In this case, the recovery process would be as follows. When you apply transaction log backups after a filegroup restore, only the transactions that affect the restored filegroup will be restored.

1. Make a backup of the orphaned transaction log.

2. Restore the backup of filegroup C.

3. Apply the two transaction log backups taken on Thursday and the one taken Friday at noon.

4. Apply the backup of the orphaned log.

## Using a Standby Server

Although a standby server can be an expensive solution, having one can provide a greater level of comfort than a data recovery strategy if you have a zero downtime tolerance for your database application. Standby server solutions are most appropriate when:

- You have no tolerance for downtime.
- You have a stable backup strategy in place.
- You can justify the cost for a minimal downtime solution.

The underlying concept with a standby server is to have two identical servers; one is your production server and the other is a mirror of that server. The basic strategy is that whenever you make a backup from your production server, you will apply that backup to your standby server as illustrated in Figure 1.5.

**F I G U R E  1.5**

Using a standby server

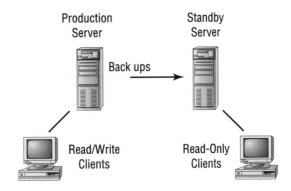

As you can also see from Figure 1.5, standby servers can be used for load balancing read-only activities. As long as the clients interacting with the standby server make no data modifications, the resources of the server can be used to offload query activities from the production server.

## Using a Cluster

Clustering is different from using a standby server, although it has some of the same load balancing advantages. In a cluster, two computers will share the same set of hard drives, each computer handling its own client requests. Clustering, which is illustrated in Figure 1.6, has two primary advantages:

1. Load balancing
2. Fault tolerance/fallback support

**FIGURE 1.6**

SQL Server on
a cluster

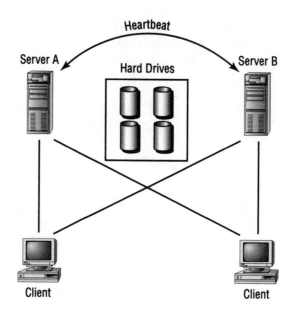

## Load Balancing

Because the two servers share the same set of hard drives, either one of the two servers could respond to a client request and return the same results. Any modifications made by one server would be visible to clients connecting through the other server. Locks held by a transaction through one server would be enforced for connections coming from the other server.

By increasing the server resources, the operating system, especially the I/O subsystem, becomes significantly less bottlenecked. This permits the combination of the two servers to do more work than either one could do independently.

## Fault Tolerance

Although media failure is always a concern, more can go wrong with a server machine than simply media failure. Other server components can also fail. A cluster helps to protect against these types of failures.

When two servers are clustered together, they establish a "heartbeat" between them. This enables the two servers to track each other's status. If one of the servers fails, all of the traffic can be diverted to the other server. Although this means that performance will be adversely affected, the application will stay up because traffic is diverted to the functional server. Note that clustering does not protect you against media failure, only server failure.

Clustering requires SQL Server 7 Enterprise to be running on Windows NT Enterprise. If you are running the Standard Edition of SQL Server, you will not have cluster support.

# Develop a Migration Plan

The migration of data from one SQL Server to another or even between two heterogeneous data sources is a common practice; however, it should not be taken lightly. When you are working with your data, especially production data, integrity is paramount.

In this section, we will look at two approaches for migrating data. We will begin with a discussion of upgrading data from an earlier version of SQL Server to SQL Server 7. We will then discuss the migration of data from other non-SQL Server data sources to the SQL Server 7 environment.

## Upgrading

SQL Server supports an automated upgrade utility that allows you to transfer data from a SQL Server 6.*x* installation to SQL Server 7. This upgrade can be performed on a single computer, or it can be performed on two computers by defining an export and import server. Before you upgrade, you should consider the following:

- You must install Service Pack 3 or later for SQL Server 6.5. The SQL Server 7 CD ships with SQL Server 6.5 Service Pack 4.

- Back up all 6.*x* databases, including the Master database so that you can recover if necessary.

- The Tempdb database in the 6.*x* server must be at least 10MB in size.

- Any stored startup procedures in the 6.5 server should be disabled. The service will stop and start during the upgrade, and there should be no startup procedures present to interfere with this process.

- All applications connecting to the 6.5 server must be terminated before the upgrade.

If the upgrade will take place on two different computers, the MSSQLServer service on both machines should use a single domain user account that is a member of the administrators group on both machines. Servers that are involved in replication cannot be upgraded using the two-computer approach.

You can only upgrade a SQL Server 6.x server to SQL Server 7. If you want to upgrade an earlier version of SQL Server, you must either upgrade that server to version 6.5 before upgrading to version 7 or use another data transfer process, such as Data Transformation Services, and object scripting.

## Performing the Upgrade

When you install SQL Server 7, a program group called Microsoft SQL Server-Switch is installed. You will find the upgrade utility in this group. A switch utility that will switch the active server back and forth between SQL Server 6.5 and SQL Server 7 is also in this group. This utility allows you to make any needed administrative modifications to the SQL Server 6.5 installation even after SQL Server 7 is installed.

When you begin the upgrade process, you will be presented with many options in a series of dialogs. Table 1.2 lists some of the upgrade information collected by the Upgrade Wizard.

| **T A B L E  1.2** | **Option** | **Description** |
| --- | --- | --- |
| Upgrade Information Collected by the Upgrade Wizard | Data transfer method | Named pipe is preferred for a simultaneous data transfer. Tape is also supported. |
| | Export server | Server that is being upgraded. |
| | Import server | Server that will receive and store the upgraded information. For a single computer upgrade, import and export will be the same computer. |
| | Administrator password | The "sa" password for each server. |

| **T A B L E** 1.2 *(cont.)* | **Option** | **Description** |
|---|---|---|
| Upgrade Information Collected by the Upgrade Wizard | Include databases to be upgraded | Select which databases you want to upgrade to the new format. |
| | Scripting code page | Select the code page to be used to transfer data. Should be the same code page as both servers. |
| | Create database scripting | Accept or modify the default file layout for the upgraded databases. |
| | ANSI nulls | Select On or Off for ANSI null-default behavior. |
| | Quoted identifiers | Select On, Off, or Mixed for quoted identifiers. |

At the conclusion of the upgrade process, you can uninstall the 6.*x* server by choosing Start ➢ Microsoft SQL Server-Switch ➢ Uninstall SQL 6.5 from the Windows Start menu. This will remove the existing SQL Server 6.5 installation and also remove the Microsoft SQL Server-Switch menu item because they are no longer needed.

## Migrating Non-SQL Data

Data can also be migrated from data sources other than Microsoft SQL Server using a tool called Data Transformation Services (DTS). DTS is more than a simple data movement utility. It is a full-featured data transfer and transformation package that allows data from any ODBC or OLE DB-compliant data source to be migrated to SQL Server 7 or any other ODBC or OLE DB-compliant data source.

Planning for DTS use is really quite simple. If you have the disk space to accommodate the imported data and the computers hosting both sides of the transfer can *see* each other on the network, you can use DTS quite effectively.

When using DTS, you can choose to have DTS create the tables in SQL Server for you, or you can create them yourself and simply append the migrated data from the non-SQL data source to the SQL Server tables.

# Develop a Replication Strategy

 **S**QL Server supports numerous approaches to replication that can be used to move data throughout the network. Depending on the reason for replicating data or the organizational model of your business, some replication models may be more appropriate than others.

In this section, we will look at two aspects of replication planning. First, we will look at the different replication models available and evaluate how these models match different organizational and infrastructural models. Then we will look at the different types of replication supported by SQL Server 7 and evaluate how these might be used to fulfill business needs.

## Replication Models

SQL Server replication is very flexible and can be used to respond to many different business needs. There are many models to choose from, each of which can be tuned to specific organizational or infrastructural characteristics of your business. Some of the SQL Server replication models include:

- Single Publisher, multiple Subscriber
- Multiple Publisher, single Subscriber
- Multiple Publisher, multiple Subscriber
- Remote Distributor

### Single Publisher, Multiple Subscriber

This is the most traditional approach; with it a single server publishes information to multiple subscribing servers. This model, illustrated in Figure 1.7, allows information to be distributed from a single source to other servers, which will use the information in decision support systems. This approach is most common when a single server accepts all data modifications and this information must be distributed to reporting servers.

**FIGURE 1.7**

A single-Publisher
replication model

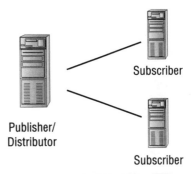

Publisher/
Distributor

Subscriber

Subscriber

The single Publisher model supports smaller organizations with simple data distribution needs. It does not effectively support organizations that must move data between multiple servers.

## Multiple Publisher, Single Subscriber

The multiple Publisher, single Subscriber model, sometimes referred to as the central Subscriber model, allows data to be gathered from multiple servers and relayed to a single Subscriber. This approach is most commonly used in organizations that have a very strong centralization tendency.

Often, each publishing server will actually maintain portions of a single table, publishing that information to a central Subscriber. In this scenario, pictured in Figure 1.8, the central Subscriber collects all of this information to a single table or group of tables. This allows the Publishers to maintain "local" data while having a "headquarters" that always has complete data.

## Multiple Publisher, Multiple Subscriber

This approach, where SQL Servers act as both Publishers and Subscribers, is most common in organizations that are very decentralized. In the previous example, only the central Subscriber ever had the "big picture" of what the data looked like everywhere in the organization. For organizations that are more autonomous at the local level, this might not be appropriate. If every node must have full data, then each server must be both a Subscriber and a Publisher. Figure 1.9 illustrates this approach.

**FIGURE 1.8**

The central Subscriber

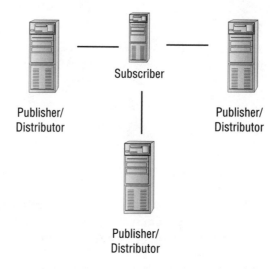

Subscriber

Publisher/
Distributor

Publisher/
Distributor

Publisher/
Distributor

**FIGURE 1.9**

The multiple
Publisher, multiple
Subscriber approach

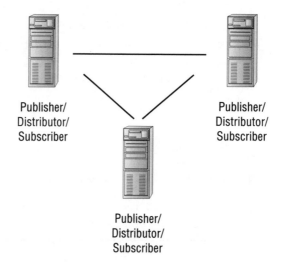

Publisher/
Distributor/
Subscriber

Publisher/
Distributor/
Subscriber

Publisher/
Distributor/
Subscriber

If each server is publishing and subscribing to the same table, you must use a server-specific key to ensure that each server modifies only data local to that server.

## Using a Remote Distributor

In all of the previous examples, the publishing server also served as the distribution server. In larger organizations, there may be an advantage to isolating the distribution server. This can be done for a number of reasons:

1. To dedicate a server to distribution tasks due to the overhead that the distribution activities place on a production server

2. To provide a distributor across a slow link, minimizing the cost involved in replicating across large geographical areas

In the first example, you may still have multiple Publishers and Subscribers; however, all of the traffic will be routed through a single Distributor. This allows all of the distribution overhead to be confined to a single server. Figure 1.10 illustrates this approach.

Publishers                    Subscribers

Distributor

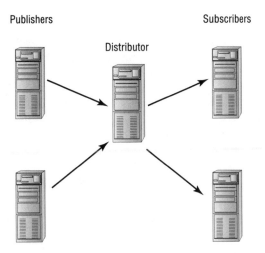

In the case of slow link services, you need to minimize the activity across the slow link as much as possible for both efficiency and cost. In the scenario presented in Figure 1.11, data from two Publishers in Los Angeles must be replicated to two Subscribers in Tokyo. It would not be cost-effective for each of the Publishers to replicate directly to each of the Subscribers. Instead, we will funnel the activity down to a single stream of communication.

**FIGURE 1.11**

Remote distribution
across a slow link

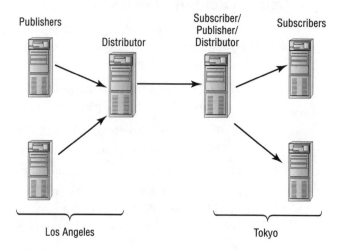

**FIGURE 1.11**

Remote distribution
across a slow link

In this example, both Publishers use a single Distributor. This Distributor replicates across the slow link to a single Subscriber. In turn, this Subscriber then publishes and distributes the replicated data to all Subscribers on the other side of the slow link. Using this approach, only a single replication operation must occur across the slow link.

## Replication Types

SQL Server supports three different types of replication that define the content and process of the replication. These different types of replication range in flexibility and data isolation. The replication types are:

- Transactional
- Snapshot
- Merge

The difference among these types is focused on the trade-off between data integrity and data independence. Where data integrity is favored, you are limited to where data modifications can be made. However, where data independence is favored, you are allowed to make data modifications on any participating server, even if data integrity is sacrificed.

## Transactional Replication

Transactional replication is a unidirectional replication model. Data modifications are made to the publishing server only. The distribution server periodically pulls transactions from the transaction log of the published database and stores them in the distribution database. These transactions are then replicated to the subscribing servers according to the schedule defined in the distribution database.

This approach is used when there is a significant amount of data to be replicated and data integrity is of the utmost importance. When this approach is used, all data modifications must be made at the publishing server and all subscribed data must be treated as read-only.

## Snapshot Replication

Snapshot replication is also a unidirectional model, but it does not depend on the transaction log of the Publisher. Unlike transactional replication, the entire replicated article is copied to the subscribing server with every scheduled replication task. This ensures that the data is always resynchronized with every replication.

This type of replication is most useful when managing relatively small replication jobs. Large tables that are replicated using snapshot replication cause too much of a strain because the entire article is replicated every time.

## Merge Replication

The merge replication model is bidirectional in nature. Data modifications can be made at any server. When two servers replicate, they merge their data modifications together. If any replication conflicts occur, such as key violations, the conflicts must be resolved at the offending server.

The merge replication model is very popular for the mobile workforce and the disconnected network. For example, if you have a mobile sales force with laptop computers running Windows 98, you could install the SQL Server Desktop Edition on each laptop. Each sales representative would be able to modify data when disconnected and merge the modifications with the host server when the laptop was connected. Eventually, all of the modifications would be replicated to every laptop through the central server.

**WARNING**   Merge replication requires servers to be licensed using the per-seat licensing approach rather than the per-server approach. You are legally allowed to transition a server once from per server to per seat, but you are not allowed to go back.

---

**STUDY QUESTIONS**

---

## Develop a Security Strategy

**1.**  The two authentication modes supported by Microsoft SQL Server are _____ and _____.

**2.**  The primary advantage of a mixed authentication mode is _____ _____ _____.

**3.**  Which authentication mode prevents unencrypted passwords from traveling on the network?_____

**4.**  Which two objects can a database administrator use to aggregate users' permissions in a SQL Server database?

_____

**5.**  Of the two objects listed in Question 4, which would be the most appropriate in a mixed authentication mode? _____ _____

**6.**  The three classifications of SQL Server roles are _____, _____, and _____.

**7.**  The role db_denydatareader is an example of which type of role? _____ _____.

**8.**  Which of the three types of roles can be dropped? _____ _____.

**9.** The _____ service is the Windows NT service that acts as the data engine, while the _____ service supports automation.

**10.** Which service supports the ability to issue a transaction to two individual servers?

_____

**11.** When configuring SQL Server services to interact with Windows NT, you can use either the _____ account or a _____ account.

**12.** To allow the SQL Server to communicate with other SQL Servers on the network, the services must be configured to use _____ accounts that are members of the _____ group.

**13.** If you want to allow users to connect to a SQL Server without providing a valid login, you must enable the _____ account.

**14.** Which Microsoft product presents middle-tier security options for managing SQL Server security? _____

**15.** True or False. Windows NT users can be associated with SQL Server roles.

_____

**16.** True or False. SQL Server logins can be part of Windows NT groups.

_____

**17.** The system administrator's role is a _____ role.

**18.** True or False. A client connecting to a SQL Server database from a Windows 98 workstation is able to connect in a Windows NT authentication mode.

_____

**19.** True or False. A client connecting to a SQL Server database from an MS-DOS–based workstation running LAN Manager is able to connect in a Windows NT authentication mode.

_____

**20.** True or False. A client connecting to a SQL Server database from a Linux workstation is able to connect in a Windows NT authentication mode.

_____

**21.** Your network has 125 workstations. Of these, 120 are Windows-based workstations and 5 are Macintosh computers. Which authentication mode would you select to ensure that you had the tightest possible security, but every workstation is allowed to connect to the SQL Server? _____

**22.** SQL Server is installed on a member Windows NT Server. You have created a local Windows NT group called SQLUsers. The Primary Domain Controller in this domain has defined a global group called SQLDomain, and all domain users that must access SQL Server are placed into this global group, including a user named Jon. The SQLDomain global group has been added to the local SQLUsers group. The SQLUsers group has been given system admin authority in the inventory database. Jon logs into the domain and creates a table in the inventory database. Who will be the registered owner of the table?

_____

## Develop a SQL Server Capacity Plan

**23.** Every database must contain at least two files. They are the _____ file and the _____ file.

**24.** Which software-based RAID solution, disk mirroring or disk striping with parity, requires more CPU time? _____

**25.** True or False. When RAID is not being used, database files and transaction log files for the RAID database should be placed on the same physical disk for recoverability reasons. _____

**26.** Describe how a RAID 5+1 structure should be implemented for a SQL Server database. _____ _____

**27.** Any file not explicitly added to another filegroup is part of the _____ filegroup.

**28.** Much of the I/O advantage offered by filegroups can also be obtained by using _____.

**29.** The minimum processor requirement for SQL Server 7 is _____ _____.

**30.** If you need to increase the size of your database by 50 percent, which server resource should you consider increasing along with the required disk space? _____

**31.** Which Transact SQL command would you use to increase the size of a database?

_____

**32.** If you created a database and set values for the maximum size and file-growth options, what additional actions would you need to take to increase the size of the database when needed?

_____

_____

**33.** Which hardware resource will be affected the most by the addition of an OLAP (on-line analytical processing) application to a SQL Server?    _____

## Develop a Data Availability Solution

**34.** List the four types of backups supported by SQL Server.

_____

_____

_____

_____

**35.** True or False. A well-planned RAID strategy is a valid replacement for backup/restore.

_____

**36.** If you have a small database and a tolerance for a small amount of data loss, your backup strategy should consist of _____.

**37.** If you have a moderately sized database with moderate data modification and no data loss tolerance, your backup strategy should include _____ _____.

**38.** True or False. Full database backups usually take longer to make than transaction log backups. _____

**39.** True or False. Differential backups are a replacement for transaction log backups. _____

**40.** File/filegroup backups are usually most appropriate for what size of databases? _____

**41.** To ensure that no data is lost, you should always back up the _____ before rebuilding or restoring a database.

**42.** If you have a very large database organized into _____, you might consider performing _____ backups to improve backup efficiency.

**43.** Differential backups make a record of all of the data pages that were modified since the last _____ backup.

**44.** If you have no tolerance for downtime and are fearful of data loss due to a media failure, you might consider using a _____ solution.

**45.** The two primary advantages to using a cluster are _____ and _____.

**46.** The two primary advantages to using a standby server are _____ and _____.

**47.** True or False. Clustering is a good way to protect against media failure.

_____

**48.** True or False. Data managed by standby servers cannot be modified through a client transaction.

_____

**49.** The _____ solution uses two servers, each managing their own hard drives.

**50.** The _____ solution uses two servers with a common set of hard drives.

**51.** If you want to use a cluster solution, you must install the _____ version of Windows NT and the _____ version of SQL Server 7.

## Develop a Migration Plan

**52.** True or False. The Upgrade Wizard supports only migrations from SQL 6.*x* versions.

_____

**53.** Before you can upgrade a SQL Server 6.5 database, you must first install _____ _____ and ensure that the Tempdb database is at least _____ MB in size.

**54.** The SQL Server 7 Upgrade Wizard supports two upgrade methods. They are _____ _____ and _____.

**55.** In the upgrade process, the server hosting the SQL 6.*x* database to be upgraded is called the _____.

**56.** In the upgrade process, the server running SQL 7 is called the _____. _____.

**57.** The service used to migrate non-SQL data is called _____.

**58.** True or False. DTS can only be used to import data into SQL Server 7. _____

**59.** True or False. DTS supports SQL Server 4.2 as an import server. _____

**60.** The SQL Upgrade Wizard does not allow a two-computer upgrade process if the upgraded databases are used for _____.

**61.** True or False. The Upgrade Wizard will automatically uninstall the SQL 6.*x* Server after the upgrade is complete. _____

## Develop a Replication Strategy

**62.**   When replicating across slow link services, you should use a _____ replication model.

**63.**   Which replication model is the most appropriate for replicating a small amount of data in a confined geographical area? _____

_____

**64.**   Which replication model provides the best support for a very centralized organization with multiple field locations? _____

**65.**   You have an organization that is very decentralized. Each of the three regional field offices maintains its own sales data on a SQL Server. Each of the field offices needs to have copies of all of the sales data from the other offices for reporting. The data coming from other field offices will not be modified. Which replication model is the most appropriate?

_____

**66.**   Which replication type is the most appropriate for replicating a very small amount of data to multiple Subscribers? The Subscribers will use the data as a lookup table, and it will not be modified. It is critical that the data is regularly synchronized with the publisher.

_____

**67.**   If you choose to use merge replication, your servers must be licensed in _____ _____ mode.

## STUDY QUESTIONS

**68.** You have four Publishers and three Subscribers on a network. Production performance on the publishing servers is critical. What can you do to maximize performance on the publishing servers without sacrificing the performance of the replication tasks?

_____

_____

**69.** Which of the three replication types places the highest priority on data independence?

_____

**70.** Which of the three replication types places the highest priority on data integrity?

_____

**71.** You have a moderately sized mobile sales force that travels extensively. You have provided mobile computers for them to use to enter sales data while they travel. Every night they connect to the main network through RAS and replicate their data to the central database. Which replication type best supports this scenario?

_____

**72.** You have a large SQL Server database that receives all data modifications for all inventory figures in the company. This information must be replicated to three other servers that will use the data for decision support services. The replicated data will not be modified on the subscribing servers. Which replication type is the most appropriate for this scenario?

_____

**73.** Your company has a central office in Boston and regional field offices in Atlanta and Baltimore. You want to allow each office to maintain its own sales figures and replicate this information to Boston. It is not necessary for Atlanta and Baltimore to see each other's sales figures. Which replication model is the most appropriate?

_____

**74.**  You have two servers in your network that both accept data modifications. The activity on each server must be replicated to the other such that both servers always look exactly the same. There is no tolerance for data latency. Would merge replication be an acceptable solution? Why or why not? _____

_____

**75.**  Other than merge replication, what approach might be used to satisfy the conditions relayed in the previous question? _____

**76.**  Which Windows NT service would be used to support the best solution to the scenario posed in Question 74? _____

## SAMPLE TEST

**1-1** You are attempting to issue a distributed transaction from a SQL Server stored procedure. The transaction fails to run. The MSSQLServer service is running on both computers involved in the transaction and you have appropriately authenticated to both computers. What else could be causing the problem?

  **A.** The SQLAgent service is not running.

  **B.** Distributed transactions cannot be called within a stored procedure.

  **C.** The MSDTC service is not running.

  **D.** The servers are not appropriately linked.

**1-2** Only one of the following servers can support a complete installation of SQL Server 7. Which is it?

  **A.** Pentium 200 with 24MB RAM and 500MB hard drive

  **B.** Pentium II 300 with 48MB RAM and 150MB hard drive

  **C.** Dec Alpha with 128MB RAM and 200MB hard drive

  **D.** Pentium 133 with 64MB RAM and 500MB hard drive

**1-3** If you want your SQL Server to participate in replication with other SQL Servers, which of the following NT authentication modes would be most appropriate for the SQLAgent service?

  **A.** Use the local system account.

  **B.** Use a local user account with administrative rights.

  **C.** Use the administrator account.

  **D.** Use a domain user account with administrative rights.

**1-4**    You have a company that uses a very centralized business model. Managers at headquarters need to run regular reports on data gathered throughout the company and replicated to headquarters. Which replication scenario would be the most appropriate?

    **A.** Transactional

    **B.** Merge

    **C.** Snapshot

    **D.** Snapshot with immediate updating subscribers

**1-5**    You have five publishing servers that must replicate to 10 Subscribers across a slow link. Which replication model would be the most appropriate?

    **A.** Single Publisher, multiple Subscriber

    **B.** Multiple Publisher, single Subscriber

    **C.** Multiple Publisher, multiple Subscriber

    **D.** Remote Distributor

**1-6**    The server being upgraded to SQL Server 7 using the Upgrade Wizard is called:

    **A.** Import server

    **B.** Export server

    **C.** Scripting server

    **D.** Source server

**1-7** You have implemented a Windows NT security model for SQL Server. The Windows NT account Bill is a member of the Windows NT group called DBAdmin. The DBAdmin group is a member of the db_owner fixed database role in the Inventory database. Bill logs in and creates a table in the inventory database. Who owns the table?

    **A.** Bill

    **B.** db_owner

    **C.** DBAdmin

    **D.** Administrator

**1-8** You have a very large database that is organized into multiple filegroups. The volatility of the data is very high and the database is so large that you cannot back up the entire database without affecting production. What backup strategy would be the most appropriate?

    **A.** Full database backups with transaction log backups

    **B.** Full database backups with differential backups

    **C.** Rotating filegroup backups

    **D.** Backup to the null device to increase speed.

**1-9** Which of the following role types can you drop from SQL Server? (Select two answers.)

    **A.** Fixed-server role

    **B.** Application role

    **C.** Fixed-database role

    **D.** User-defined database role

**1-10**    You have a mission-critical database with minimal downtime tolerance. You want to protect yourself against the possibility of media failure. You would also like to increase the performance of data read operations. Which of the following solutions will provide these benefits?

    **A.** Clustering

    **B.** Standby server

    **C.** Creating a volume set

    **D.** Implementing a RAID array

**1-11**    You have a mission-critical database application that performs extensive OLAP activities. You are concerned that increased user activity will adversely affect performance. Which of the following techniques might address these issues?

    **A.** Clustering

    **B.** Standby server

    **C.** Creating a volume set

    **D.** Implementing a RAID array

**1-12**    You want to perform merge replication from remote Subscribers in the field to a central Publisher at headquarters. Which of the following licensing restrictions applies to this scenario.

    **A.** Publisher must be licensed per server.

    **B.** Publisher must be licensed per seat.

    **C.** Subscriber must be licensed per server.

    **D.** Subscriber must be licensed per seat.

**1-13**  Your company uses a small table in the Orders database to store your product price list. Changes are occasionally made to this price list. These changes are always made at one server, but the table must be replicated regularly to other servers on the network. The table is small; however, maintaining data integrity on the table is essential. Which replication type would be most the appropriate?

**A.** Transactional

**B.** Merge

**C.** Snapshot

**D.** Transactional with immediate updating subscribers

**1-14**  You have numerous Macintosh clients on your network. You must give them access to a SQL Server database. Which of the following security configurations should you use?

**A.** Map NT user accounts in a Windows NT–only mode.

**B.** Create SQL Server user accounts in a Windows NT–only mode.

**C.** Map NT user accounts in a mixed mode.

**D.** Create SQL Server user accounts in a mixed mode.

**1-15**  Which of the following is not a benefit of using NT clusters?

**A.** Load balancing

**B.** Media protection

**C.** Fail-over support

**D.** Scalability

# UNIT

# 2

Installation and Configuration

# Test Objectives: Installation and Configuration

- **Install SQL Server 7.0.**

  - Choose the character set.

  - Choose the Unicode collation.

  - Choose the appropriate sort order.

  - Install Net-Libraries and protocols.

  - Install services.

  - Install and configure a SQL Server client.

  - Perform an unattended installation.

  - Upgrade from a SQL Server 6.*x* database.

- **Configure SQL Server.**

  - Configure SQL Mail.

  - Configure default American National Standards Institute (ANSI) settings.

- **Implement full-text searching.**

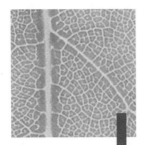

In this unit, we will explore the installation and configuration of SQL Server 7. We will begin with a discussion of the server installation process, including the installation of client utilities, unattended installations, and upgrading. We will then look at the configuration process for the SQL Mail utility and the Full-Text Search service.

# Install SQL Server 7

**S**QL Server supports an automated setup utility for installing a server and the client utilities. This setup utility can be launched from the initial setup screen, pictured in Figure 2.1, which will AutoPlay from the SQL Server CD. Follow the link for Install SQL Server 7 Components, which will present the options for installing the SQL Server products.

**FIGURE 2.1**

The SQL Server installation start screen

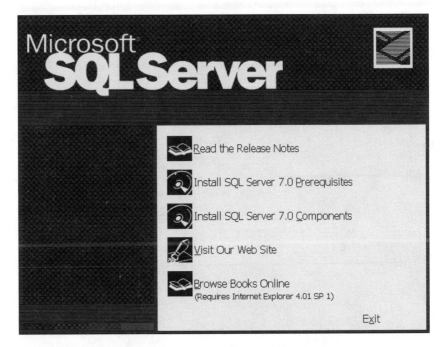

Although SQL Server 7 supports three distinct versions, this guide assumes that the user will be installing the Standard Server Edition, as opposed to the Enterprise or Desktop Editions.

Stepping through the installation, the Installation Wizard will gather information about your desired configuration and then set up the server accordingly. During setup, you will be asked many important questions. You will need to select the:

- Character set
- Sort order
- Unicode collation sequence
- Service accounts
- Network libraries

## Character Sets

A character set, also called a code page, is a set of mappings that relate numerical values to character representations. Most character sets used today store characters as a single byte per character. Because 8 bits equals a byte, 256 unique characters are allowed in the character set. Table 2.1 lists some of the character set choices for a SQL Server 7 installation.

Choose your character set carefully. If you change your mind later, modifying the character set is a tedious task that involves rebuilding your entire SQL Server on the new character set.

It is important that you select a character set based on two criteria:

- It must support the characters you need to store in the database.
- It must be compatible with the client applications and the operating system.

| **T A B L E  2.1** | **Code Page** | **Use** |
|---|---|---|
| Available Character Sets | 1252 (ISO 8859-1) | This is the default character set. Provides the greatest compatibility with Windows. Extended characters support some internationalization. |
| | 850 (multilingual) | Contains characters commonly used in the Americas and Europe. Select this character set if additional internationalization is required beyond CP 1252. |
| | 437 (U.S. English) | Although this is the most commonly used character set in the United States, it is often a poor choice for databases because the extended characters are not frequently found in data stores. |

If you are using only the first 128 characters of the character set in your application, stick with the default character set. All of the character sets listed in the table have the same first 128 characters, and the default character set gives you more flexibility for future growth.

## Unicode Collation Sequence

SQL Server supports special Unicode character data types (nchar and nvarchar) that store character data in Unicode rather than as an ANSI character set. Unicode differs from the character sets that we have already evaluated in that it requires two bytes of storage space rather than one for each character. This increase allows up to 65,536 characters to be stored in the Unicode character set.

The advantage to this representation is that it supports internationalization. Rather than swapping character sets around to support additional characters, Unicode, a universal code page, supports most of the world's most common characters in a single character set.

The Unicode collation sequence defines how Unicode data is sorted. You should use a Unicode collation sequence that is compatible with your standard sort order. This will make it easier to move data between Unicode and non-Unicode formats.

The default Unicode collation sequence is *general, case-insensitive*. You should match the case sensitivity with the standard sort order. Otherwise, you should not change the sequence without a compelling, strategic reason.

## Sort Order

Sort orders dictate how characters compare and sort with respect to other characters. The sort order that you select can have a significant impact on:

**1.** The performance of sorts and comparisons

**2.** The requirements of the client application using the server

Table 2.2 lists some of the more common sort order options that you have to choose from when you install your server.

| T A B L E  2.2 Sort Order Options for a SQL Server Installation | Sort Order | Effect |
| --- | --- | --- |
| | Dictionary-order, case-insensitive | Default. Characters sort and compare in dictionary order without regard to case. |
| | Dictionary-order, case-sensitive, uppercase preference | Characters sort based on case, but case is not considered when performing comparisons. |
| | Dictionary-order, case-sensitive | Faster. Characters sort and compare based on case. |
| | Binary | Fastest. Characters sort in true binary order. |

One of the most important things to consider when selecting a sort order is the client application. If the client has already been developed, it was created assuming a specific approach to case sensitivity. You must install the server with the required sort intact.

If the client application has not yet been developed, you should consider the sort order as part of the application's planning phase. This helps to ensure that you have considered all the benefits and drawbacks of the different sort orders.

When you are selecting sort order in your application, be as cautious as you were when selecting your character sets. If you choose to modify your sort order, the same process of rebuilding your server on the new sort order is required.

## Network Libraries

SQL Server is designed to provide its data services in a network environment; however, this network functionality is effectively abstracted from the database developer. This allows the database developer to focus on the core business problem without having to write code to interface with the network.

The Net-Library (network library) is the SQL Server attribute that makes this all possible. A network library is a thin layer of software that lies between the SQL Server data services and the network. This library instructs SQL Server on how to successfully negotiate the network, organizing data into a Tabular Data Stream (TDS). Network packets are built around the TDS packets.

Although some of the network libraries use the same name as the network protocols with which they were designed to interact (such as TCP/IP Sockets and NWLink), they are not actually protocols, but rather abstraction software. The network libraries abstract the actual implementation of the protocols for the DB Library API. This means that your SQL Server and client applications don't have to know anything about how the protocols actually interact with the data. Table 2.3 lists the network library options that you have when installing SQL Server. Asterisks (*) identify the network libraries that are installed by default.

A server can have multiple network libraries installed and can utilize each of them, depending on how the clients initiate contact. Clients can communicate only with a single SQL Server using one network library, but they can communicate with multiple servers using different network libraries.

| TABLE 2.3 | Library Name | Use |
|---|---|---|
| SQL Server Network Libraries | Named Pipes* | Used to move data between client and server using a single Microsoft-supplied protocol. |
| | Multiprotocol* | Uses named pipes to move data across multiple Microsoft-supplied protocols. Supports encrypted transmission. |
| | TCP/IP sockets* | Interacts with the TCP/IP protocols. |
| | NWLink | Supports the NWLink protocol. |
| | AppleTalk | Needed when using AppleTalk rather than TCP/IP to communicate with Macintosh clients. |
| | Banyan Vines | Supports a Banyan Vines network. |

*These Net-Libraries are installed by default.

**WARNING** Because Microsoft does not ship the AppleTalk or Banyan Vines protocols, you must acquire and install these protocols before the network libraries can be used. Also note that Windows 95/98 using a Desktop server installation does not support named pipes.

## Installing the Services

Running the SQL Server setup installs three (optionally four) services:

**MSSQLServer**  The SQL Server data engine

**SQLAgent**  The SQL Server automation engine

**MSDTC**  The distributed transaction coordinator

**Microsoft Search**  Full-Text Search service (optional)

The important decision that you will make during installation is how these services (particularly the MSSQLServer and SQLAgent) will access the operating system and the network. You have two options. You can configure the services to log on to NT Server using either of the following:

- The local system account
- A user account

If you use the local system account, the services will only be able to access resources on that NT Server. If you want the SQL Server to interact with other servers on the network, such as using replication or linked servers, you should use a domain user account for the services.

Add this account to the local administrators group to give the SQL Server services full access to the server resources. A single domain account can be used for all SQL Servers in the domain or trusting domains.

Service logon accounts can also be modified using the Services applet in the Windows NT Control Panel. Note also that the Desktop Edition of SQL Server runs as a background application rather than as a Windows NT service, therefore requiring no login accounts for its services.

## Installing Clients

When you install SQL Server, the client utilities are automatically installed by default whenever you perform a typical or custom installation. You can, however, choose to install only the client utilities. To do this, you must perform a *custom* setup. When presented with the component list, locate and select only the management tools and client connectivity options as illustrated in Figure 2.2.

**F I G U R E  2.2**

Installing client utilities

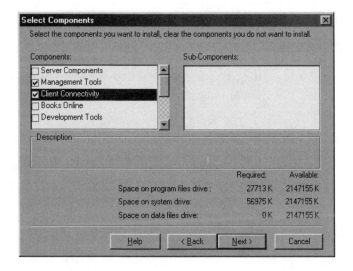

After installing the clients, you may want to configure the network library through which the clients communicate with the servers in the network. Use the Client Network utility to perform this task.

This utility allows you to specify which network library the clients on that computer will use to communicate with each server on the network. Click the Add button in the utility main screen to present the dialog pictured in Figure 2.3. This dialog allows you to configure access to a server on the network using a specified network library. In this case, the library is Named Pipes.

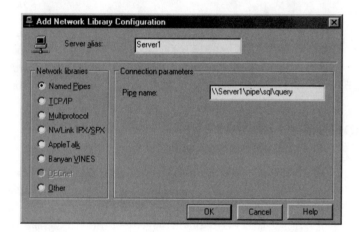

 To configure the Enterprise Manager to display system databases and objects, you must edit the server registration properties. Right-click the server name in the Enterprise Manager, and select "Edit SQL Server Registration Properties." From the dialog, select the option to show system objects.

## Unattended Setups

If you intend to install a large number of identically configured SQL Servers in your network, it may be more efficient to use an unattended setup process. Because SQL Server uses InstallShield as its setup utility, you can simply customize an InstallShield response file (.iss) to control the installation process. SQL Server ships with some .iss files and batch files that control the setup of different server components. Table 2.4 lists these files and their uses.

| **T A B L E  2.4** | **Batch File** | **Response File** | **Use** |
|---|---|---|---|
| Setup Batches and Response Files | Sql70cli.bat | Sql70cli.iss | Installs the SQL Server management tools |
| | Sql70ins.bat | Sql70ins.iss | Performs typical installation of SQL Server |
| | Sql70cst.bat | Sql70cst.iss | Performs a custom installation of SQL Server |

While each of these batch/response file pairs will perform an unattended installation with no further configuration required, you might want to customize the installation to suit your own individual needs. The easiest approach is to select the response file that is closest to the finished configuration that you require and customize it to create the installation that best meets your needs.

## Upgrading from SQL Server 6.x

A very well defined upgrade path comes with SQL Server 7. The upgrade utilities can help you leverage your existing investment in SQL Server and bring your application into SQL Server 7 as quickly and painlessly as possible.

The SQL Server Upgrade Wizard is a menu-driven upgrade process that will take your data and objects from a SQL Server 6.x installation to a SQL Server 7 implementation. Before you can upgrade the 6.x server, you should take the following prerequisite steps:

1. Back up all of your system and user databases to enable an easy recovery if required.

2. Run DBCC checks on the 6.x databases to ensure that they are valid.

3. Ensure that the Tempdb database is at least 10MB in size.

4. Disable any startup stored procedures. The Upgrade Wizard stops and restarts the services. No startup stored procedures should be active during this process.

5. Stop the replication process.

**6.** Disconnect any client applications that may be hitting the SQL Server.

**7.** If you plan to migrate data from a SQL Server 6.*x* installation on a computer other than the one running SQL Server 7 (a two-computer upgrade), the MSSQLServer service on both computers should be running on domain user accounts with administrative access.

If the upgraded service is running SQL Server 6.5, you must have Service Pack 4 or higher installed to perform the upgrade.

To begin the upgrade process, install the SQL Server 7 software as you would for a normal installation. Configure the server as desired. This will install the SQL Server Upgrade Wizard, which you will use to upgrade the data from a 6.*x* server. It is perfectly safe to install SQL Server 7 on a computer that is already running SQL Server 6.*x*. The installation of the version 7 software will not corrupt the 6.*x* installation, and it will enable you to migrate your databases later, when you are ready.

Select the SQL Server Upgrade Wizard from the Windows Start menu. This option is located at Start ➤ Programs ➤ Microsoft SQL Server-Switch ➤ SQL Server Upgrade Wizard. The first form of the Wizard, pictured in Figure 2.4, presents the default options for moving data from a SQL Server 6.5 to a SQL Server 7. The mode of transport is a named pipe.

**FIGURE 2.4**

Preparing to upgrade

You will subsequently have the option to select the servers that will participate in the upgrade process. If you installed SQL Server 7 on a computer that is already running SQL Server 6.*x*, you will identify the same server as the source and destination. This is called a single computer upgrade. If you want, you can also identify another server in the network running SQL Server 6.*x* and then migrate the databases to your target machine. This is a two-computer upgrade. Figure 2.5 illustrates the form in the Wizard that you will use to configure the export and import servers.

**F I G U R E　2.5**

Configuring export and import servers

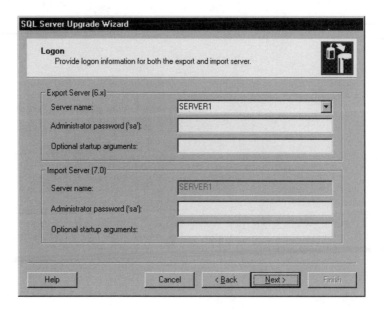

The subsequent forms of the Upgrade Wizard will allow you to customize the upgrade to perform many functions such as:

- Selecting databases to upgrade
- Changing the disk/file layout of the target database
- Transfer server configurations
- Transfer ANSI settings
- Transfer SQL Executive tasks to SQL Agent jobs

Once the SQL information concerning the SQL Server upgrade has been provided, you can launch the upgrade process. Many tasks are involved in this process. The Microsoft SQL Server Books Online provides the following list of tasks that occur during the upgrade process:

- Starts SQL Server 6.*x*
- Updates ODBC and SQL-DMO components on SQL Server 6.*x*
- Examines SQL Server 6.*x* databases
- Exports replication settings
- Exports server configuration settings from the `master` database.
- Exports logins
- Exports database owners
- Exports SQL Executive objects and settings from the Msdb database
- Exports database objects for all databases chosen
- Shuts down SQL Server 6.*x*
- Starts SQL Server 7
- Creates databases
- Modifies SQL Executive objects and settings to SQL Server 7 formats
- Imports logins
- Imports database objects
- Simultaneously exports data from SQL Server 6.*x* and imports it into SQL Server 7
- Imports modified SQL Executive objects and settings into SQL Server 7
- Imports replication settings
- Examines SQL Server 7 databases
- Verifies that the upgrade is successful
- Sets database options in SQL Server 7
- Marks server and databases as moved (for subsequent runs of the Wizard)
- Drops temporary Tempdb files

After the upgrade, you can remove the previous versions of SQL Server from your computer and your network. The upgrade process does not destroy or corrupt the previous version server or its databases. You can continue to use the Switch utility to switch between the previous installation and SQL Server 7 until you are ready to uninstall the previous server version.

# Configure SQL Server

**A**fter the installation or upgrade of your SQL Server, you will want to make come configuration adjustments to your server. Although SQL Server 7 is intended to be primarily self-tuning, two areas require some minor configuration when you are using dynamic allocation of resources. These areas are configuring the SQL Mail client and the ANSI compatibility settings.

## SQL Mail

SQL Server includes a MAPI-compliant mail client. This enables the SQL Server to interact with system administrators and other users via any MAPI-compliant mail system. Any questions on the exam regarding mail integration will assume that you are using Microsoft Exchange as your mail system.

Configuring the SQL Mail client requires us to look back a few steps in the installation process to the point at which we provided a user account for the services to log on to the operating system. In order to allow the SQL Mail client to access the mail system, a mail account must be created for this logon on the Exchange server.

If you already have a Microsoft Exchange server installed and available on the domain, you should be prompted for mail account information at the time when you add the user account.

After creating an Exchange account for the SQL Server logon user account, you will need to configure a default profile for that account. To configure the profile, you should log on to the SQL Server computer interactively, using the account that you provided for the services. Once logged in, you can configure the default profile for that account.

To configure the profile, open the SQL Server Enterprise Manager and locate the server in the tree view on the left side of the Explorer interface. Right-click the server, and select Properties from the Shortcut menu. In the Properties dialog, click the Server Settings tab. This should present a dialog like the one pictured in Figure 2.6.

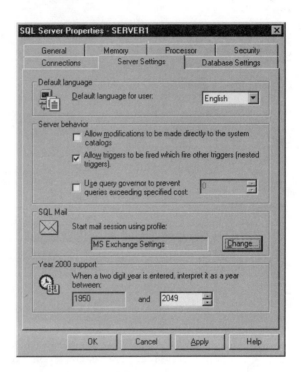

If you want to change the profile, click the Add button and select any profile from the list. When the SQL Server services access the mail system, they will do so using the profile configured in this dialog.

A profile provides a set of configurations for accessing an underlying message source. It is somewhat analogous to the concept of a data source name for ODBC data access.

# ANSI Settings

Some SQL Server settings are not compliant with the ANSI defaults for server behavior. To provide administrators the ability to support ANSI compliance, server and database settings are available. Configuring these settings may change the way your database or client application behaves; however, if you want to have an application that is truly ANSI compliant, you might consider setting some of these options.

We will look at the ANSI server settings. To access these settings, navigate to the server properties and click the Connections tab as pictured in Figure 2.7. The options available include:

- ANSI warning

- ANSI padding

- ANSI nulls

- ANSI null defined on

- ANSI null defined off

**FIGURE 2.7**

Setting ANSI options

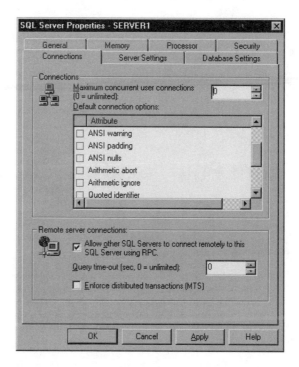

### ANSI Warnings

When the ANSI warning option is selected, warnings are issued when nulls appear in aggregate functions or a divide-by-zero error occurs. Without this option set, no warnings are issued and a divide-by-zero or arithmetic overflow error returns a null.

### ANSI Padding

When fixed-length data types are used, ANSI padding preserves trailing blanks when assigning them to varchar variables. Trailing zeros are preserved for varbinary variables.

### ANSI Null

The ANSI standard requires that a null will always fail all comparisons. In other words, if you have a query with a where clause that reads *column = null* or *column <> null,* both would return no rows. Turn this switch on to initiate this behavior.

### ANSI Null Defined On/Off

When you create a table, you can explicitly state whether each column will allow null values to be stored in the column. If you do not explicitly request nulls to be allowed, the SQL Server default will not allow nulls in a column. The ANSI standard is just the opposite, allowing nulls in columns where nullability is not explicitly stated. When the ANSI null defined on option is set, SQL Server complies with the ANSI requirements.

# Implement Full-Text Searching

One of the more challenging aspects of maintaining a SQL Server is optimizing the performance of queries. Selects against large character columns often prove to be among the most problematic queries to tune. This is because of the inability of standard indexes to provide useful assistance when selecting data when the criteria are based on comparisons with characters inside the column.

Full-text indexes differ from standard indexes in three primary ways:

- Rather than indexing only high-order elements in the column, the full-text index tracks search information for the entire text of a large character column.

- Although standard indexes are updated automatically when modifications are made to the database, full-text indexes remain static. They must be updated at regular and appropriate intervals to reflect the changing data in the character columns.

- Full-text indexes are not actually stored in the database. They are stored in the file system. This means that they are not backed up with the databases and must be rebuilt when the databases are restored.

## Installing the Full-Text Search Service

The Full-Text Search service, also called Microsoft Search, is not installed by default when you install SQL Server. You must perform a custom installation and select the Full-Text Search from the list of server components as illustrated in Figure 2.8.

**FIGURE 2.8**

Installing
Microsoft Search

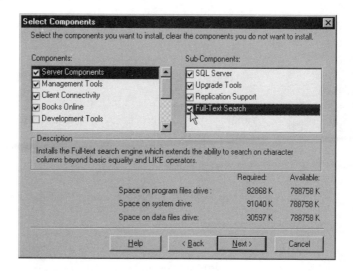

Once installed, the Full-Text Search service will be visible in the support services folder of the Enterprise Manager. Right-click the service and select Properties from the Shortcut menu to access the configuration options for the service including the location of full-text catalogs and error logs.

## Enabling and Implementing Full-Text Searching

After the service is installed, you must enable full-text searching on databases and tables before you will be able to create and maintain full-text indexes. Working with full-text can be performed by using either the Enterprise Manager interface or Transact-SQL code.

Using the Enterprise Manager, you can enable and configure full-text searching for a database and tables within a database using the Full-Text Indexing Wizard. This easy-to-use Wizard has many functions, including:

- Enables full-text searching on a database.

- Enables full-text searching on a table.

- Specifies the unique column for the indexed table (required for full-text indexing).

- Identifies the character columns that you want to index.

- Identifies which catalog you will use to store the index, or alternately allows you to create a new catalog. A catalog is a collection of full-text indexes.

- Specifies a population schedule for the catalog.

To access the Full-Text Indexing Wizard, click the database that you want to enable in the Enterprise Manager and select Tools ➤ Full-Text Indexing from the menu.

Alternatively, you can use system stored procedures to enable full-text indexing on a database or table. The relevant stored procedures are:

- **sp_fulltext_database** Enables full-text indexing for a database

- **sp_fulltext_table** Enables full-text indexing for a table

- **sp_fulltext_column** Marks a column to participate in a full-text index

- **sp_fulltext_catalog** Creates a full-text catalog

Once the full-text catalogs have been created, you must populate them before they can be of any significant use. To populate a full-text catalog, expand the database in the Enterprise Manager and locate the full-text catalogs from the list of database objects as pictured in Figure 2.9. Right-click the catalog to rebuild or repopulate the catalog.

Rebuilding a full-text index will actually re-create the entire full-text index. Use this option when you modify table structure or need to redefine your indexes. Because full-text indexes are not updated dynamically, you may also need to repopulate the index. This will ensure that the index contains up-to-date information about the table structure. The distinction between repopulate and rebuild is important for the exam.

You have two options for repopulating an index. You can do a full repopulation or an incremental repopulation. Full repopulation will restructure the entire index, while incremental repopulation will modify entries only for modified data.

**FIGURE 2.9**

Locating full-text catalogs

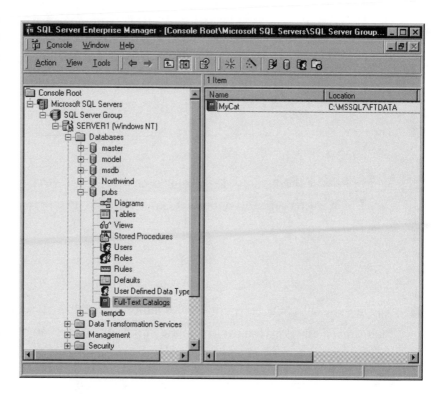

WARNING

Rebuilding and repopulating full-text catalogs can be a very time-consuming task. However, because these indexes are static, it is a task that must be performed. Try to schedule the task for a time when there is less activity on the database.

## Install SQL Server 7

**1.** Which two installation decisions cannot be reversed without rebuilding the server and all of its databases?

_____

**2.** What purpose does the character set serve in a SQL Server installation?

_____

_____

**3.** The default character set in SQL Server is _____.

**4.** True or False. If the application uses only the first 128 characters in the character set, the choice of character set is less important because there is no difference in the first 128 characters across code pages.

_____

**5.** You must install a SQL Server that stores information gathered from both domestic and international offices in eastern Canada and Europe. It is important that the character set you choose support these locales. Which character set should you use?

_____

**6.** You have a network that consists of only U.S. English builds of Windows 98 and Windows NT Workstation clients. You want to select a SQL Server character set that will provide the most compatibility with the client workstations. Which character set should you select?

_____

**7.**   Which sort order provides the best possible performance for sorts and comparisons?

_____

**8.**   Which general types of sort orders are the fastest, case-sensitive or case-insensitive? Why?

_____

_____

_____

_____

_____

**9.**   What factors should you consider when selecting a sort order for a server?

_____

_____

**10.**   How many bytes are used to store a single character using the Unicode character set?

_____

**11.**   When should you consider using Unicode characters in your data storage?

_____

_____

_____

**12.**   You have determined that you will use a dictionary-order, case-sensitive sort order for your SQL Server. Which Unicode collation sequence should you use on this server?

_____

**13.** The default Unicode collation sequence is_____.

**14.** What is the purpose of a Net-Library (network library) on a SQL Server?

_____

_____

_____

_____

**15.** What three network libraries are installed by default on a SQL Server?

_____

_____

_____

**16.** Which two network libraries are most commonly used to communicate with Macintosh clients?

_____

**17.** Your network uses NetWare as its primary network operating system. You want to install a Windows NT Server to host a SQL Server on this network. To allow clients in this network to access the SQL Server database application, you must install the _____ protocol on the NT Server and the _____ network library on the SQL Server.

**18.** Which network library uses a named pipes inter-process communication (IPC) mechanism and supports data encryption? _____.

**19.** SQL Server services can log on to the Windows NT operating system using either the _____ account or a _____ account.

**20.** You have installed a SQL Server on a server named *Server1*. The SQL Server services will not access any resources on any server other than Server1. Does it make a difference which account type you use? Why?

_____

_____

_____

**21.** If you require the SQL Server services to be able to make trusted connections to other servers, you must provide _____ accounts as logon accounts for the SQL Server services.

**22.** Which service supports atomic transactions on multiple SQL Server in the network?

_____.

**23.** Which service acts as the automation engine for the SQL Server?

_____.

**24.** Which service is not installed in a typical installation of SQL Server?

_____.

**25.** The _____ Edition of SQL Server cannot act as a Publisher in a transaction replication model because its services do not support a logon using domain user accounts and, therefore, cannot create trusted connections to other servers.

**26.** Unattended setups require which two files?

_____

_____

**27.** Which response file supports an unattended typical installation of SQL Server?

_____

**28.** True or False. You must uninstall SQL Server 6.5 on a server before you can install SQL Server 7.

_____

**29.** Before you upgrade a SQL Server 6.5 server to version 7, you must ensure that the Tempdb database is at least _____ in size.

**30.** By default, data is moved between servers in an upgrade through a_____.

**31.** When an upgrade is being configured, the server that houses the 6.*x* database is called the _____ server, and the server that houses the version 7 server is called the _____ server.

## Configure SQL Server

**32.** The SQL Server mail client uses an open API set called _____ to communicate with a mail service.

**33.** What must you do before you can set the default messaging profile for the SQL Server services account?

_____

_____

_____

**34.** True or False. By default, SQL Server 7 is completely compliant with ANSI database requirements.

_____

**35.** The ANSI setting that forces errors to be raised when a divide-by-zero error occurs is called

_____.

**36.** True or False. With ANSI null option selected, the clause _column = null_ will return 0 rows even if that column contains null values.

_____

**37.** What does the ANSI null-defined on switch do?

_____

_____

**38.** What is the primary benefit of making your application and server ANSI compliant?

_____

_____

_____

**39.** Where would you find the ANSI settings in the Enterprise Manager interface?

_____

_____

**40.** How do you configure the Enterprise Manager to display information about system objects such as system databases and tables?

_____

_____

## Implement Full-Text Searching

**41.** List some of the differences between standard indexes and full-text indexes.

_____

_____

_____

**42.** Which stored procedure would you use to enable full-text indexing on a column of a table?

_____

**43.** How do you install the Full-Text Search service?

_____

_____

**44.**   True or False. You can use a Full-Text Search index to locate information in a column defined as a money data type.

_____

**45.**   Before you can build a full-text index on a table, the table must have a _____

_____.

**2-1** You have a large mission-critical application and have decided to use SQL Server as your database management system. Your server has 4GB of physical memory. You want to use as much of this memory as possible for your SQL Server data cache. You also want to install the server on a Windows NT cluster for fail-over support. You are concerned about price and want to use the most cost-effective installation possible. Which SQL Server installation should you use?

    **A.** Desktop

    **B.** Standard

    **C.** Enterprise

    **D.** Application

**2-2** You want to install SQL Server on a computer in New York and a computer in Germany. These two servers must be able to exchange data; however, the server in New York uses extended characters in the ISO-Latin1 character set and the server in Germany uses extended characters in code page 850. How should you plan the installation?

    **A.** Install both servers with the Latin1 character set.

    **B.** Install both servers with code page 850.

    **C.** Install each server with a character set that is appropriate for each locale.

    **D.** Build the server tables to use Unicode data types for all string data.

**2-3** You have implemented full-text searching in your web application. You have modified a moderate amount of information in one of the indexed tables and you are no longer getting valid results. It is very important that you conserve server resources. What should you do to solve the problem?

    **A.** Do nothing. The index will automatically be maintained during idle time on the server.

    **B.** Do an incremental repopulation.

**C.** Rebuild the index.

**D.** Do a full repopulation.

**2-4**   You have configured your SQLServerAgent service to log into Windows NT under an account called SQLAgent. How do you configure the SQLServerAgent service to send e-mail through Microsoft Exchange?

   **A.** Log into Exchange as SQLAgent and set mailbox properties.

   **B.** Add the SQLAgent account to the db_mailadmins role.

   **C.** Log into SQL Server as SQLAgent and configure the mail profile.

   **D.** Do nothing. SQLServerAgent is autoconfigured for Microsoft Exchange.

**2-5**   You have configured all of your SQL Server clients to use the Named Pipes network library to interact with a Desktop installation of SQL Server running on Windows 98. Your clients are unable to connect. What might be causing the problem?

   **A.** The Desktop Edition of SQL Server does not support remote clients.

   **B.** The Desktop Edition of SQL Server on Windows 98 does not support the Named Pipes network library.

   **C.** You must configure a port number before you will be able to connect.

   **D.** Use the client network utility to add the multiprotocol network library.

**2-6**   Steve wants to implement SQL Server in a small workgroup. His goal is to provide data services for a small application that will never have more than three users connected at any time. He is willing to support a Windows NT Server for his data services, but would rather use Windows 98 if possible. Which version of SQL Server should Steve install?

   **A.** Desktop

   **B.** Standard

   **C.** Enterprise

   **D.** Application

**2-7** Sue has a SQL Server 4.2 installation that she wants to upgrade to SQL Server 7. She wants to upgrade all of the data and other database objects to version 7. Which of the following upgrade paths will accomplish this goal?

**A.** Use Data Transformation Services to migrate the data and objects.

**B.** Upgrade the server to SQL Server 6.5, then upgrade again to SQL Server 7.

**C.** Bcp the data into SQL Server 7 and script your other objects.

**D.** Use the SQL Server 6.5 Transfer Management Interface to push the data and objects from version 4.2 to version 7.

**2-8** Bill wants to upgrade his SQL Server 6.5 databases to version 7. He does not have the money for a second server and wants to upgrade his SQL Server using only the single server. There is a problem with the upgrade that requires some alterations to be made to the original SQL Server 6.5 database. How should Bill proceed?

**A.** Remove the SQL Server 7 installation, reinstall SQL Server 6.5, and repeat the upgrade.

**B.** Install SQL Server 6.5 on another server and repeat the upgrade.

**C.** Use the SQL Server switch utility to switch to the 6.5 installation, make the changes and repeat the upgrade.

**D.** Attach the SQL Server device files directly to the SQL Server 7 installation.

**2-9** You are performing a two-server upgrade from SQL Server 6.5 to SQL Server 7. Which of the following conditions would prevent the upgrade from completing successfully?

**A.** SQLExecutive tasks cannot be upgraded to SQLAgent jobs.

**B.** SQL Server 7 cannot accept SQL Server 6.5 Unicode data formats.

**C.** SQL Server 7 does not support multiserver upgrades.

**D.** Replication Publishers cannot be upgraded using a two-server upgrade path.

**2-10**   Which sort order will perform the fastest string comparisons?

   **A.** Case-sensitive

   **B.** Case-insensitive

   **C.** Binary

   **D.** Unicode

**2-11**   Which ANSI setting will maintain trailing blanks for varchar data rather than trimming the trailing blanks?

   **A.** ANSI padding

   **B.** ANSI trim

   **C.** ANSI warnings

   **D.** ANSI nulls

**2-12**   Which of the following is *not* a difference between standard indexes and full-text indexes?

   **A.** Standard indexes store data only on high-order elements of the indexed columns.

   **B.** Full-text indexes are not stored in the database while standard indexes are.

   **C.** Full-text indexes are not dynamically maintained like standard indexes.

   **D.** All of the above are differences between standard indexes and full-text indexes.

# UNIT

# 3

Configuring and
Managing Security

# Test Objectives: Configuring and Managing Security

- Assign SQL Server access through Windows NT accounts, SQL Server logins, and built-in administrator logins.

- Assign database access to Windows NT accounts, SQL Server logins, the *guest* user account, and the *dbo* user account.

- Create and assign SQL Server roles. Server roles include fixed server, fixed database, *public*, user-defined database, and application.

- Grant to database users and roles the appropriate permissions on database objects and statements.

- Audit server and database activity.

**O**ne of the primary responsibilities of the database administrator (DBA) is to secure the server and its data structures against unauthorized access. To assist the DBA in this task, SQL Server supports an extensive security system that allows the DBA to control access down to the column level.

In this unit, we will explore the SQL Server 7 security system, including controlling access to the server, database, and database object. We will also look at the differences between managing server access and database security in the Windows NT only mode versus the mixed mode. Finally, we will apply the SQL Profiler utility as a means of logging and auditing database activity.

# Secure Server Access

**B**efore users can obtain access to a database object, they must first provide the necessary credentials to the server. These credentials can be provided in one of two different ways:

**1.** Accessing a SQL Server through a trusted Windows NT login

**2.** Providing a SQL Server login and password at connection

If the server authentication mode is set to *SQL Server and Windows NT* as illustrated in Figure 3.1, then either authentication method is allowed. If the Authentication mode is set to *Windows NT only*, only trusted Windows NT logins are allowed to access the server. SQL Server logins and passwords are not accepted.

**WARNING**  When you change the authentication mode of the server in this dialog, you must stop and restart the SQL Server service before the changes will take effect.

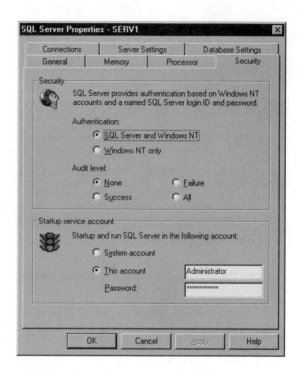

## Adding SQL Server Logins

SQL Server stores all login and password information in the syslogins system
table, which is stored in the Master database. When you add a standard SQL
Server login account, you are actually adding a row to this system table. You
can use either of two approaches to add standard SQL Server logins. You can
use the Enterprise Manager graphical interface, or you can implement the
system stored procedures in the Transact-SQL code.

For the purposes of the exam, you should pay special attention to the
Transact-SQL code examples. The exam heavily emphasizes the Transact-
SQL approach to administration tasks.

## Using the Enterprise Manager to Add SQL Logins

When you use the Enterprise Manager to add standard SQL Server login accounts, drill into the tree view on the left side of the interface through the Security folder, as shown in Figure 3.2. Under Logins you will see the logins (both NT accounts and standard SQL Server logins) that have been recognized by the server.

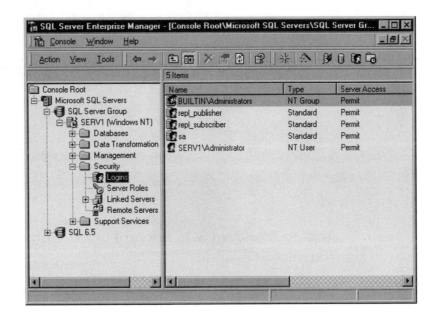

To add a new standard SQL Server login, right-click the Logins folder in the Enterprise Manager, and select New Login from the Shortcut menu. Click the SQL Server authentication option button and enter the login name and password as pictured in Figure 3.3. When you click OK, you will be asked to confirm the new password. Your new SQL Server login will now be visible in the logins list in the Enterprise Manager.

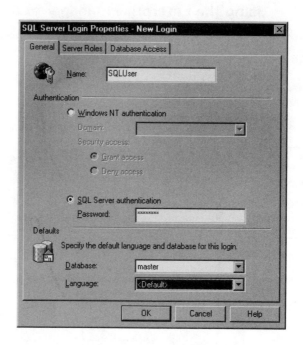

## Adding Standard SQL Server Logins with Transact-SQL Code

Table 3.1 lists the stored procedures used to manage SQL Server logins. Only the sa login or members of the system administrators or security administrators server roles can use these procedures.

| TABLE 3.1 | Procedure | Use |
|---|---|---|
| Login Management Stored Procedures | sp_addlogin | Add a new SQL Server login to the syslogins system table of the Master database. |
| | sp_droplogin | Remove a SQL Server login. |
| | sp_password | Change the password for an existing SQL Server login. |

To add a login named *SQLUser* with a password of *password* and Pubs as the default database, you would use the following procedure call:

```
EXEC sp_addlogin 'SQLUser', 'password', 'pubs'
```

To drop this login, use the following call:

```
EXEC sp_droplogin 'SQLUser'
```

When used by an administrator, the sp_password stored procedure requires you to provide the name of the login. To change the password from *password* to *newpassword* for SQLUser, issue the following call:

```
EXEC sp_password 'password', 'newpassword', 'SQLUser'
```

Because users can also change their own passwords, SQLUser would also be able to issue the sp_password call using the following syntax to change his or her own password.

```
EXEC sp_password 'password', 'newpassword'
```

# Adding Windows NT Account Access

Because Windows NT accounts already exist in the domain or on the server, you don't actually add the Windows NT account to SQL Server again. You simply grant SQL Server access to existing Windows NT logins or groups. You can also deny SQL Server access to Windows NT logins or groups to prevent them from obtaining access to a SQL Server. Just as before, you can either use the Enterprise Manager or the Transact-SQL code to perform this task.

## Granting Windows NT Account Access with Enterprise Manager

To add a Windows NT account to SQL Server, open the New Login dialog pictured earlier in Figure 3.3. To grant access rights to the NT login, select the Windows NT authentication option button and select the computer or domain name that hosts the Windows NT account from the drop-down list. Then type the name of the Windows NT login or group in the Name text box.

Note that in the case of Windows NT logins, the password text box is disabled. This is because SQL Server "trusts" that Windows NT has performed the authentication, and it does not reauthenticate the account. Note that you can also specify the option to either grant or deny access to the Windows NT account; this option is not needed for standard SQL Server accounts.

## Managing the Builtin\Administrators Account

SQL Server includes a predefined trusted account for all NT administrators called Builtin\Administrators. You should not remove this account; however, you may choose to restrict access to this account by setting the account properties. Right-click the account in the Enterprise Manager and select Properties from the Shortcut menu. In this dialog, you will be able to modify default database, grant/deny, and role membership attributes of the account.

Note that by default this account is recognized as the dbo user in every database and is a member of the sysadmins server role. You should change these attributes if it is inappropriate for the network admins to have this level of authority in the server.

## Managing Windows NT Account Access with Transact-SQL

Windows NT login and group accounts are managed in SQL Server through three stored procedures. These procedures, listed in Table 3.2, give the DBA control over which NT users are allowed to access a SQL Server.

| T A B L E   3.2 | Procedure | Use |
|---|---|---|
| NT Account Management Stored Procedures | sp_grantlogin | Grants SQL Server access rights to a specified Windows NT login or group account |
| | sp_denylogin | Prevents the specified NT login or group account from gaining access to the SQL Server |
| | sp_revokelogin | Revokes previous grants or denials to specified Windows NT login or group account |

Using these stored procedures, if you wanted to grant SQL Server access to a Windows NT login named *Steve* in the Accounts domain, the procedure call would be:

```
EXEC sp_grantlogin 'Accounts\Steve'
```

To deny access to every member of a Windows NT group called *SQLDeny* in the Corporate domain, you would use the following call:

```
EXEC sp_denylogin 'Corporate\SQLDeny'
```

Finally, to revoke either previously configured grant or deny settings on an account, you would use the following call:

```
EXEC sp_revokelogin 'Accounts\Steve'
```

In addition to using the single quotes as identifiers in this situation, you can also use square braces as in the following call: EXEC sp_grantlogin [Accounts\Steve].

# Configure Database Access

**E**ven though users have properly authenticated to SQL Server, they must be granted access rights to a database before they will be able to access any of the resources in that database. There are two primary approaches to granting database access:

1. Assign a database user name to the login for the desired database.

2. Create and configure a guest user in the database. This allows any server login without an assigned user name in the database to access as the guest user.

## Adding Users with the Enterprise Manager

You can take either of two approaches to add users to a database. You can use the Database Access tab of the Login Properties dialog, or you can go directly to the users list of the database and add a new user there. If you intend to map a single login to multiple databases at the same time, using the Login Properties dialog is more convenient.

The Database Access tab of the Login Properties (pictured in Figure 3.4 ) allows you to select the databases to which you want to grant access to the login. Simply select the checkbox next to the database name and type a user name in the text box on the right side of the database name. Figure 3.4 illustrates the Login Properties dialog for the SQLUser login. This login has been granted access to the Pubs database under the user name SQLUser.

**F I G U R E 3.4**

Configuring
Database Access

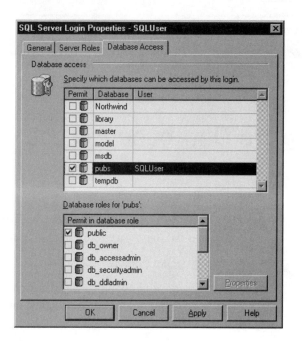

In this example, the login and the user name are the same, SQLUser. This is often convenient, but it is not required. You can use any unique name for the user name associated with any login.

## Adding Users with Transact-SQL

Using the Transact-SQL code, you grant database access to a login by providing a name within that database that maps to the login account. Table 3.3 lists the stored procedures used to manage database access in SQL Server 7.

| T A B L E  3.3 Database Access Stored Procedures | Procedure | Use |
|---|---|---|
| | sp_grantdbaccess | Adds a user in the database that maps to a specified login. |
| | sp_revokedbaccess | Removes the user account in a database for the specified login. |
| | sp_change_users_login | Remaps a database user name to a different login. |
| | sp_changedbowner | Transfers ownership of a database to the specified login. That login will then be the dbo user in the database. |

Using the stored procedures listed in the table, you would add a user name called *NewUser* to the Pubs database that maps to the *SQLUser* login with the following call:

```
USE pubs
EXEC sp_grantdbaccess 'SQLUser', 'NewUser'
```

To add a user name in the database that is the same as the login, you can omit the second argument, which defines the user name in the database. The statement EXEC sp_grantdbaccess 'SQLUser' would add a user called SQLUser in the current database that maps to the SQLUser login.

To remove the NewUser database user name previously granted to the SQLUser login in the Pubs database, use the sp_revokedbaccess procedure as follows:

```
USE pubs
sp_revokedbaccess 'NewUser'
```

To remap the SQLUser database user name in the Pubs database to a new SQL Server login or NT account named *NewLogin*, use the following procedure call:

```
USE pubs
sp_change_users_login 'Update_One', 'SQLUser', 'NewLogin'
```

The 'Update_One' value in the previous statement provides a value for the *@action* parameter of the procedure. This value states that you will update just the named database user account to the named login.

## Using the Guest Account

User databases do not contain a *guest* user by default. If you want to add a guest user account in the database, this account will provide access to any authenticated server login that does not have configured access to the database. To create the account, issue a statement like the following:

```
USE pubs
EXEC sp_grantdbaccess 'guest', 'guest'
```

If you want to have a guest account to all new user databases that you create, add the guest account to the Model database. This account will then be part of any new user database that you create from that point forward on that server.

## Configuring the DBO User

The database owner (dbo) of a database has full control of the database and its objects. To transfer ownership of a database to a new login account, you can use the sp_changedbowner stored procedure. This procedure assigns the dbo user name to the specified login.

Because a login can have only one user name in any single database, you must revoke database access for that login before you can execute this procedure. This will remove any existing user identification in the database for the login. The procedure will then associate that login with the dbo user name. Use the following format:

```
USE pubs
EXEC sp_changedbowner 'NewLogin'
```

# Manage Roles

**R**oles allow the database administrator to consolidate all access rights and permissions. Permissions are assigned to roles and roles are then associated with logins and users. SQL Server 7 supports four types of roles:

1. Fixed server

2. Fixed database

3. User-defined database

4. Application

 Fixed roles, both server and database, are not configurable. They cannot be altered or dropped.

## Fixed Server Roles

Fixed server roles define sets of rights to perform server-level configurations and tasks. Server roles are associated with server logins. The server roles supported in SQL Server are listed in Table 3.4.

| **TABLE 3.4** Fixed Server Roles | Role | Authority |
| --- | --- | --- |
| | sysadmin | Performs all server-related activities |
| | securityadmin | Creates and manages server logins |

| **T A B L E 3.4** *(cont.)* Fixed Server Roles | **Role** | **Authority** |
| --- | --- | --- |
| | serveradmin | Manages server-level properties and configurations |
| | setupadmin | Installs and manages replication |
| | processadmin | Manages SQL Server processes |
| | diskadmin | Manages disk space and file allocation |
| | dbcreator | Creates and manages databases |

Server roles can be assigned to logins with the Enterprise Manager by using the Server Roles tab of the Login Properties dialog. Figure 3.5 shows the SQLUser login associated with the sysadmins server role.

**F I G U R E 3.5**

Assigning server roles

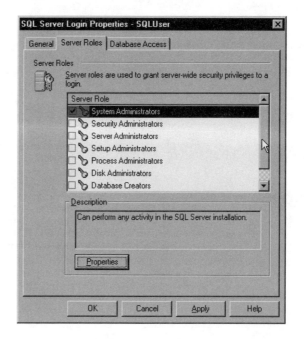

SQL Server provides two stored procedures for assigning and dropping server roles to logins. They are:

- sp_addsrvrolemember
- sp_dropsrvrolemember

To associate the sysadmin server role with the SQLUser login, you would make the following call:

```
EXEC sp_addsrvrolemember 'SQLUser',sysadmin
```

To revoke a previously granted ability to create databases from the Windows NT group called DBAdmins in the Accounts domain, use the following code:

```
EXEC sp_dropsrvrolemember 'Accounts\DBAdmins',dbcreator
```

## Fixed Database Roles

Fixed database roles are associated with database user accounts. They determine which database activities a user has permissions to perform. These permissions can range from full dbo access to denying rights to read tables. Table 3.5 lists the fixed database roles supported by SQL Server 7.

| T A B L E 3.5 Fixed Database Roles | Role | Authority |
|---|---|---|
| | public | Provides default database permissions. All users are members of the public role. |
| | db_owner | Performs all database activities. |
| | db_accessadmin | Creates and manages database users and roles. |
| | db_ddladmin | Adds, drops, and modifies all database objects. |
| | db_securityadmin | Assigns permissions to roles and users. |
| | db_backupoperator | Performs the backup and restoration of databases. |
| | db_datareader | Can read from all tables in the database. |

| **TABLE 3.5** (cont.) | **Role** | **Authority** |
| --- | --- | --- |
| Fixed Database Roles | db_datawriter | Can modify data in all tables in the database. |
| | db_denydatareader | Cannot read from any table in the database. |
| | db_denydatawriter | Cannot modify data in any table in the database. |

It is very important for the exam that you have a firm understanding of the functionality of each server and database role.

You can use the Enterprise Manager to associate server roles with database user accounts. Two different dialogs support this process. You can use the Database Access tab of the Login Properties dialog as pictured in Figure 3.4. In addition, you can also user the Role Properties dialog pictured in Figure 3.6. Click the Add button to select a user to add to the role.

**FIGURE 3.6**

Adding role members through role properties

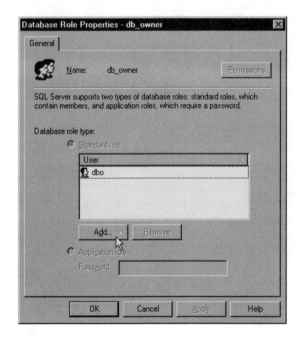

SQL Server provides two system stored procedures to configure association with database users. These procedures are:

- sp_addrolemenber
- sp_droprolemember

To associate a database user named *Dave* with the db_owner fixed database role, you would issue the following call:

```
EXEC sp_addrolemember 'db_owner','Steve'
```

To remove a user named *Sally* from the db_ddladmin fixed database role, use the following call. Note that you cannot remove a user from the public role.

```
EXEC sp_droprolemember 'db_ddladmin','Sally'
```

## User-Defined Database Roles

In addition to fixed roles, databases also support user-defined roles. User-defined roles are those that you create. You can assign permissions to them, and you can also drop them if necessary.

To create user-defined roles with the Enterprise Manager, navigate to the Roles folder of the target database as illustrated in Figure 3.7. Right-click the Roles folder, and select New Database Role from the shortcut menu.

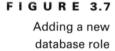

**FIGURE 3.7**

Adding a new database role

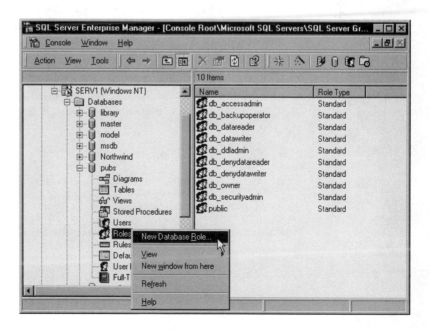

Using the Transact-SQL code, you will implement two system stored procedures to add and drop database roles. They are:

- sp_addrole
- sp_droprole

To add a role called *ReadAuthors* to the Pubs database, you would use the following procedure call. Note that the second parameter in the procedure specifies the owner of the role, which should be dbo.

```
EXEC sp_addrole 'ReadAuthors', 'dbo'
```

The following command would result in dropping the same role from the database.

```
EXEC sp_droprole 'ReadAuthors'
```

Once you have added user-defined roles to the database, you can associate user accounts with roles in exactly the same manner as with fixed database roles, using the sp_addrolemember and sp_droprolemember stored procedures.

## Application Roles

Application roles work differently from other types of roles in that logins or users are not associated with application roles. Instead, application roles are activated from within an application when a client connects to the SQL Server.

When a client invokes an application role, all permissions assigned to the current user are discarded and the permissions of the application role are used for the duration of that connection. When the client disconnects from the server, the application role context is terminated and must be reinvoked if desired upon the next connection. Using an application role comes in three steps:

1. Create the application role.

2. Assign permissions to the application role.

3. Invoke the application role in a client connection.

Step three, assigning permissions, will be discussed later in this unit.

## Creating an Application Role

When you create an application role, you will provide a role name and a password. The password is used when you activate the role from the client connection. This secured the permissions of the application role so that they can be activated only by the application making the connection.

You can create an application role using the Enterprise Manager by using the New Database Role dialog illustrated in Figure 3.8. This dialog shows the addition of a new application role called *AppRole* with a password of *password*.

**FIGURE 3.8**

Adding an
application role

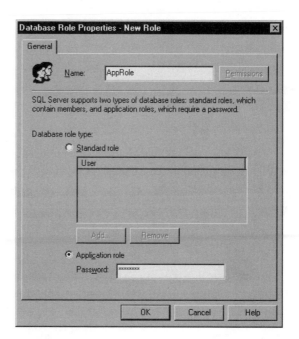

To add the application role using the Transact-SQL code, you will use the sp_addapprole stored procedure. This procedure has two arguments, namely rolename, and password. To create an application role called *AppRole* with a password of *password*, you would use the following stored procedure call:

```
EXEC sp_addapprole 'AppRole', 'password'
```

### Implementing an Application Role

To implement the application role, you must use the sp_setapprole stored procedure. When this stored procedure is in the context of a client connection, all permissions assigned to the application role replace any permissions assigned to the user or the user's associated roles.

The sp_setapprole stored procedure supports three arguments, namely rolename, password, and encryption. In the following code example, the application role is called, encrypting the password in transit using ODBC encryption. The "N" before the password in the command indicates that the password should be converted to Unicode format, required for encryption:

```
EXEC sp_setapprole 'AppRole', {ENCRYPT N'password'},'ODBC'
```

# Manage Permissions

**B**efore users will be allowed to access individual database objects, they must be assigned the appropriate permissions for those objects. Different objects support different actions and, therefore, different permissions. For example, select permissions are very applicable to tables, but you can't select from a stored procedure. Execute permissions are appropriate for stored procedures. Table 3.6 lists the permissions that are appropriate for different types of objects. These are called object permissions.

| **T A B L E  3.6** Object Permissions | **Object** | **Select** | **Insert** | **Update** | **Delete** | **References** | **Exec** |
|---|---|---|---|---|---|---|---|
| | Table | X | X | X | X | X | |
| | View | X | X | X | X | X | |
| | Column | X | | X | | X | |
| | Proc | | | | | | X |

A database administrator can also grant users the rights to execute specific types of commands. These commands are primarily those used to create database objects, but they also include specific backup rights. These are called statement permissions. The set of statement permissions is listed here:

- Create Database
- Create Table
- Create View
- Create Procedure
- Create Rule
- Create Default
- Backup Database
- Backup Log

Permissions are assigned and removed through the use of three Transact-SQL statements: Grant, Deny, and Revoke. Both statement and object permissions are managed with these three statements.

 If you have statement permissions to create an object, you do not need permissions to perform any actions on the underlying objects. However, you will not be able to execute your object unless you have the necessary permission on the underlying objects.

## Granting Permissions

The GRANT statement is used to grant either statement or object permissions to database users or roles. Database users can be mapped to either SQL Server logins or to Windows NT user or group accounts. To grant statement permissions, use the following syntax:

```
GRANT {ALL|statement[,…n]}
TO security_account[,…n]
```

Implementing this syntax, you would grant CREATE TABLE permissions to the c_table database role in the Pubs database with the following statement:

```
USE pubs
GRANT CREATE TABLE
    TO c_table
```

Granting object permissions is very similar; however, when you grant object permissions you must identify the object name as well as the permission being granted. The basic syntax is:

```
GRANT {ALL|permission}
    ON object_name
    TO security_account
```

Implementing this syntax, you would grant SELECT permissions on the Authors table of the Pubs database to the Accounts\AuthSel NT group using the following code example:

```
USE pubs
GRANT SELECT
    ON authors
    TO [Accounts\AuthSel]
```

 If a user is associated with multiple roles, the user will inherit the aggregate of all permissions assigned.

# Denying Permissions

The DENY statement is used to deny a permission to a specified account. The DENY overrides GRANT. If a user is a member of one group that has been granted permissions on an object and another group that has been denied permissions on an object, the user will be denied access to the object. In this way, DENY is very similar to the "No Access" right used in Windows NT security.

The syntax of the DENY statement is almost identical to the GRANT statement. Simply substitute the term DENY in place of GRANT. The syntax for denying statement permissions is shown here:

```
DENY {ALL|statement[,...n]}
    TO security_account[,...n]
```

To implement this statement, you might use the following code example that denies all statement permissions to the role named no_creates:

```
DENY ALL
    TO no_creates
```

Similarly, the DENY statement also supports virtually identical syntax for the assignment of object permissions. The code to deny UPDATE permissions on the Authors table of the Pubs database to an application called *no_update_approle.*

```
USE pubs
DENY UPDATE
    ON authors
    TO no_update_approle
```

## Revoking Permissions

The REVOKE statement is used to revoke permissions for an account on an object. REVOKE removes both affirmative and negative access rights previously placed on an account by using the GRANT and DENY statements. In other words, REVOKE will bring you back to where you started, with no permissions either granted or denied.

The syntax of the REVOKE statement is again very similar to the GRANT and DENY. The only substantive difference is that you don't revoke permissions TO an object, you revoke permissions FROM an object. Note the difference in the object permission syntax here:

```
REVOKE{ALL|permission}
    ON object_name
    FROM security_account
```

For example, if you previously denied all statement permissions to the no_creates role, you could revoke that denial by issuing the following statement. If a user were a member of another role that allowed them statement permissions, they would be able to exercise those permissions after the REVOKE was executed.

```
REVOKE ALL
    FROM no_creates
```

# Miscellaneous Issues

**O**ne of the tricks in managing permissions and roles is understanding how different roles and permissions work together. Every rule has an exception, and SQL Server security also falls into this category. Some of the special situations include:

- Working with security modes
- Special access conditions

## Security Modes

You will recall from our earlier discussion that SQL Server supports two security modes. The default mode supports both SQL accounts and NT authentication. This is often referred to as mixed mode. In addition, SQL Server supports a Windows NT–only authentication mode. Applying these modes correctly can be extremely important in planning your security requirements.

Consider the following scenario. Suppose that a user's NT account has been denied access to the SQL Server. This means that the user will not be able to log in to the SQL Server using Windows NT authentication even if the user is a member of another Windows NT group that has been granted access to the server.

If the server is running in Windows NT–only mode, this user would not be able to access the server unless the DENY was removed from the user. However, if the server is running in mixed mode, the user could log in to the server using a standard SQL Server account. This means that if the server is running in mixed mode, any user who has access to a SQL Server account will be able to access the SQL Server, no matter what access rights have been granted to their NT account.

## System Administrator Rights

One of the previously stated rules says that if users are denied access to a resource, they will not be able to access the resource even if they are associated with another role that permits access to that resource. The exception to this rule is the System Administrator server role.

The sysadmin server role allows the user access to all resources on the server. For example, suppose that a user who is associated with the sysadmin server role is also associated with the db_denydatareader database role in the Pubs database. Under normal conditions, this would prevent the user from selecting data from any of the tables in the database. However, because the user is associated with the sysadmin server role, none of the database role restrictions apply.

# Audit Activity with SQL Profiler

The SQL Profiler utility provides the DBA the ability to monitor and audit database activity. Whether the goal is to monitor performance or security, this utility provides the functionality to find out what is really going on with your SQL Server and who is issuing the commands.

To start the SQL Profiler, select Start ➢ Programs ➢ Microsoft SQL Server 7.0 ➢ Profiler. This will start the Profiler application. The next step is to create a new trace. A trace is a collection of settings that specify which activity will be traced and which data columns will be returned about that activity. To begin a new trace, select File ➢ New ➢ Trace from the Profiler menu.

You can also use a very complete set of extended stored procedures to create, manage, and replay profiler traces. This gives you the added benefit of scheduling trace activity and controlling traces procedurally.

The resulting dialog is the Trace Properties dialog. In the General tab, you will provide a name for the trace, and if you want to capture the output to a file or a SQL Server table, you can indicate your choices here.

If you want to save your trace so that you can replay it again later, save the trace to an operating system file or a SQL Server table. Saving to a file is the more efficient approach. Trace files can be replayed on any server for performance analysis, and they can also be used by the Index Tuning Wizard to determine the best index structure for the database.

By clicking on the Events tab, you begin the real work of creating a trace. You can capture events such as session connects and disconnects, transaction activity, individual Insert, Update, and Delete statements, and a whole host of other options. Figure 3.9 illustrates a trace that captures Connect, Disconnect, and Select activities. This type of trace might be used if you notice suspicious read activity in a database.

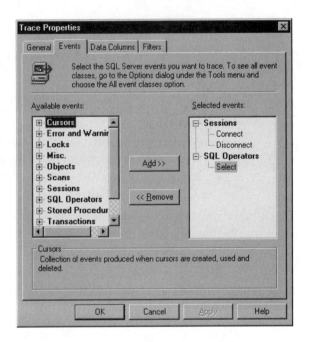

Click the Data Columns tab to specify which columns of data will be extracted for every row produced by an event. This tab allows you to specify groups if you want to consolidate some of the information into groups. For example, you might choose to group by SQL User Name and then look at the detail within the group in the trace output.

Figure 3.10 illustrates a trace definition that extracts the Event Class, SQL User Name, NT User Name, and Application Name for every event. No grouping is used in this example.

**FIGURE 3.10**

Setting trace
output columns

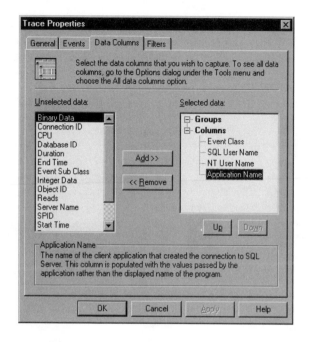

The Filters tab allows you to filter out any unwanted activity. For example, the filter automatically excludes the SQL Profiler activity from appearing in the output. You could also add additional filter such as the one pictured in Figure 3.11, which filters out activity created by the Windows NT Administrator account.

When you are finished defining the trace, you can close the dialog and the trace will begin to run. Figure 3.12 illustrates a running trace. Notice that you have to ability to stop, pause, and start the trace as needed by clicking the appropriate buttons on the Profiler toolbar. The trace illustrated in Figure 3.12 was defined as follows:

- Events

    - Sessions: Connect

    - Sessions: Disconnect

    - SQL Operators: Select

    - TSQL: SQL StmtStarting

- Data Columns
  - Event Class
  - Text
  - Application Name
  - NT User Name
  - SQL Server Name
- Filters
  - Application Name Exclude: SQL Server Profiler

**FIGURE 3.11**

Setting trace filters

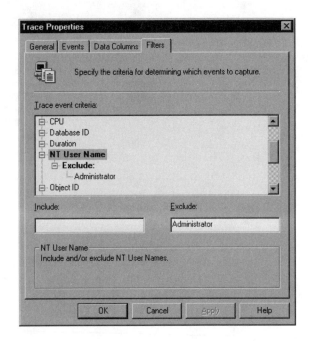

**F I G U R E  3.12**

A trace running in the
SQL Profiler

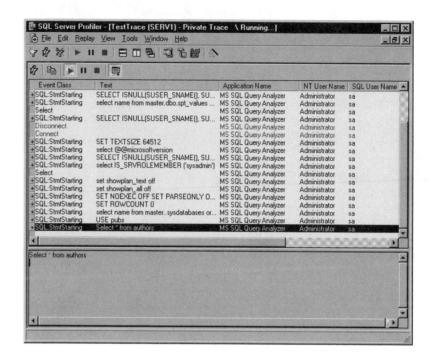

**F I G U R E  3.12**

A trace running in the
SQL Profiler

To generate this trace, Query Analyzer was accessed in SQL Server authentication mode as the sa login. The query SELECT * FROM authors was
subsequently executed.

## Secure Server Access

**1.** The two security modes supported by SQL Server are _____ and

_____.

**2.** To create a new SQL Server login, you can either use the Enterprise Manager or the

_____ stored procedure.

**3.** True or False. Unless you are running the SQL Server in mixed security mode, you are not

allowed to use SQL Server logins for server authentication.

_____

**4.** True or False. When you are not running the SQL Server in mixed security mode, you are not

allowed to use Windows NT groups for authentication.

_____

**5.** To configure server access for a Windows NT account, you can use either the Enterprise

Manager or the _____ stored procedure.

**6.** To prevent a Windows NT account from accessing the SQL Server, you can use the

_____ stored procedure.

**7.** True or False. You can deny SQL Server access to a standard SQL Server account.

_____

**8.** The SQL Server account that is granted sysadmin authority by default is the
_____ account.

**9.** The Windows NT account that is granted sysadmin authority by default is the
_____ account.

**10.** True or False. You can change the password of a mapped NT Server account from SQL
Server by using the sp_password stored procedure.

_____

## Configure Database Access

**11.** True or False. Every database has a guest user account by default.

_____

**12.** By default, the dbo user is mapped to the _____ login account.

**13.** To map a login to a user account in a database, you can use the _____
stored procedure.

**14.** To associate a new login with the dbo user account in a database, use the
_____ stored procedure.

**15.** If you want to transfer all of a user's rights and permissions in a database to a new login
account, you would use the _____ stored procedure.

## Manage Roles

**16.**   The four types of roles supported by Microsoft SQL Server are:

_____

_____

_____

_____

**17.**   List at least four fixed server roles.

_____

_____

_____

_____

**18.**   To associate a login with a server role, you should use the _____ stored procedure.

**19.**   Which server role allows the login to manage physical storage space on a SQL Server?

_____

**20.**   To use the KILL keyword, you must either be a member of the _____ role or the _____ role.

**21.**   To use the RECONFIGURE statement, you must either be a member of the
_____ role or the _____ role.

**22.**   Every database user is associated with which fixed database role?

_____

**23.**   By default, the sa login is associated with the _____ and
_____ fixed database roles in every database.

**24.**   The _____ database role allows the user to add additional user
accounts to the database while the _____ role allows the user to
assign permissions to accounts.

**25.**   The _____ role will prevent a user from reading any data in the
database while the _____ role prevents a user from writing data to
any table in the database.

**26.**   True or False. To restrict permissions, you can remove a user from the public role.

_____

**27.**   True or False. You cannot drop server roles.

_____

**28.** To remove a user from any database role other than public, you can execute the _____ stored procedure.

**29.** To create a custom role, you should execute the _____ stored procedure.

**30.** The two parameters of the sp_addrole procedure are _____ and _____.

**31.** To override all permissions assigned to a user while only in the context of a specific application connection, you should use a _____ role.

**32.** How long do application role permissions last?

_____

**33.** True or False. An application requires a password in order to activate.

_____

**34.** Which stored procedure would you use to drop a server role?

_____

**35.** Which roles provide the ability to perform database backups?

_____

_____

## Manage Permissions

**36.**   Which database object supports the "execute" permission?

_____

**37.**   Which two database objects support all object permissions other than execute?

_____ and _____

**38.**   Permissions can be classified into two general categories based on their function. These are called _____ permissions and _____ permissions.

**39.**   The three Transact-SQL statements that you use to manage permissions are _____, _____, and _____.

**40.**   If you want to prevent a user from accessing a database object even if the user is associated with another role that allows object access, you should use the _____ statement.

**41.**   You have denied access to an object for a specific NT group. To allow this group access to the object through another role, you should use the _____ statement.

**42.**   Which optional argument of the GRANT statement can you use to give the permission recipient the ability to grant the same permission to other users?

_____

**43.**   True or False. You can grant object permissions directly to Windows NT groups.

_____

**44.**   The DENY keyword will have no effect on your database permissions if you are associated with the _____ server role.

**45.**   To control database access for the guest user account, you should set very restrictive permissions on the guest user and the _____ database role.

**46.**   Does the db_backupoperator database role have the permission to restore databases? (Yes or No.)

_____

**47.**   True or False. If a user is associated with multiple roles, that user will inherit the least restrictive permissions assigned to all of the roles to which that user is associated.

_____

**48.**   The REVOKE keyword will remove all security configurations previously applied through either the _____ or _____ statements.

**49.**   True or False. If a SQL Server is running in mixed security mode, a user would be able to access SQL Server through a standard SQL Server account even if that user's NT account had been denied access to the server.

_____

**50.**   If the SQL Server is not running in mixed mode, you will not be able to access the SQL Server using a _____ login account.

## Auditing Activity with SQL Profiler

**51.** The SQL Server Profiler can capture trace results to either a _____ or a
_____.

**52.** The most efficient way to capture a SQL Server trace is to capture to a
_____.

**53.** True or False. You can replay a SQL Server trace on another SQL Server to test performance
on that server.

_____

**54.** Which wizard uses Profiler traces to optimize data access?

_____

**55.** Explain the function of an Exclude statement in a Profiler trace.

_____

_____

---

**SAMPLE TEST**

---

**3-1** Which SQL Server security mode allows both standard SQL Server logins and the Windows NT account to be authenticated?

    **A.** Windows NT–Only

    **B.** Trusted

    **C.** Mixed

    **D.** Integrated

**3-2** You are running a SQL Server in Windows NT–only mode. You are a member of a Windows NT group called *localusers* that has been denied access to a SQL Server named *ORDERS*. You are a member of another NT group called *admins* that has access to the server. You are unable to connect. What can you do to gain access to the server?

    **A.** Connect to SQL Server through a standard SQL Server account.

    **B.** Remove your account from the localusers group.

    **C.** Connect using an application role.

    **D.** Add the admins group to the public role.

**3-3** Your Windows NT account has been configured to access the *Inventory* database; however, your account has been denied SELECT permissions on the Products table in the database. What can you do to provide yourself SELECT access to the Products table?

    **A.** Associate your user with the db_owner role in the Inventory database.

    **B.** Associate your user with the db_datareader role in the Inventory database.

    **C.** Add your NT user account to the sysadmin server role.

    **D.** Add your NT account to another NT group that has access to the Products table.

**3-4** You have been denied access to a table to the SQLUsers role. Which SQL keyword would you use to remove this DENY from the role?

    **A.** REMOVE

    **B.** DENY

    **C.** GRANT

    **D.** REVOKE

**3-5** Which fixed role (server or database) would you use to grant only user account management rights in a single database?

    **A.** db_securityadmin

    **B.** db_accessadmin

    **C.** db_owner

    **D.** securityadmin

**3-6** You have a team of users who work on short, temporary projects with a small number of users. These users access only a single table to store data about the project. What is the best way to manage security for this environment?

    **A.** Add NT users to a database role that provides access to each table.

    **B.** Add NT groups and allow each group access to their respective tables.

    **C.** Create standard SQL logins for the users and set their permissions to the tables individually.

    **D.** Give all of the NT users sysadmin access to the server.

**3-7** What are the minimum permissions that you need to create a view that selects data from the Authors table?

    **A.** You need CREATE VIEW only permission.

    **B.** You need CREATE VIEW and SELECT permissions on the Authors table.

    **C.** You must be a db_owner.

    **D.** You must be a sysadmin.

**3-8** You want to monitor activity on multiple SQL Servers on your network and forward all of the information to a central server. You are concerned that if one of the monitored servers fails, this will prevent the server from forwarding any additional information to your central server. What is the best way to configure the servers to prevent this from happening?

    **A.** Use the Performance Monitor to pull the data to the monitoring server.

    **B.** Use Profiler extended stored procedure calls and mark them as startup procedures.

    **C.** Add the trace activity to an AutoExc.bat file.

    **D.** Use Performance Monitor alerts to inform you when a server goes down and recovers manually.

**3-9** You notice that your NT administrators have access to some very sensitive data in the Inventory database. You want to prevent them from accessing this data, but they must be able to continue with the NT admin activities. What is the easiest way to accomplish this?

    **A.** Deny the administrators access to the inventory database.

    **B.** Remove the administrators from the public role in the Inventory database.

    **C.** Remove them from the NT Administrators group.

    **D.** Remove the Builtin\Administrators from the sysadmin role.

**3-10**   Sue uses a non-admin NT account and needs dbo access to a database, but you must be able to trace the activity through her NT user name. How can you do this?

   **A.** Add a SQL login for Sue.

   **B.** Map Sue's NT account to the db_owner role.

   **C.** Use sp_changedbowner to give ownership of the database to Sue.

   **D.** SQL Server does not allow you to trace database activity through an NT login name.

**3-11**   Jerry is responsible for maintaining inventory information through a custom developed client application. You want Jerry to be able make the modifications to the inventory data through this application but not through other applications such as the Query Analyzer. How can this be accomplished?

   **A.** Have Jerry use a database user account that has the needed permissions when using the custom client.

   **B.** Give Jerry the needed permissions and remove his access to the Query Analyzer utility.

   **C.** Implement an application role in the client application.

   **D.** Assign a restrictive SQL Server login account to Jerry.

**3-12**   You have been assigned the responsibility to perform emergency recovery for the Orders database if data loss on the server ever occurs. Which of the following roles will provide the minimum permissions needed to perform this task?

   **A.** db_backupoperator

   **B.** db_owner

   **C.** sysadmin

   **D.** diskadmin

# U N I T

# 4

Managing and Maintaining Data

# Test Objectives: Managing and Maintaining Data

- **Create and Manage databases.**

  - Create data files, filegroups, and transaction log files.

  - Specify growth characteristics.

- **Load data by using various methods. Methods include the INSERT statement, the SELECT INTO statement, the *bcp* utility, Data Transformation Services (DTS), BULK INSERT, and the BULK INSERT statement.**

- **Back up system databases and user databases by performing a full database backup, a transaction log backup, a differential database backup, and a filegroup backup.**

- **Restore system databases and user databases from a full database backup, a transaction log backup, a differential database backup, and a filegroup backup.**

- **Manage replication.**

  - Configure servers, including Distributor, Publisher, and Subscriber.

  - Create publications.

  - Set up and manage subscriptions.

- **Automate administrative tasks.**

  - Define jobs.

  - Define alerts.

  - Define operators.

  - Set up SQLAgentMail for job notification and alerts.

- **Enable access to remote data.**

  - Set up linked servers.

  - Set up security for linked databases.

---

Exam objectives are subject to change at any time without prior notice and at Microsoft's sole discretion. Please visit Microsoft's Training & Certification Web site (www.microsoft.com/Train_Cert) for the most current exam objectives listing.

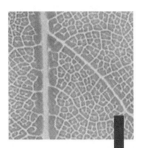

In this unit, we will look at managing and maintaining your data. We will begin with a discussion on how to create a database, fill it with data, and then make backups of your data. We will take a brief look at the management of replication, which includes the configuration and installation of your publishing, distribution, and subscription servers. We will then look at reducing your total cost of ownership by implementing automation. Finally, we will review linked servers, how to use them, and how to set up security for them.

# Create and Manage Databases

SQL Server 7 uses two types of files to store your database information. There are one or more database files and one or more transaction log files. As part of your role as a database creator, you must decide how large to make these database files, what type of growth characteristics they should have, and their physical placement on your system.

In SQL Server 7, a new user database is really a copy of the model database. Everything that is in the model database will show up in your newly created database. Once the copy of the database has been made, it is then expanded to the size you requested. When you create a database in SQL Server 7, you must specify at least one file to store data and hold your system tables and another file to hold the transactions.

Your database files have a default extension of .MDF. The transaction log is stored on one or more files with a default .LDF extension. If you create a database that spans multiple database files, then the additional database files have a default filename extension of .NDF. Additional transaction log files don't change their extensions. There are several important things to remember about your data and log files:

- All data and log files that are managed by a particular SQL Server must reside on that SQL Server machine.

- Only one database is allowed per data file. A single database can span multiple data files.

- Transaction logs must reside on their own file, and they can also span multiple log files.

- Database files fill up their available space by striping across all data files in the filegroup. In this manner, you can eliminate hot spots and reduce contention in high volume OLTP (Online Transaction Processing) environments.

- Transaction log files do not use striping, but fill each log file to capacity before continuing on to the next log file.

You should place your transaction logs on separate physical hard drives. In this manner, you can recover your data up to the second in the event of a media failure. If you are using RAID 5 (striping with parity), you should create your data files on the RAID 5 array and then create a mirror set (RAID 1) on two other hard disks and place your transaction log there.

When you create a database, you specify the database name, the filegroup, the file's logical name, and the physical location of your file. Optional parameters include the maximum size that the database is allowed to grow to, as well as the growth characteristics.

You can use the ALTER DATABASE statement to specify new database growth parameters. You can alter the MAXSIZE and FILEGROWTH properties very simply.

In this example, we will create a database that has data spanning two files and a transaction log. We will also set the autogrowth parameters and maxsize parameters.

```
CREATE DATABASE Complex
ON PRIMARY
(NAME = Complex_Data1,
 FILENAME = 'C:\MSSQL7\Data\Complex_Data1.mdf',
```

```
  SIZE = 5MB,
  MAXSIZE = 10MB,
  FILEGROWTH = 1MB)
 (NAME = Complex_Data2,
  FILENAME = 'C:\MSSQL7\Data\Complex_Data2.ndf',
  SIZE = 2MB,
  MAXSIZE = 10MB,
  FILEGROWTH = 2MB)
 LOG ON
 (NAME = Complex_Log1,
  FILENAME = 'D:\Logs\Complex_Log1.ldf',
  SIZE = 2MB,
  MAXSIZE = 8MB,
  FILEGROWTH = 1MB)
```

This code creates a database with an initial size of 9MB (5MB for the first file, 2MB for the second file, and 2MB for the log). The database has a maximum size of 28MB.

**WARNING**   You should always specify a maximum size for data and transaction log files that have an autogrowth feature. If you do not, it is possible for the file to fill the entire hard disk partition. If this happens, Windows NT will no longer allow you to use that partition. If the partition also has the Windows NT system files on it, you will not be able to use Windows NT until the situation is remedied.

When you want to shrink your database, you can choose to shrink individual files within the database or all files in the database. There are several methods that you can use to shrink your database:

- The Enterprise Manager
- The DBCC SHRINKDATABASE commands
- The DBCC SHRINKFILE commands
- The autoshrink database option

To shrink a database using T-SQL, you can use the DBCC SHRINK–DATABASE command, which will attempt to shrink all files in the database, or you can use the DBCC SHRINKFILE command, which will attempt to shrink a specific database file. The SHRINKFILE command allows you to shrink a single database file. Here is an example that will attempt to leave 10 percent of your database as free space.

```
DBCC SHRINKDATABASE (Foo, 10%)
```

# Loading Data Using Various Methods

**D**ata can be entered into your database through many various ways. In this section, we will look at the INSERT statement, SELECT INTO, bcp, DTS, BULK INSERT, Transfer Manager, and HDR.

## Using the INSERT Statement

When you use the INSERT statement, you will add a single row of data to your table. There are variations of the INSERT statement that will allow you to add multiple rows of data by selecting data from another table. You can also use the SELECT INTO statement to move data from one location to another.

Before you can use the INSERT statement, you must know a little about the structure of the table into which you want to insert data. You should know the number of columns in the table, the data type contained in these columns, the column names, and any defaults or constraints (like IDENTITY) that are on a particular column.

The easiest way to work with the INSERT statement is to insert data into the table by specifying data for each column in the table (each column that requires data), in the same order that the columns were defined. In the Categories table, the CategoryID field is an IDENTITY column and will automatically generate a value. You need to specify the CategoryName, Description, and Picture fields. You can add a new record to the Categories table by running the code shown here. Note the last set of quotation marks is a placeholder for the Picture field, which you are not adding. This will add a single row to the table.

```
INSERT INTO Categories VALUES
('Beer', 'Beers of the World', '')
```

When you insert character data, you must enclose the characters in single quotation marks. When you insert numeric data, you do not use quotation marks.

Remember these facts about the INSERT statement:

- Generally, it adds a single record at a time.
- The inserted record *is* a logged transaction.
- If there is an index, it will be updated as well.
- You must have INSERT permission on the table to which you want to add records.

## Using SELECT INTO to Manage Data

The SELECT INTO statement is used to create new permanent tables or new temporary tables filled with data from another table. It is essentially a copy table command.

To use the SELECT INTO command to create a permanent table in your database, you must first enable the SELECT INTO/bulk copy database option. This can be done either in the Enterprise Manager or through the sp_dboption stored procedure. To create a temporary table, you must precede the temporary table name with the pound symbol (#). This is used to create a local temporary table. You can also create global temporary tables by using two pound symbols, as in ##MyGlobalTempTable.

You can use spaces in your naming conventions. To do this, you must enclose the identifier in square brackets. For example, a table named *Order Details* would be referred to as [Order Details]. Although you can use spaces in your naming conventions, we strongly suggest that you use the underscore (_) or mixed case. Here is an example of using the underscore: Order_Details. Mixed case pushes all of the words together and uses both uppercase and lowercase characters to make it more readable. For example: OrderDetails.

When you set the SELECT INTO/bulk copy database option, you are specifying that you are about to perform a non-logged insert of data. You can enable this option using the Enterprise Manager or by using the sp_dboption stored procedure.

This example will generate a new table called *tblNewCategories* in the Northwind database and fill it with the data from the old Categories table. In this script, the sp_dboption stored procedure is used to both enable and then disable the SELECT INTO/bulk copy database option.

```
USE Northwind
GO

EXEC sp_dboption 'Northwind', 'select into/bulkcopy', True
GO

SELECT * INTO tblNewCategories
FROM Categories
GO

EXEC sp_dboption 'Northwind', 'select into/bulkcopy', False
GO
```

As with any non-logged transactions, the recoverability of your database is at issue. You should perform a backup of your data as soon as possible.

Keep these things in mind when you are working with the SELECT INTO statement:

- To create a permanent table, you must have the SELECT INTO/bulk copy database option enabled.

- To create local temporary tables, you must prefix your table name with a pound sign (#).

- To create global temporary tables, you must prefix your table name with two pound signs (##).

- To run the SELECT INTO command, you must have CREATE TABLE permissions in the database.

- To set the SELECT INTO option, you can use the sp_dboption stored procedure.

Running a SELECT INTO statement performs a non-logged operation, so you should ensure your data by backing it up.

## Working with BCP

Bulk copy or "bcp" is a command line utility that is lightning fast for moving data between a flat file and your SQL Server 7 database. The upside of bcp is its speed and compatibility. If you do not have indexes created on your tables and you also have the SELECT INTO/bulk copy database option set, then reading an ASCII file into your server is very quick. However, using bcp has several downsides, including the cumbersome interface. It is a command line utility and, as such, requires you to remember a bunch of different switches as well as case sensitivity. Another disadvantage is that bcp transfers *only* data. The bcp utility will not transfer other database objects like tables, views, and schema. The last downside is the fact that bcp cannot do data transformations. Data transformations include things like converting a text string to a numeric value or vice-versa, splitting a Name field into a First-Name and LastName field, as well as many other types of transformations.

Keep these points in mind when working with bcp:

- With bcp you can append data to an existing table just like you would if you were using a third-party utility like Visual Basic, but the bcp program is generally much quicker.

- When you export data using bcp, you will always overwrite the old flat file (if it exists).

- To use bcp, you must have the appropriate permissions. When you want to move data from a flat file into SQL Server 7, you must have READ permissions on the file itself (if using NTFS) and you must have INSERT permissions on the SQL Server table into which you would like to move the data.

- To use bcp to move data from SQL Server to a flat file, you must have NTFS permissions for either Change or Full Control on the directory and the file. If you are using a FAT or FAT32 partition, this is not an issue because neither of these types of file systems support permissions. Within SQL Server, you must have SELECT permissions on the table or view from which you want to pull your data.

- Character mode is the most flexible method of bulk copy. This is because all data is treated as characters. This means that SQL Server and most other applications can work with the data. When you use character mode to export data, it will be stored as an ASCII text file. Native mode uses the internal SQL Server data types and can be faster for data transfers from one SQL Server to another SQL Server database.

When you are working with the data files, bcp needs to know where one field ends and another begins. Bcp also needs to know where one row of data ends and another begins. To do this, specify a common character to be a terminator.

When you perform a bulk copy to import data, you can do it in normal mode, which means every insert is logged, or you can do it in fast mode in which inserts are not logged. To operate in fast mode, you must enable the SELECT INTO/bulk copy database option and you must drop all indexes that are affected by the data transfer. Once you have done this, you can quickly add your data using bulk copy. There are a few other items you should be aware of when you do a fast bulk copy:

- SELECT INTO/bulk copy must be enabled.

- You must drop all affected indexes.

- Defaults and data types will always be enforced.

- Rules, triggers, and constraints will always be ignored.

Because rules, triggers, and constraints are ignored during a fast bulk copy, you should check the validity of your data by running queries or other stored procedures.

Once you have completed a bulk copy, you should re-create your indexes and then back up your database as it is now unrecoverable.

## Using BULK INSERT

The BULK INSERT command is a new Transact-SQL statement in SQL Server 7. The BULK INSERT command treats data files like OLE-DB recordsets. Because SQL Server thinks the file is an OLE-DB recordset, it can move multiple records per step. You can move the entire file in one batch or in several batches.

One major difference between bcp and BULK INSERT is that BULK INSERT cannot move data from SQL Server to a file. Essentially, BULK INSERT gives you bulk copy capabilities through the use of T-SQL. Because bcp is a command line utility, it can be placed into batch files, whereas BULK INSERT cannot. In order for you to use the BULK INSERT command, you must be a member of the sysadmins server role.

## Using Data Transformation Services

Most companies store their data in a variety of locations and in a variety of formats. Using DTS you can import and export data between these different sources and destinations. When you are working with data from two SQL Server 7 computers, you can also transfer database objects and schema. This includes the stored procedures, views, permissions, table layouts, and other information. You can accomplish this through the Transfer Manager.

SQL Server can move data through any OLE-DB– or ODBC-compliant data source and data destination. The DTS interface itself is a set of COM (component object model) based objects. These COM-based objects allow you to:

- Transfer data to and from Access, Excel, SQL Server, Oracle, DB2, ASCII text files, and other sources

- Create DTS packages that are integrated with other COM-compliant third-party products

- Schedule DTS packages

Because COM-based objects are language independent, any computer language that supports COM can be used to interact with your DTS Packages. This includes scripting languages like VBScript, JavaScript, and PerlScript. You can also use full-fledged programming languages like Visual Basic and C++ to interact with the DTS Packages that you create.

Keep these definitions in mind when you are working with DTS.

## DTS Package

A set of tasks is designed into a workflow of steps. These steps and tasks are then grouped together into a package. You can create packages using the Import and Export wizards, through a scripting language, from the command line using dtswiz and dtsrun or visually through the DTS Designer. Once you have created a package, it becomes a completely self-contained COM object. You can interact with this object through the Enterprise Manager, Task Scheduler, as well as the command-line and COM-compliant languages. You can store your DTS Packages in several different formats and enforce several different security mechanisms.

## Task Objects

Each task defines a particular action that should be taken or some type of processing. Task objects can be used to perform the following activities:

- Move data from one OLE-DB– or ODBC-compliant data source to an OLE-DB– or ODBC-compliant data destination. This is often referred to as a Data Pump task.
- Run a Transact-SQL statement.
- Run a T-SQL batch.
- Execute external programs, batch files, or command executions.
- Execute another DTS package.
- Execute COM-compliant scripts (VBScript, JScript, and PerlScript are currently supported within DTS itself).
- Gather results from other running DTS Packages.
- Send e-mail using SQL Mail and the xp_sendmail stored procedure.

## Step Objects

Task objects are self-contained units; however, they will never run if they are not referenced by a step object. A step object is used to coordinate the flow of your tasks. If a task object does not have an associated step object, that task will not be executed. Essentially, step objects are used to structure workflow.

Step objects can be executed in several different situations:

- Run step only when the prior step completes successfully.
- Run step only when the prior step fails to complete.
- Run step after a prior step completes regardless of success or failure.

Task objects can be associated with multiple steps; however, a particular task can have only one instance of itself running at any given time.

Precedence constraints can be applied to steps. Precedence constraints are assigned by specifying that the next step will execute in one of several situations:

**On Success**  This specifies that the next step will wait until the first step has completed successfully before beginning.

**On Failure**  This specifies that the next step will wait until the first step issues a failure and then begin processing.

**Unconditional**  This option specifies that the next step will execute regardless of the success or failure of the previous step.

**Return Codes**  This option requires you to gather the return codes generated by calling a scripting language module. The scripting language allows you far more flexibility for working with your steps.

## Connection Objects

In order to move data around, you must connect to both a data source and a data destination. DTS uses connection objects to accomplish this. These connection objects contain all of the information necessary to make a connection. This includes the login IDs, passwords, filenames, locations of the data, format of the data, etc. There are two types of connection objects:

**Data file**  A data file connection object specifies the location and data format of an ASCII file that will be used during the DTS process.

**Data source**  A data source connection object is used to specify OLE-DB– or ODBC-compliant data source and destination servers. This includes the server location, data format, login credentials, and passwords.

Connections remain dormant until they are invoked. Once invoked, the connection will remain active until the DTS Package has completed.

### Data Pump Object

The DTS data pump object is an OLE-DB service provider that takes care of your importing, exporting, and the data transformation. It is an in-process COM server that runs in the process space of the SQL Server 7 application. The data pump gathers data from one or more data sources and can then transform the data before sending it out to one or more data destinations.

## Transfer Manager

Through the Data Transformation Services Import and Export wizards, you can transfer objects, security, and/or data from one SQL Server 7 database to another SQL Server 7 database. When you use this method, the objects, data, and security in the original database are unaffected; they are copied to the receiving database and not actually moved.

In SQL Server 6.5, the Transfer Manager Interface was a stand-alone component incorporated into the Enterprise Manager. In 7.0, this component has been incorporated into the DTS Import and Export wizards.

Because new objects are being created, the user performing the transfer needs SELECT permissions in the source database and DBO permissions in the destination database.

Because this process moves not only data but also schema from one SQL Server 7 computer to another SQL Server 7 computer, it is ideal for situations where you want to transfer data from one platform to another. For example, you may want to move both data and schema from a 7.0 server on an Intel platform to a 7.0 server on an Alpha platform. You can also move data from one sort order and character set to another.

## Other DTS Details

DTS Packages can be stored with both an operator password and an owner password. Owners can edit and execute the package. Operators can only execute the packages.

DTS Packages can be stored in three locations:

**COM Object**   As a COM object, your DTS package can easily be e-mailed to other users. It can also be referenced by COM-compliant languages like C++, Visual Basic, and Java.

**Microsoft Repository**   When your DTS package is stored here, you can track the lineage or history of changes to your data and to your package.

**SQL Server**   When your DTS package is stored here, you can execute whenever you want. Other SQL Servers can also execute your DTS package on the SQL Server where it is stored.

# SQL Backups

**Y**ou have several choices when backing up your data, including:

**Full Database Backups**   Full database backups are created when the entire database is backed up. Although they are the easiest to implement and restore from, full database backups may not be practical because of the amount of time required for very large databases.

**Transaction Log Backups**   Because the transaction log records all changes made to a database, backing up the log (after performing an occasional full database backup) allows you to re-create the database without having to do full database backups every time.

**Differential Database Backups**   New with SQL 7, differential backups only back up data that has changed since the last full backup. This could be more efficient than transaction log backups for databases with existing data that changes often. For example, if a person's bank account changed 10 times in one day the transaction log backup would contain all 10 changes while the differential backup would contain just the final amount.

**File Group Backups**   Also new with SQL 7, file group backups allow you to back up different pieces of the database, based on the various files that make up the database. Usually file group backups are performed when the time required to complete a full database backup is prohibitive.

## Creating a Backup Device

SQL Server backs up databases to an object called a *backup* (dump in earlier versions) device. SQL has no built-in backup devices—you will need to create all of your backup devices and configure your backups in order to have databases that are backed up regularly.

Because SQL Server keeps the database files open while SQL Server is running, the databases don't get backed up during regular Windows NT backups. You need to configure SQL Server's backups, because the default settings will not back up any of your databases! Once a backup has been made to a backup device, the device is closed and can be backed up normally during Windows NT backups.

Backup devices can be created with the sp_addumpdevice command. The syntax for the command specifies the logical name for the device, and the path to the file that will be created after the backup is completed. You can also use the Enterprise Manager.

Syntax: Sp_addumpdevice 'type', 'logical name', 'path'

SQL Server 6 referred to backup devices almost exclusively as dump devices, even in Enterprise Manager.

From the Query Analyzer, you can run the following code to create a backup device:

```
sp_addumpdevice 'disk', 'master_backup',
'c:\MSSQL7\Backup\master.bak'.
```

A backup device is mainly just a pointer that SQL Server remembers so that it knows where to put the backup file when the backup is actually done. Because of this, files are not created when a backup device is defined; they are created when the backup is actually performed.

## Backing Up Transaction Logs

If the database is not set to Truncate Log on Checkpoint, the transaction log can be backed up and restored separately from the database.

Although the option to Truncate Log on Checkpoint will automatically keep the log cleaned, it is not recommended for production environments because you cannot recover transactions that happened between database backups. If you do use the Truncate Log on Checkpoint option, make sure you perform frequent (at least nightly) database backups.

Another advantage of backing up the transaction log is that it can be restored up to a certain point in time. For example, if you had a backup of the transaction log for Wednesday and you discover a major error occurred at 4:05 P.M., you could restore the data up to 4:00 P.M.

The log can be backed up by issuing the command:

```
BACKUP LOG 'dbname' to 'device' [TRUNCATE
ONLY|NO_LOG|NO_TRUNCATE]
```

Various switches can be added to the command to change the way the backup works, as listed in Table 4.1.

| T A B L E  4.1 Backup Switches | Switch | Usage |
|---|---|---|
| | TRUNCATE_ONLY | This switch is used to truncate (clean out) the log. You might want to use this switch if the database is backed up in its entirety every night, thereby making maintaining a log backup redundant, but the log still needs to be cleaned out. Another option to consider if this switch was used on a regular basis would be to set the database to Truncate Log on Checkpoint. |

| TABLE 4.1 *(cont.)* | Switch | Usage |
|---|---|---|
| Backup Switches | NO_LOG | This switch can be used as a last resort if the log becomes so full that none of the other switches work. Normal backups of the log first make an entry to record that the log has been backed up, and then the log is cleared out. If the log is completely full, the record of the backup can't be made, so the backup fails, along with the truncating of the log. |
| | NO_TRUNCATE | This switch does the opposite of the truncate_only switch—it backs up the log without truncating or cleaning it out. The main purpose for this switch is to make a new backup of the transaction log when the database itself is either too damaged to work or is completely gone. |

With SQL Server 7 you must have at least one .MDF file (database file) still working in order for the NO_TRUNCATE option to successfully back up data from the transaction log.

## Differential Database Backups

SQL Server 7 has the ability to create a differential database backup, which records the final state of any added, edited, or deleted rows since the last full database backup.

Differential backups, unlike transaction log backups, cannot be restored to a particular point in time, as only the final state of the data is recorded. Transactions in progress are rolled back upon restoration. For this reason, you should back up the transaction log at the time you perform a differential backup. In this fashion, those last few transactions can be applied to your differential restoration.

To perform a differential backup using T-SQL syntax, simply open a Query Analyzer window and issue the following command:

```
BACKUP 'dbname' TO 'device' WITH DIFFERENTIAL
```

### Filegroup Backups

SQL Server 7 also allows you to back up files and filegroups independently from the database. For example, suppose you have three data volumes (N:, O:, and P:) and three file groups (Employees, Customers, Orders), each residing on a different data volume. If the entire database took too long to back up, you could back up the Employees files on Monday, the Customers filegroup on Tuesday, and the Orders on Wednesday. Because backing up files or filegroups does not back up the transaction log, make sure you also perform a transaction log backup after backing up the filegroup.

To perform the filegroup backup using T-SQL, issue the following command:

```
BACKKUP 'dbname' FILE = 'file name', filegroup = 'filegroup'
TO 'device'
```

# SQL Recovery

**T**he process of restoring SQL databases can be summed up in the following steps:

- Attempt to back up the transaction log.

- Find and fix the cause of the failure.

- Restore the database from a database backup or from a file or filegroup backup.

- Restore the transaction log from a log backup or restore the differential database backup.

## Attempt to Back Up the Transaction Log

You should always attempt to create a transaction log backup after a database failure in order to capture all of the transaction up to the time of the failure. You should use the no_truncate switch, which backs up the log when the database is unusable. If you successfully back up transactions to the point of the failure, simply restore this new transaction backup set after you restore the other transaction log backups.

## Find and Fix the Cause of the Failure

This step involves troubleshooting NT and/or SQL Server to determine the cause of the failure. There are two basic reasons for determining the cause—obviously, the first is to fix the problem, and the second is to take the appropriate steps to prevent it from happening in the future.

## Restore the Database

Enterprise Manager can restore databases quickly. Simply highlight the database to be restored, select the backup, and choose Restore. You can also restore a database without having to re-create it because the restoration procedure will create the database if it doesn't already exist. To automatically re-create the database, simply choose a backup set to restore from. If the database doesn't exist, it will be re-created. If a database by the same name as that in the backup set already exists, it will be overwritten. If you want to restore a backup set to a differently named database, use the Replace switch.

Although the syntax to do a restoration starts out simple, there are many options that let you control exactly what is restored from which backup set.

The syntax to do a restoration is:

```
Restore Database <database> from <device> <options>.
```

The most common options are:

**Dbo_only**  Tags the restored database as Read_Only.

**Recovery**  Recovers any transactions and allows the database to be used. This is the default if not specified.

**No_recovery**  Allows additional transaction logs to be restored, and does not allow the database to be used until the Recovery option is used.

If you use this option by mistake (or end up not having any logs to restore), you can issue the command Restore Database <database> Recovery to activate the database.

**Replace** Required when the name of the database being restored is different than the one that was backed up.

**Standby** Allows the database to be read-only between log restores. This is used for standby servers or for other special purposes, such as testing the data contained in each transaction backup set.

**Restart** Usually used with tape backups. Restart allows you to restart an operation at the point of failure. For example, suppose you have five tapes, and on the last tape you insert the wrong one. By using the Restart switch, you can simply insert Tape 5 and quickly finish the job.

SQL Server wipes out the old database when you restore a full backup of a database—there is no merging of data.

## Restore the Log

Enterprise Manager or the Restore Log command can be used to restore transaction logs. Restoring transaction logs can be thought of as reapplying all the transactions just as they occurred.

The T-SQL command to restore the log is:

Restore Log <database> from <device> <options>

All the options that apply to the Restore Database command also apply to the Restore Log command, with the exception of the Replace option, which is not supported for log restorations.

Unlike restoring the entire database, restoring transaction logs literally reapplies all the transactions that took place between the time of the full database backup and the time of the transaction log backup, appending any changes to the database.

**Restoring to a Certain Time**   SQL Server can restore transaction log backup up to a certain point in time. To do this, just choose a date and time from the Restore window, or specify the stopat parameter in the Restore command.

## Restore Differential Backups

Restoring a differential backup works very much like restoring transaction log backups. You must first do a full database restoration, then select the most recent differential backup to restore.

The T-SQL syntax to restore a differential backup is the same as for restoring the entire database.

## Restore Filegroups

Restoring filegroups can be done by using either Enterprise Manager or T-SQL syntax. It is done in Enterprise Manager in much the same fashion as full database restorations.

The T-SQL syntax for restoring files and file groups is:

```
Restore Database <database> from <device>
File=<logical filename>
Filegroup=<logical filegroup name>
```

# Manage Replication

**T**o successfully install and enable replication, you must install a distribution server, create your publications, and then subscribe to them. Before any of this can take place, you must first configure your SQL Server.

## SQL Server Configuration

Before you can configure your SQL Server for replication, the computer itself must meet the following requirements:

- All servers involved with replication must be registered in the Enterprise Manager.

- The replication agents use the same Windows NT account that the SQL Server Agent uses. This account must have administrative rights and be a member of the Administrators group.

- The SQL Server Agent account must have the "Log On As a Service" advanced user right.

- If the servers are from different domains, then trust relationships must be established before replication can occur.

- Any account that you use must have access rights to the distribution working folder on the distribution server.

- The server must have a minimum of 32MB of RAM with 16MB allocated for SQL Server 7.

- You must enable access to the distribution working folder on the distribution server. For an NT Server, this is the \\ServerName\ C$\MSSQL7\ReplData folder. For the defaults to operate properly on a Windows 9*x* computer, you must use the share name C$. (The $ means that only accounts with administrative rights can access that particular share.)

You should use a single Windows NT Domain account for all of your SQL Server Agents. Do *not* use a LocalSystem account because this account has no network capabilities and will, therefore, not allow replication.

## Installing a Distribution Server

Using the Enterprise Manager is the easiest way to install a distribution server. Keep the following in mind when you choose your Distributor:

- Ensure that you have enough hard disk space for the distribution working folder and the distribution database.

- You must manage the distribution database's transaction log carefully. If that log fills to capacity, replication will no longer run. This can adversely affect your publishing databases as well.

- The distribution database will store all transactions from the Publisher to the Subscriber. It will also track when those transactions were applied.

- Snapshots and merge data are stored in the distribution working folder.

- How many and how large are the articles being published?

- Text, ntext, and image data types are replicated only when you use a snapshot.

- More latency can significantly increase your storage space requirements.

- How many transactions per synchronization cycle are there? For example, if you modify 8,000 records between synchronizations, then there will be 8,000 rows of data stored on the Distributor.

- In order to successfully enable a publication database, you must be a member of the sysadmin fixed-server role. Once you have enabled publishing, any member of that databases db_owner role can create and manage publications.

## Adding a Publication

When you add a new publication, you need to determine the type of replication that will be used, the snapshot requirements and Subscriber options like updating or anonymous Subscribers. You can also partition your data and decide whether or not you will allow push or pull subscriptions.

Each publication will use a separate publishing agent by default. You can override this option.

## Creating a Subscription

As part of the subscription process you will be able to specify the Publishers you want to subscribe to, a destination database to receive the published data, verify your security credentials, and set up a default schedule.

# Automate Administrative Tasks

All of the scheduled jobs, alerts, and e-mail operator information is stored in the Msdb database. The Msdb database is a system database that is automatically created when you install SQL Server. Because the Msdb database contains all your jobs, alerts, and operators, it should be backed up on a regular basis.

If you rebuild the Master database for some reason, the Msdb database will be rebuilt also. You can then restore your backup of Msdb to recover your jobs, alerts, and e-mail operators.

## The SQLAgentMail

The SQLAgentMail can be thought of as an optional helper service for SQL Server. Nothing it does is technically required to make SQL Server work, but it does enough that you will probably want to enable it.

The SQLAgentMail service is in charge of finding and carrying out jobs and alerts, and notifying operators about the success and/or failure of those jobs and alerts.

The SQLAgentMail is installed by default. Although the SQL Setup program attempts to correctly configure the service for your system, it may not be entirely successful.

Two main settings are required for the SQLAgentMail to work properly:

- A user account, with appropriate rights, should be assigned to the service.

- The service should be configured to start automatically (if it is set to manual, you will have to start it by hand every time you reboot your server).

 When using the Desktop version of SQL Server with Windows 95/98, you cannot assign an account to the SQLAgentMail. Not assigning an account to the agent will not affect any jobs or alerts on the local computer. The major limitation on Windows 95/98 computers is that they cannot be assigned as job managers for other servers.

There are three parts to setting up the SQL Agent user account:

- Create the user account using the Windows NT User Manager or User Manager for Domains utility.

- Give the user account appropriate rights. Make the user account for the SQL Agent a member of the Administrators group and also a member of the Domain Administrators group if you want that account to be usable on any and all SQL Servers in the domain. Assign the "Log On as a Service" right to this account.

- Assign the user to the service.

# Alerts, Jobs, and Events

Let's look at what happens to a common error before and after the SQLAgent-Mail service has been configured. Suppose that the Pubs2 database log fills up and generates an 1105 error (the standard error code generated for a full log). SQL Server's own internal error generator will create the 1105 error, but without SQLAgentMail to watch for and handle the error, the problem will need to be fixed by hand.

With a predefined alert and job, the alert engine could look for the 1105 error in the Windows NT application log and will be ready to trigger a backup job that will truncate (clean out) the log. The database log is truncated, and users can resume using the database normally. If the backup failed to work, another error could be generated. At that point, the operator could be sent an e-mail message and/or paged.

For an alert to be seen by SQLAgentMail, it must be written to the Windows NT Application Log.

## Creating and Managing Jobs

SQL Server supports four general types of jobs:

**TSQL jobs** These jobs are written using T-SQL commands. They are often used to back up the database, rebuild indexes, and perform other various routine database maintenance activities.

**CmdExec jobs** These jobs literally open a command prompt and run some sort of batch file. Common CmdExec jobs are those created by the Database Maintenance Plan Wizard or by the SQL Server Web Assistant and can be run as well.

**Replication jobs** These jobs deal with replication. Normally you would use the Replication wizards and prompts to help set up replication jobs, although monitoring these jobs is an important step in maintaining replication.

**Active Script jobs** These jobs can run Visual Basic or Java script regular intervals.

**Multiple Server Jobs**    SQL Server 7 has the ability to create jobs that run on multiple servers. In order to create multiple server jobs, you must ensure that all servers involved are running SQL Server 7 on Windows NT.

- Designate one server as the master server (MSX).

- Designate a master server operator (MSX Operator).

- Designate one or more servers as target servers when you create the job.

Target servers can report to only one master server at a time, and the SQLServerAgent needs to use a service account. (The local system account cannot be used.)

You should also choose the MSX Operator carefully because that account is the only one that will be notified about multiserver jobs.

Another feature of multiple server jobs is that target servers will automatically upload their job completion status to the master server.

## Creating Jobs

The required elements of a job are the name, schedule, and command to be executed during one or more steps.

The Database Maintenance Plan Wizard creates one or more jobs for a given plan. For any given plan, you will probably see separate jobs for the optimizations, integrity checks, and backups.

Jobs can be scheduled in one of four ways:

**When the SQL Agent starts** A job can be created that automatically executes whenever the SQL Agent starts. This would be good for an automated system of some kind.

**When the CPU is idle** A job can be scheduled to start after the CPU has been idle a certain amount of time, which is configurable in the Properties screen of the SQL Agent.

**One time only** A one-time-only job is usually created for a special purpose; it executes only once on its scheduled date and time.

**Recurring** A recurring job happens on a regular basis. The job's frequency can be daily, weekly, or even monthly.

You can modify a job to change its name, type, command, or schedule by editing the job in the Jobs folder in the Console Tree. You can also run the job manually by right-clicking the job and choosing Start Job.

A very helpful feature of Enterprise Manager is that it keeps a record (job history) of each job's time of execution, as well as whether the job was successful or not. You can check the job history to verify that your jobs are running properly.

You may also delete jobs; however, you should disable the job rather than delete it. This way you can quickly re-enable the job if needed.

## Creating and Managing Alerts

SQLAgentMail , via the alert engine, looks in the sysalerts table in order to determine which errors it should be looking for. By defining an alert, you are telling SQL Server which error codes to look for in the NT application.

**Creating an Alert** Creating alerts is somewhat intuitive. There are several basic steps:

1. Define the type of alert, either an alert based on a SQL Server error message or one based on a performance monitor counter.

2. If based on a SQL Server error message, define the error to look for. Alerts can be based on a generic error-message number, the error's severity, or an error happening in a specific database.

3. Optionally, define the database in which the error must happen. An alert can filter error messages based on the database. For instance, an

alert can be created to watch the Pubs database in case it fills up. This alert would operate only on the Pubs database; if any other database filled up, the alert wouldn't do anything.

4. If based on a performance monitor counter, define which counter to monitor and the threshold that will trigger the alert.

5. Define the response of the alert. Alerts can be set to trigger jobs automatically and/or to alert operators that the alert was activated.

6. If the alert is meant to perform a job, define (or select) the job to be done. Alerts are usually created to perform a job when the alert condition is met. You can define a job that will run when the alert is triggered.

7. If the alert is meant to notify someone, define who will be notified and how this will be done. You can specify operators and whether they should receive an e-mail message and/or be paged when an alert is triggered.

8. Activate the alert by selecting the Enabled box inside the Edit Alert dialog box (it is selected by default but can be deselected to temporarily disable an alert).

After you've created an alert, you can easily make changes to it in much the same way that you worked with jobs. Simply return to the Manage Alerts and Operators window, highlight the alert you want to change, and click on the Edit Alert button.

**Forwarding Alerts**   If you have more than one server running SQL Server, you can define a central server that will receive alerts from other servers. The server that receives these events is called an *unhandled-event forwarding server*.

The server that is designated as the unhandled-event forwarding server must be registered in Enterprise Manager.

Windows 95/98 cannot forward events to, or act as, an unhandled-event server.

## Creating and Managing Operators

SQL Server is MAPI-compliant, which means that SQL Server can send and receive e-mail. This gives you the ability to define operators and their e-mail addresses in SQL Server and have SQL Server notify those operators about the success and/or failure of scheduled or triggered jobs and alerts.

SQL Server also supports many paging services and can be configured to page operators if an alert is triggered. These paging services depend on your e-mail system's ability to decode an e-mail message in order to send a page message.

### Enabling MAPI Support for E-mail

Installing MAPI support for Windows NT 4 has five basic steps:

1. Create a user account for SQLAgentMail and MSSQLServer service accounts to use.

2. Create a post office box for these accounts. (You should use a single account for both the SQLAgentMail and MSSQLServer services. This allows you to use a single e-mail account through which both services can send mail.)

3. Log into the SQL Server computer as the SQL user account and create an Exchange profile that points to the post office.

4. Log into the SQL server as someone with Administration and sa rights and assign the SQL user account (created in Step 1) to the MSSQLServer and SQLAgentMail services. Stop and restart both services.

5. Assign the profile (created in Step 3) to the SQL Mail portion of SQL Server. Start the SQL Mail session.

After you've set up your operators, you can designate a fail-safe operator in case no other operators are on duty when an alert is triggered.

# Enable Access to Remote Data

**O**ne of the great new features of Microsoft SQL Server 7 is the ability to use distributed queries. A distributed query allows you to gather and manipulate data from multiple databases. These databases may or may not be hosted by Microsoft SQL Server. To accomplish this task, you can use linked servers. By definition, the Microsoft SQL Server that the user is connected to is considered the *local server* while all other databases, whether they are Microsoft SQL Servers or not, are considered *remote servers*. If you are connecting to these remote servers through the OLE-DB providers in Microsoft SQL Server 7, then these remote servers are referred to as *linked servers*.

## What Is a Linked Server?

With Microsoft SQL Server 6.5, you could set up your Microsoft SQL Server to allow your users to pull or manipulate data on remote servers; however, these remote servers were required to be Microsoft SQL servers. Another drawback to the remote server configuration used in SQL Server 6.5 was that the user could only execute stored procedures on the remote servers. Of course, these remote procedures had to be created in advance and had to reside on the remote server.

If the user wanted to pull data from a remote server, then a stored procedure had to be created on the remote server to perform the SELECT statement. If the user wanted to manipulate data on the remote server, then another stored procedure had to be created on the remoter server to perform the INSERT, UPDATE, or DELETE statement. The user was not able to connect or JOIN tables that resided on separate physical servers.

Now that Microsoft SQL Server 7 allows remote servers to be linked, they are not required to be Microsoft SQL Servers. Linked servers are remote database servers that are accessed via an OLE-DB provider from the local Microsoft SQL Server 7 computer. As a result, your users can create SELECT statements that JOIN two or more tables that reside on separate servers. The fact that these tables are not on the local server is transparent to the user.

Generically, an OLE-DB provider (from the viewpoint of Microsoft SQL Server) is a registered COM object, which can establish a connection to a specific type of database. This COM object can translate statements issued from the local server into statements understood by the remote server.

For backward compatibility, Microsoft SQL Server 7 can still be configured to use remote servers that only allow for the execution of remote stored procedures. If you have a SQL Server 6.5 computer that is using remote servers, you can upgrade this server to SQL Server 7 and still maintain compatibility. Once this upgrade has been performed, you can then upgrade the remote servers to linked servers.

Once you have set up your linked servers, you can create and run distributed queries. In the next section, you will take a closer look at distributed queries.

Suppose one of your users needs information from a couple of databases that do not reside on his or her SQL Server 7 computer. If the other database servers have been linked, then the user could create and run a distributed query.

As long as the user is connected to the local SQL Server 7 computer that has been linked to the remote database servers, he or she could execute a query that would pull information from some or all of the databases.

In order to reference a table that resides on a linked server, you must use a "fully qualified name" as in (*LinkedServerName.Database.Owner.Table*). If you are using a third-party OLE-DB provider, then the accompanying documentation supplied by the vendor should give you a more detailed explanation on which parts of the fully qualified name are required.

When executing a SQL statement in SQL Server 7, the local server is also considered the default server. If your SQL statement does not specify a server name, SQL Server 7 will default to the local/default server.

## Installing and Configuring Linked Servers

Creating and configuring linked servers involves two main steps:

1. Configure the link from the local server to the remote servers.

2. Configure login security on the linked server(s) for the user(s).

Only Microsoft SQL Server administrators (*sa*, or members of the sysadmin fixed server role) can set up linked servers, and they must be set up from the SQL Server 7 computer that you want to designate as the local server.

When you create a link to a remote server, you have to provide up to seven pieces of information:

**Server Name** The name your users will use to reference the linked server. (Mandatory.)

**Product Name** The name of the database software hosting the remote database. This parameter defaults to "SQL Server" if the provider name supplied is "SQLOLEDB."

**OLE-DB Provider Name** The name of the OLE-DB COM object as it is registered with the local server. (Mandatory if the product name is not "SQL Server.")

**Data Source** The remote database name/alias or remote database file name depending on which OLE-DB provider is used.

**Location** The physical location of the remote database depending on which OLE-DB provider is used.

**Provider String** The setup string passed to the remote server to establish the connection or link. This string may contain a remote login, remote password, remote database name, etc., depending on which OLE-DB provider is used.

**Catalog Name** The remote catalog or database name depending on which OLE-DB provider is used.

When you purchase and install a new OLE-DB provider, you should receive documentation from the vendor specifying the parameters required and what type of information you should supply for them.

Only two parameters are mandatory for all providers: server name and provider name. The remaining five parameters may be required, have defaults, or are not used at all depending on which OLE-DB provider you choose.

As of this writing, only four OLE-DB providers have been tested for use with SQL Server 7: SQL Server 7, Oracle, Access, and ODBC-compliant OLE-DB providers.

## Linking to a Remote SQL Server 7 Computer

Linking to a remote SQL Server 7 database is the most straightforward type of linking to configure. You have to supply only two parameters:

- The *server name* of the remote SQL Server 7 computer
- The *product name,* which is "SQL Server"

The server name should be the actual server name (the name you would use to register the remote SQL Server 7 computer in Enterprise Manager). If you decide to use a server name other than the actual name, then you will have to specify the actual name of the remote server for the data source parameter.

To link to a remote SQL Server 7 database, follow these steps:

1. Open Enterprise Manager and connect to the computer that you want to use as the local server.

2. Right-click the Linked Servers icon and choose New Linked Server from the Context menu.

3. Enter the remote server's name for the Linked Server option.

4. Select SQL Server as the Server Type.

### Linking to a Remote SQL Server 6.5 Computer

Linking to a SQL Server 6.5 database is almost as straightforward as creating a link to a remote SQL Server 7 computer. Before you can create a link to the remote SQL Server 6.5 computer, you will need to prep the remote server by executing a SQL script using the sa account or an account with SQL Admin privileges on the SQL Server 6.5 computer. You must run an INSTCAT.SQL query on the SQL Server 6.5 computer. This file can be found on your SQL Server 7 installation disk under the \INSTALL directory or in the \MSSQL7\ INSTALL directory on your local SQL Server 7 computer. Once you have done that, the rest of the installation is practically identical to the SQL Server 7 linked server installation.

### Linking to an Access Database

Linking to an Access database can be a bit tricky. A new parameter called the *data source* is introduced. In the data source parameter you must specify the complete path to the Access database. If it is on a remote server, you may need to map a drive letter or use the UNC naming convention.

Take a look at this scenario:

- The Access database is on a machine named *ATLANTA*.

- The directory in which the Access database is located is shared as INVENTORY.

- The database filename is InvDB.MDB.

The data source parameter that you would need to specify is:
`\\Atlanta\Inventory\InvDB.MDB`

You can use the same Microsoft.Jet.OLEDB4.0 driver to link to an Excel spreadsheet.

### Linking to an Oracle Database Server

When setting up a link to an Oracle database, you will have to install two pieces of software onto your local server: Oracle Client Software and Oracle's SQL*Net software. The version you will need to install will depend on your OLE-DB provider.

If you use the supplied Microsoft OLE-DB provider for Oracle, you will need to install Oracle Client Software Support File Version 7.3.3.0.4 or later and SQL*Net version 2.3.3.0.4 or later.

Oracle implements databases in a fundamentally different way than Microsoft SQL Server. In order to access a database on Oracle from SQL Server 7, you will have to set up an alias to the Oracle database using Oracle's SQL*Net software.

The documentation accompanying the SQL*NET software will detail how to set up a SQL*NET alias to an Oracle database.

SQL*Net is the networking software used by a database system (including other Oracle servers) to talk to a remote Oracle server over a network.

If you were to examine how these software packages work together, you would see that SQL Server talks to the OLE-DB layer which talks to the Oracle Client Software layer which talks to the SQL*Net layer which in turn talks to the TCP/IP stack which then sends the data onto the wire. Figure 4.1 illustrates this.

## Linking to an ODBC Database Server

You can link to an ODBC-compliant database in one of two ways:

- Through a predefined ODBC data source name (DSN)

- By supplying all connection information in the *provider string* parameter

Whether you use a predefined ODBC DSN or the *parameter string*, you will still need to have the ODBC files necessary to connect to your remote database.

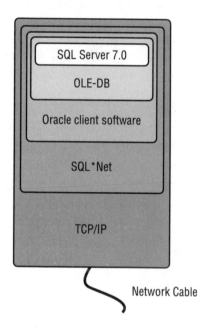

**FIGURE 4.1**

Communicating with
an Oracle Server

Network Cable

Generally, the ODBC files (.DLLs) necessary to connect to the remote database
will be supplied by the vendor from which you bought the ODBC connectors.

Make sure you specify "Other data source" as the Server Type, MSDASQL
for the Provider name option, and a valid DSN for the DSN option.

## Establishing Security for Linked Servers

Once you have created a link to a remote server, you then have to set up the
security to the linked server. Because security mechanisms differ from system
to system, you need to specify what login ID and password you want the
local SQL Server 7 computer to use on the remote system on behalf of your
individual local clients or group of local clients.

If you have a client who is logging onto the local SQL Server 7 computer
as "JohnD," you need to tell SQL Server 7 what login ID and password to
use when logging into the remote database server when "JohnD" tries to

gain access to the remote database. If everyone on your local server is to use a different login ID and password on the remote database system, then you will have to tell SQL Server 7 about each of them. To make things easier, you can designate a login ID and password on the remote database system for a group of local logins.

If you are using a Windows NT local or global group as the login account, then you can map this NT group to a remote database login ID and password.

When you are setting up the security to a remote database server, you will have to provide up to five pieces of information:

**Remote Server Name**  The name you used as the server name when linking the server. (Mandatory.)

**Useself Logical**  This is a TRUE or FALSE parameter to specify whether or not the local SQL Server should send the local login ID's Windows NT credentials when logging onto the remote server The default is FALSE. (Mandatory.)

**Local Login ID**  The login ID on the local server that you want to map to a remote login ID. This local ID can be an NT login ID, an NT group, or the login ID the client uses to log onto SQL Server. (Mandatory.)

**Remote Login ID**  The login ID to use on the remote server. Your local login ID will map to the Remote Login ID.

**Remote Password**  The password that the Remote Login ID will use on the remote server.

With security account delegation, users authenticated by Windows NT to access the local SQL server would have their NT credentials sent to the remote Microsoft SQL Server to access the remote database. The useself parameter is used to specify whether or not to send the NT credentials.

Windows NT 4 does not support security account delegation. This type of authentication will not be implemented until Windows 2000. Until that time, the useself parameter should be set to FALSE. In addition, if the remote database server is a Microsoft SQL Server, that SQL Server needs to be configured to accept nontrusted connections.

## STUDY QUESTIONS

## Create and Manage Databases

**1.** SQL Server uses *.MDF and *. _____ files to store data and
*._____files to store database transaction logs.

**2.** When you create a new database, SQL Server makes a copy of the _____database
and then expands it to the specified size.

**3.** Should you separate your transaction logs and database files on different physical hard
drives? (Yes or No.)

**4.** To create or resize a database, you must have the _____permissions or be
a member of the _____ or fixed server role.

**5.** When you create a database and decide to use the autogrowth characteristics, you should
specify the _____ parameter so that your database does not grow to fill the
entire disk.

**6.** You can use the DBCC _____ to shrink all files in a database or
the DBCC _____ to shrink individual database files.

**7.** If you create a database that has 10MB on Data1.MDF and 10MB on Data2.NDF and 5MB
on Log1.LDF and another 5MB on Log2.LDF, what size is your database?

_____

## Loading Data Using Various Methods

**8.**    True or False. You can use the INSERT statement to add multiple rows to a table.

_____

**9.**    To use the INSERT statement, you must have _____ permissions on the table or view to which you are adding data.

_____

**10.**    True or False. Performing inserts is a logged transaction.

_____

**11.**    You can create both new permanent and new temporary tables using the _____ command.

**12.**    To specify a local temporary table in SQL Server, you must prefix the table name with _____, and to specify a global temporary table, prefix the table name with _____.

**13.**    True or False. Local temporary tables are available to all connections to the local database.

_____

**14.**    To perform a SELECT INTO command, you must have the _____ database option enabled.

_____

## STUDY QUESTIONS

**15.**   True or False. Running a SELECT INTO statement is a logged transaction and because it is logged, you should not worry about making a backup.

_____

**16.**   You must have _____ permissions in the database in order to perform a SELECT INTO command.

**17.**   True or False. Bcp can move data from a flat file into SQL Server and from SQL to a flat file.

_____

**18.**   True or False. Bcp is a command line utility and requires no permissions in the database to operate.

_____

**19.**   True or False. Bcp can be used to transform data as the data is processed.

_____

**20.**   Bcp requires _____ permission on the table in the database you to which you want to import.

_____

**21.**   Bcp requires _____ permissions on the table in the database from which you want to export.

**22.** True or False. Bcp can be used to insert records into a local temporary table.

_____

**23.** To perform a fast bulk copy, you must enable the _____ database option and drop all affected _____.

**24.** Bcp enforces _____ and _____ and will always ignore _____, _____, and _____.

**25.** True or False. Fast bulk copies are non-logged operations and as such, you should immediately back up your database.

_____

**26.** The _____ command is a T-SQL version of bulk copy and can only be used to move data into SQL Server.

**27.** True or False. The BULK INSERT command can read ASCII data files as if they were OLE-DB recordsets.

_____

**28.** To transfer data between SQL Server 7 and Access, Excel, Oracle, and other SQL Servers, you can use _____.

**29.** _____ creates COM- compliant packages that can interact with COM compliant scripting languages like _____, _____ and _____.

**30.** A DTS _____ is a set of tasks that are grouped together and can then be scheduled.

**31.** You can use the _____ to programmatically create a DTS Package. You could then run that package using the _____ command line program.

**32.** True or False. A task object can move data to and from any OLE-DB–compliant data source and data destination.

_____

**33.** True or False. Task objects can run T-SQL statements, run T-SQL batches, and run command line execution.

_____

**34.** True or False. A DTS task object can execute COM-compliant scripts, send mail, and execute other DTS Packages.

_____

**35.** Every task object must be associated with a _____ object if the task is to be executed.

**36.** You use _____ to coordinate the workflows of DTS Packages.

**37.** True or False. Task objects can be associated with multiple step objects and can run simultaneously.

_____

**38.** When you are working with step objects, you can have them run under three different criteria. What are the criteria that allow the next step to run?

_____

_____

_____

**39.** All of the information necessary to make a connection is stored in the connection object. There are two types of connection objects _____ and _____.

**40.** A _____ connection object is used to specify OLE-DB– or ODBC-compliant data source and data destination server. It includes information about the server location, data format, and login credentials.

**41.** A _____ connection object is used to specify the location and format of an ASCII file that will be used by DTS.

**42.** Importing, exporting, and transformation of your data is handled by the _____ object.

**43.** DTS is moving data into your SQL Server and is logging all of the entries. You can minimize the size of the transaction log during this process by setting the _____ database option to _____.

**44.** True or False. A DTS import can be used to create new tables in SQL Server based on the data DTS is reading from a data source.

_____

**45.**   There are two types of security that you can place on your DTS package. They require an _____ password or an _____ password.

**46.**   You can store your DTS packages in three locations. You can store them as _____ objects, which can easily be e-mailed to others. You can store them in the _____ , which allows you to track the lineage of your data. You can also store them in SQL Server.

**47.**   You can use the _____ to move data, schema, and database objects between two SQL Server 7 computers.

**48.**   True or False. The item listed in Question 47 can be used to move data from one platform to another platform and from one character set and sort order to a different character set and sort order.

_____

**49.**   You must have _____ permissions in the source database and you must be the _____ in the destination database to use the Transfer Manager.

**50.**   True or False. Unicode is standard across all SQL Server 7 implementations. This means that you can use DTS, bcp, or even Transfer Manager to move Unicode data from one Unicode collation sequence to another Unicode collation sequence.

_____

## SQL Backups and SQL Recovery

**51.** When you perform backups in SQL Server, it is possible to make backups of the following types: full backup, _____, _____, _____, and _____.

**52.** To make a permanent backup, you must back up to a _____, which can be created with the Enterprise Manager or through code using the _____ stored procedure.

**53.** When you have the Truncate Log on Checkpoint database option set, which of the following backups can you successfully perform? (Full, Log, Differential, Filegroup, File)

_____

**54.** True or False. You can restore SQL Server 6.5 backups in your 7.0 database.

_____

**55.** True or False. You can restore a SQL Server 7 backup to a 7.0 database even though the character set or sort order is different.

_____

**56.** True or False. You can restore a SQL Server 7 backup to a 7.0 database even though the Unicode collation sequence is different.

_____

**57.** A _____ backup is the only type of backup that allows you to recover to a particular point in time.

**58.** You have moved a large amount of data into SQL Server with the Select Into/bulk copy switch set. You now want to ensure the integrity of your database. You decide to perform a full database backup and reset the switch. Is this a good solution?

_____

**59.** If you do not want to make a backup of the transaction log, but you do want to clear out the log, you should use the _____ switch as part of the backup command.

**60.** If your transaction log becomes full, you can no longer perform a backup because a backup itself is a logged transaction. You can use the _____ switch as part of the backup command to clear the log without backing it up.

**61.** A differential backup stores all of the changes to the database since the last _____
_____.

**62.** When SQL Server 7 performs a backup, it captures the active portion of the transaction log as part of the backup process. When you restore your database, you must specify whether or not to replay that active portion of the log. This can be accomplished with the _____ and _____ commands.

**63.**  You use the _____ command only for the last statement in your backup process. This will roll forward all committed transactions that were saved as part of the backup. It will also rollback uncommitted transactions saved as part of the backup. All other restorations to be performed prior to this last command should use the _____ command.

**64.**  During a full database backup process, several modifications to the database were completed successfully and several were still in process when the backup completed. You restore the full backup and use the NO RECOVERY command. Will the successful completions show up in the recovery? Will the in-process transactions show up? (Yes or No.)

_____ , _____

**65.**  During a full database backup process, several modifications to the database were completed successfully and several were still in process when the backup completed. You restore the full backup and use the RECOVERY command. Will the successful completions show up in the recovery? Will the in-process transactions show up? (Yes or No.)

_____ , _____

**66.**  You have a 50GB database. You decide to use five 10GB filegroups. This has advantages for you because you can now perform filegroup backups throughout the week and still maintain data integrity. What other backup must you do in addition to your filegroup backups in order to maintain integrity?

_____

## Manage Replication

**67.** The distribution working folder is located on the distribution server. \\ServerName\
C$_____ is the default share name for this folder. This folder
is used primarily by _____ replication.

**68.** True or False. If the distribution database's transaction log fills to capacity, the distribution
server can no longer receive replicated transactions. When this happens, you will no longer
be able to truncate the transaction logs of the published databases.

_____

**69.** The default conflict resolution process when using Merge replication is based on site priority.
Each site is assigned a priority level and based on that priority, one site's data may be considered more important than another site's data with a lower priority. Which site by default
has the highest priority level?

_____

**70.** Before transactional replication can begin, you must first move a copy of the data to be replicated over to the Subscribers. You can do this using a _____ as part of the
initial synchronization process.

**71.** True or False. In order to maintain the integrity of your replication scenario, you can perform various types of backups. The best backup scenario is to perform a backup of the
Publisher, then the Distributor, and finally the Subscriber. This way all of the backups are
in synch.

_____

**72.** True or False. To ensure that there are no problems with security during your replication process, you should use the same domain account for all of your SQLAgentMail logins involved with the replication scenario.

_____

**73.** You want to subscribe to only one article in a publication in SQL Server 7. How can this be done? Explain.

_____

_____

_____

**74.** Transactional replication takes advantage of the msrepl_commands table as a store-and-forward container for transactions to be read from a Publisher and sent to a Subscriber. After synchronization occurs, the sp_repldone stored procedure is run, and this procedure marks the transactions that have been transferred as replicated. What distribution server process removes these marked transactions from the table?

_____

## Automate Administrative Tasks

**75.** Automation information including e-mail operators, jobs and their schedules, and alerts are stored in the _____ database and are managed by the _____ service.

**76.** Scheduled jobs can run T-SQL scripts, _____, _____, and _____.

**77.**   True or False. SQL Server 7 has the ability to create and manage jobs that run on multiple servers.

_____

**78.**   True or False. Jobs can be enabled and disabled. You can also put jobs on a schedule. When a job is scheduled, it can run once a week, once a day, once every 10 minutes, or it can even run just one time and then delete itself.

_____

**79.**   The Alerts Manager reads the _____ and looks for alerts that match alerts created and maintained in the sysalerts table of the Msdb database.

**80.**   True or False. Alerts can be fired based on a performance counter or a performance threshold being reached.

_____

**81.**   True or False. You can forward alerts to a central alerts management server.

_____

**82.**   Alerts can be fired on a specific _____ _____ or on a less specific _____ _____.

**83.**   True or False. Jobs can be run when the CPU has been set to idle for a certain period of time.

_____

**84.**   When an alert fires or a job runs with success or failure, you can have an e-mail message generated to the e-mail operator as well as a pager address (if supported by your e-mail system). You can also create a _____ operator in case no one else is scheduled to be an operator at a particular time.

**85.**   SQL Server 7 supports backward compatibility by providing a mechanism to support remote stored procedures. With the advent of OLE-DB databases, SQL Server can now add greater functionality using a concept known as _____ servers.

**86.**   You can currently execute remote stored procedures on two SQL Server 7 computers in your enterprise. This means that you have login capabilities on both computers. What do you need to do to enable distributed queries to run?

_____

_____

**87.**   You want to link an Access database to your SQL Server and run distributed queries between the two. In order to do this, you must specify the appropriate _____, which would be the share name and folder where the access database was contained. In addition to this connection information, you may need to specify security credentials as well. This information needs to reside in the _____ database.

**88.**   When you link to an Oracle database, you will need to install another piece of software. This other piece of software is called _____.

## Enable Access to Remote Data

**89.** SQL Server must map a local login ID to the remote database in order for your SQL Server users to run distributed queries in that remote database. To accomplish this, you must specify the correct security credentials for the Remote _____ and Remote _____ parameters.

**90.** If you are using NT Authentication, SQL Server is receiving your NT security credentials. In order to pass these on to a linked server, you should use the _____ parameter.

## SAMPLE TEST

**4-1**    What rights does the SQL Agent service account need? (Choose all that apply.)

    **A.** Log On as a Service right

    **B.** Administrator group membership

    **C.** Backup Operators membership

    **D.** Server Operators membership

**4-2**    What is the API set that allows SQL Server to send and receive e-mail?

    **A.** TAPI

    **B.** EAPI

    **C.** OLE

    **D.** MAPI

**4-3**    Which database holds alert and job information?

    **A.** The Master database.

    **B.** The Model database.

    **C.** The Msdb database.

    **D.** None, it is held in the Registry.

**4-4**    How can you rebuild the Msdb database?

    **A.** You can't; you must reinstall SQL Server.

    **B.** Rebuild the Master database.

    **C.** Rebuild Msdb database.

    **D.** Stop and restart SQL Server; the Msdb database will be rebuilt automatically.

## SAMPLE TEST

**4-5**   Where do alerts look for errors?

    **A.** The Windows NT Application log

    **B.** The SQL Server event log

    **C.** The Master database error log

    **D.** SQL Server sends errors directly to the alert engine

**4-6**   What kinds of jobs can be created? (Choose all that apply.)

    **A.** T-SQL (Transact-SQL)

    **B.** CmdExec (command prompt)

    **C.** Replication

    **D.** Active script

**4-7**   What is the best way to stop an alert for a couple of hours?

    **A.** Disable the alert.

    **B.** Set the hit counter of the alert to −1.

    **C.** Delete the alert.

    **D.** Deselect any operators that were being notified.

**4-8**   What is the operator of last resort called?

    **A.** Weekend operator

    **B.** Last-chance operator

    **C.** Notification operator

    **D.** Fail-safe operator

**4-9**   You want SQL Server to be able to send messages upon job completion using an Exchange operator. Which of these steps is required to create e-mail operators?

   **A.** Create an Exchange account for the SQL Agent service account.

   **B.** Assign the SQL Agent service to use a service account.

   **C.** Create an operator.

   **D.** Assign the job to notify the appropriate operator.

**4-10**   Which of the following database servers are supported as linked servers?

   **A.** Microsoft SQL Server 6.5 (Integrated Security)

   **B.** Microsoft SQL Server 6.5 (Mixed Security)

   **C.** Oracle

   **D.** Microsoft Access (Unsecured)

**4-11**   Your users are complaining that their distributed query is timing out the first time they execute it. After the first time, it executes properly. The remote Microsoft SQL Server 7 is physically located several hundred miles away. Upon further investigation, you find out that there is a slow link to that location. When you check the setup of the linked server in Enterprise Manager, you see that you are using the data source parameter. Even though this is the case, the users say it works perfectly after the first run. Which of the following is a good solution?

   **A.** Make the name in the data source parameter all uppercase.

   **B.** Make the name in the data source parameter all lowercase.

   **C.** Don't use the data source parameter, let the linked server name be the actual name and update the query.

   **D.** Delete the linked server in Enterprise Manager and set it up again because it was using the wrong name in the data source parameter.

**4-12** Your users are logging into your local SQL Server using nontrusted connections. You want to use one mapping for all the users to access the remote database. If the data is not sensitive and security to the data is not an issue, which of the following would accomplish your task?

 A. Create a server role with *public* as a member, and map this role to a remote login ID.

 B. Create a database role with *public* as a member, and map this role to a remote login ID.

 C. Make the NT global group "Domain Users" a valid login, and map it to a remote login ID.

 D. None of the above.

**4-13** Your users are logging into your local SQL Server using trusted connections. Your server and all of your users are in the workgroup SQLDOM. You want to use one mapping for all the users to access the remote database. If the data is not sensitive and security to the data is not an issue, which of the following would accomplish your task?

 A. Create a server role with *public* as a member, and map this role to a remote login ID.

 B. Create a database role with *public* as a member, and map this role to a remote login ID.

 C. Make the NT global group "SQLDOM\Domain Users" a valid login, and map it to a remote login ID.

 D. None of the above.

**4-14**     Your users are logging into your local SQL Server using trusted connections. Your server and all of your users are in the workgroup SQLDOM. You want to use one mapping for all the users to access the remote database. If the data is not sensitive and security to the data is not an issue, which of the following would accomplish your task?

**A.** Create a server role with *public* as a member, and map this role to a remote login ID.

**B.** Create a database role with *public* as a member, and map this role to a remote login ID.

**C.** Make the NT global group "SQLDOM\Domain Users" a valid login, and map it to a remote login ID.

**D.** None of the above.

**4-15**     SQL Server 7 uses a Publisher/Subscriber metaphor to implement its replication design. As a Publisher, you have made several articles available within several publications. To which of the following may authorized Subscribers subscribe?

**A.** The Publisher

**B.** The articles

**C.** The publications

**D.** None of the above

**4-16** You have many salespeople who carry laptops with them on business. You want the sales-people to be able to take orders as well as receive updates to their price lists. In order for your salespeople to keep track of what other salespeople might have quoted for a particular item, they also need to know what the other salespeople have done. In addition, a salesperson might need to add or remove items from the quote. The databases are to be updated nightly, but sometimes this is impossible and there may be a lag of as much as three days between synchronizations. Which type of replication would be best suited to this business situation?

   **A.** Transactional replication for the price lists and transactional replication for the quotes

   **B.** Snapshot replication for the price lists and merge replication for the quotes

   **C.** Merge replication for both the price lists and the quotes

   **D.** Transactional replication for the price lists and merge replication for the quotes

**4-17** You want to use replication to distribute data from the home office in Sacramento to your satellite offices in München, Hamburg, and Köln. What type of replication would be the most cost-effective, given the slow and expensive modem links?

   **A.** Central Publisher (single Publisher with multiple Subscribers)

   **B.** Central Subscriber (single Subscriber with multiple Publishers)

   **C.** Publishing Subscriber

   **D.** Multiple Publishers of one table

**4-18** You have several regional offices that need to update central headquarters throughout the day. Which of the following replication models would be the most effective?

   **A.** A central Publisher model (single Publisher with multiple Subscribers) that uses a RegionCode as part of the primary key

   **B.** A central Subscriber model (single Subscriber with multiple Publishers) that uses a RegionCode as part of the primary key

**C.** A publishing Subscriber model that uses a LocationID as part of the primary key

**D.** Multiple Publishers of one table using LocationIDs for the primary key

**4-19** You want to view the history of replications that have taken place at a particular Subscriber. That Subscriber uses a push subscription to gather its data. In addition, the data is transferred throughout the day using transactional replication. Once a week a snapshot replication is scheduled to run to refresh all the replicated data. Which of the following will allow you to view the history of snapshots applied to the Subscriber?

**A.** Use the replication monitor on the distribution server to view the Snapshot Agent history

**B.** Use the replication monitor on the subscription server to view the Snapshot Agent history

**C.** Use the replication monitor on the distribution server to view the distribution agent history

**D.** Use the replication monitor on the Subscriber to view the distribution agent history

**4-20** You have a central Publisher with a remote Distributor set up as part of your replication scenario. You have 12 Subscribers using pull subscriptions for transactional replication. You also have two additional Subscribers that are doing merge replication. How many cleanup jobs are there on the remote Distributor?

**A.** None; all cleanup jobs run on the Publisher.

**B.** 2

**C.** 12

**D.** 14

**4-21**   You are using merge replication where a central Publisher makes data available for five Subscribers. A Subscriber makes modifications to a record at 10:30 A.M. The Publisher makes modifications to the same record at 11:02 A.M. The records are converged at 12:00 P.M. and then sent back to the clients. Which of the following is true?

   **A.** This record will not be converged.

   **B.** Each Subscriber will have its own unique version of the modified record.

   **C.** The Subscriber's modification of the record will be converged to all of the other Subscribers.

   **D.** The Publisher's modification of the record will be converged to all of the Subscribers.

**4-22**   You are currently monitoring your replication model that uses transactional replication with a remote Distributor. You notice that transactions are added to the MSRepl_commands table on the distribution database. When the transactions are applied to the Subscriber, they disappear from the table a few minutes later. Which of the following is true?

   **A.** When the transactions are applied to the Subscriber, the sp_repldone stored procedure is run on the Distributor, and all applied transactions are marked.

   **B.** When the transactions are applied to the Subscriber, the sp_repldone stored procedure is run at the Subscriber and the records are marked.

   **C.** A cleanup task is run on the Distributor and all marked transactions are truncated.

   **D.** A cleanup task is run on the Subscriber and all marked transactions are truncated.

**4-23**   Which of the following is true regarding the SELECT INTO statement?

   **A.** You must have the Select Into/Bulk Copy database option enabled.

   **B.** You must be a member of the sysadmin database role.

   **C.** SELECT INTO statements are logged transactions.

   **D.** You must have CREATE TABLE permissions in the database.

**4-24**   Your environment includes a SQL Server 7 computer and an AS-400 running DB2. Only three people in your organization have access to the AS-400, but nearly 200 need access to the data. The AS-400 currently dumps large ASCII flat files to your computer. Because you are the SQL Server administrator, you must make the data available to those 200 users. Which of the following data management techniques could be used to move the ASCII files into your SQL Server computer?

    **A.** You can use the bcp utility.

    **B.** You can use the BULK INSERT statement.

    **C.** You can use the SELECT INTO statement.

    **D.** You can use the INSERT statement.

**4-25**   Your environment includes a SQL Server 7 computer and an AS-400 running DB2. Only three people in your organization have access to the AS-400, but nearly 200 need access to the data. The AS-400 currently dumps large ASCII flat files to your computer. Because you are the SQL Server administrator, you must make the data available to those 200 users. You decide that you want to use the Bulk Copy command-line utility. You also want the transfer to be as fast as possible. Which of the following will accomplish this task?

    **A.** You must drop all indexes on the affected tables to avoid transaction logging.

    **B.** You must drop all data in the affected tables to avoid transaction logging.

    **C.** You must enable the SELECT INTO/bulk copy database option to avoid transaction logging.

    **D.** You must enable the Truncate Log on Checkpoint database option to avoid transaction logging.

**4-26**  Which of the following is true about the bulk copy operation?

  **A.** Defaults and datatypes are always ignored.

  **B.** Defaults and datatypes are always enforced.

  **C.** Rules and triggers are always ignored.

  **D.** Rules and triggers are always enforced.

**4-27**  You decide that you want to use the Bulk Copy command-line utility. Which permissions are required for you to perform this bulk copy operation?

  **A.** When copying data in to SQL Server, you must have READ permissions on the file (if it is on an NTFS partition).

  **B.** When copying data in to SQL Server you must have INSERT permissions on the table that is affected.

  **C.** When copying data out of SQL Server you must have SELECT permission on the affected tables.

  **D.** When copying data out of SQL Server you must have SELECT INTO permissions on the affected tables.

**4-28**  Which of the following is true about the BULK INSERT statement?

  **A.** It is a command-line utility.

  **B.** It is a T-SQL command.

  **C.** It only reads one record at a time.

  **D.** It is reads all records in a flat file as if they are an OLE-DB recordset.

**4-29**   You have a large SQL Server 7 computer running a quad-processor Alpha-AXP computer. The server currently holds about 3 terabytes of data. For administrative reasons, you want to distribute portions of that data to SQL Server 7 computers running on Intel Pentium IIs throughout your organization. As part of the distribution process, you want to include some tables, many of the views, and several of the stored procedures. You do not want to keep the security setting, however. You decide to use the DTS Import and Export engine to move the information. Which of the following is true about this solution?

**A.** This is a poor solution because only data will be transferred, but not the views and stored procedures.

**B.** This is a poor solution because all data will be transferred, including the rules, defaults, triggers, constraints, and security information.

**C.** This is a fair solution; however, all security information will be transferred.

**D.** This is an excellent solution and fits all the required parameters.

**4-30**   You have a large SQL Server 7 computer running a quad-processor Alpha-AXP computer. The server currently holds about 3 terabytes of data. For administrative reasons, you want to distribute portions of that data to SQL Server 7 computers running on Intel Pentium IIs throughout your organization. As part of the distribution process, you want to include some tables, many of the views, and several of the stored procedures. You do not want to keep the security setting though. You decide to use the Transfer Manager to move the information. Which of the following is true about this solution?

**A.** This is a poor solution because only data will be transferred, but not the views and stored procedures.

**B.** This is a poor solution because all data will be transferred including the rules, defaults, triggers, constraints, and security information.

**C.** This is a fair solution; however, all security information will be transferred.

**D.** This is an excellent solution and fits all the required parameters.

**4-31** The task object in a DTS package can perform which of the following?

    **A.** Move data from a source to a destination

    **B.** Run a T-SQL statement or batch

    **C.** Execute external programs like .CMD files or .BAT files

    **D.** Execute another DTS package

    **E.** Execute COM-compliant scripts like VBScript

**4-32** The step object in a DTS package can run in parallel when there are no precedence constraints on it. Which of the following are step object precedence constraints?

    **A.** On Success

    **B.** On Failure

    **C.** Unconditional

    **D.** Return Codes

**4-33** You want create a DTS package that can access and work with sensitive data. When you store the package, you want to give some people the ability to run the package and others the ability to edit it. For security reasons, you also want the package encrypted. Which of the following steps should you take to accomplish these goals?

    **A.** Supply an owner password for the package.

    **B.** Supply an operator password for the package.

    **C.** Select the encrypt option for the package.

    **D.** Do nothing. Only the sysadmin can work with packages.

## SAMPLE TEST

**4-34**   You are currently running SQL Server 6.5 and are thinking about upgrading to SQL Server 7. On your SQL Server 7 computer, you want to use a different character set and sort order. You decide to upgrade the SQL Server 6.5 computer to 7.0 using the current 6.5 sort order and character sets. You then install another version of SQL Server 7 on the network with the new sort orders and character set. Which of the following methods of data transfer is the best choice to move your data from the recently upgraded SQL Server?

    **A.** Re-create the objects in the destination database and then use bcp to move your data.

    **B.** Re-create the objects in the destination database and then use DTS to transfer your data.

    **C.** Use the Transfer Manager to move all objects and data from the source database to the destination database.

    **D.** You cannot transfer data with different character sets and sort orders.

# UNIT

# 5

Monitoring and Optimization

# Test Objectives: Monitoring and Optimization

- Monitor SQL Server performance.

- Tune and optimize SQL Server.

- Limit resources used by queries.

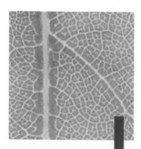

In this unit, we will look at monitoring and tuning your SQL Server. We will begin with a discussion of Performance Monitor and the principal performance counters. We will look at the SQL Server Profiler tool and how it benefits the tuning and optimization of your SQL Server. We will then review the SQL Query Governor and spend a few minutes on a series of optimization techniques.

# Monitor SQL Server Performance

SQL Server exposes more than 100 performance counters that can be used in the SQL Performance monitor to track SQL Server activity in real-time. These performance counters can even be designed to send an alert when a performance threshold has been reached. For example, a counter might generate an alert when the transaction log that it is tracking reaches 80 percent capacity.

## Using Performance Monitor

Performance Monitor comes with Windows NT and is located in the Administrative Tools folder on the Start menu. Four views are available:

**Chart** This view displays a graph of system performance. As values change, the graph will spike or dip accordingly.

**Report** The Report view looks more like what you might get on a piece of paper except that the values here change with system use.

**Alert** With Alert view, you can tell Performance Monitor to warn you when something bad is looming on the horizon, perhaps when CPU use is almost—but not quite yet—too high. This type of warning gives you time to fix potential problems before they become actual problems.

**Log** This view is for keeping records. With Log view, you can monitor your system over a period of time and view the information later, as opposed to viewing it real time (the default).

Using Performance Monitor, you can monitor SQL Server, as well as Windows NT because SQL provides its own objects and counters. The SQL counters you will be using most often have been preset for you and can be accessed through the Performance Monitor icon in the SQL Server 7 menu on the Start menu. Table 5.1 describes each of the counters in the preset Performance Monitor.

| **T A B L E  5.1** Preset SQL Performance Monitor Counters | **Object** | **Counter** | **Use** |
|---|---|---|---|
| | SqlServer:Buffer Manager | Buffer Cache Hit Ratio | This tells you how much data is being retrieved from cache instead of disk. You want this number to be as high as possible. |
| | SqlServer:Buffer Manager | Page Reads/Sec | Number of data pages that are read from disk each second. The lower the better. |
| | SqlServer:Buffer Manager | Page Writes/Sec | Number of data pages that are written to disk each second. The lower the better. |
| | SqlServer:General Statistics | User Connections | Number of user connections. Each of these will take some RAM. |
| | SQLServer:Memory Manager | Total Server Memory (KB) | Total amount of memory that SQL has been dynamically assigned. |
| | SQLServer:SQL Statistics | SQL Compilations/Sec | Number of compilations per second. This can be lowered by using stored procedures. |

Through the Performance Monitor, you can also create alerts that generate an error message to the Windows NT Application Log. This is accomplished through the SQLALRTR utility. You can create a performance alert for each of your transaction logs. To do this, create an alert that fires when the transaction log for a given database reaches 75 percent of its capacity. Then create a SQL Server alert to automatically make a backup of the database when it finds that error in the Application Log.

## Monitoring with SQL Profiler

The SQL Profiler allows you to monitor and record what is happening inside the database engine. This is accomplished by performing a *trace*, which is a record of data that has been captured about events. Traces can be stored in a table, in a trace log file, or in both. They can be either shared (viewable by everyone) or private (viewable only by the owner).

The actions you will be monitoring are called *events* and are logically grouped into *event classes*. Some of these events are useful for maintaining security, and some are useful for troubleshooting problems. Most of these events are used for monitoring and optimization.

When you work with the Profiler, an overwhelming amount of data is automatically tracked. You can use *filters* to wade through the mountains of data and work with only the data you want.

The Trace Wizard is a very handy tool for creating a "quick and dirty" trace to get some standard information. You can create a total of six traces with this wizard:

**Find the Worst Performing Queries** This trace will help identify which queries are the slowest by grouping the output according to the duration of each query.

**Identify Scans of Large Tables** This trace will identify scans of large tables. If you find such scans you may need to create some indexes.

**Identify the Cause of a Deadlock** Deadlocks, caused by multiple users trying to access the same data at the same time, can slow down all users. This trace will show the chain of events leading up to the deadlock and the object that was being accessed.

**Profile the Performance of a Stored Procedure** Stored procedures are Transaction-SQL (T-SQL) code that is stored at the server for clients to access. Improperly written stored procedures can slow down the system. This trace will help find these slow and poorly coded stored procedures.

**Trace Transact-SQL Activity by Application** This trace will show you which applications are being used the most to access SQL Server.

**Trace Transact-SQL Activity by User** This trace will help you see which of your users are accessing SQL Server the most and what they are doing while logged in.

You probably will not be able—or want—to watch Profiler constantly to see whether anything important happens. This is not a problem, because you can always replay the traces.

## Replaying a Trace File

When solving a problem or dealing with and untoward event, you will typically try to re-create the circumstances and chain of events that led up to the event. You can re-create the problem-causing events by replaying a trace. Loading your saved traces into Profiler will allow you to replay them against the local server (or any other SQL Server 7 computer) and figure out exactly where the problem occurred. An especially nice touch is that you don't have to play the whole trace all at once; you can take it step-by-step to see exactly where the problem lies.

In order to replay a trace file, you must capture the following events:

| | |
|---|---|
| Application Name | Host Name |
| Binary Data | Integer Data |
| Connect | RPC:Starting |
| Connection ID or SPID | Server Name |
| Database ID | SQL:BatchStarting |
| Disconnect | SQL User Name |
| Event Sub Class | Start Time |
| ExistingConnection | Text |

All of the following must be true in order to replay a saved trace on another computer:

- All login IDs and database users found in the trace must also be found on the target computer and target database.

- All login IDs on the target must have the same permissions they had in the source.

- All passwords must be the same for the user executing the replay.

You cannot replay a trace on another computer when any of the following are true:

- Users are connected to SQL Server through NT Authentication.

- Traces contain replication activity in their transaction logs.

- Traces contain GUIDs. GUIDs are often used for auto-numbering and in Merge Replication.

- There are non-logged bcp events like text and image updates.

Automation is a key ingredient in optimizing your systems. The Profiler is no exception. You can have the Profiler automatically start when SQL Server starts running. This is a wonderful feature, and it can make your life a bit easier. This is one more thing that you don't have to do. You can use the extended stored procedures to start and run the Profiler.

Let's extend our automation example. If you create a startup stored procedure, that startup stored procedure can call all of the necessary extended stored procedures to create and begin a trace. As part of that trace, you can specify the trace destination. This means that you can configure a SQL Server to begin tracing itself upon startup and then send the results of the trace to another SQL Server on the network.

The Profiler is a wonderful tool for monitoring database activity and reporting problems, but that is not all it can do. Profiler comes with yet another wizard that will help you further improve the performance of your queries, the Index Tuning Wizard.

## Using the Index Tuning Wizard

When SQL Server indexes are out of tune, they can slow down the entire system. Perhaps the wrong columns were indexed from the beginning, or maybe users started querying different data over time, which will require the creation of new indexes. If any of this is true, your indexes need tuning.

The Index Tuning Wizard essentially allows you to create optimized indexes for your database. The Wizard is nice because, as an admin, you don't need to know about the structure of the database or the workload of your server.

The one thing you need before you can run the Index Tuning Wizard is a workload. You get this by running and saving a trace in Profiler. It is best to get this workload during times of peak database activity to make sure that you give the Wizard an accurate load.

The Index Tuning Wizard is useful when a ton of new data is added to your database. Over time, the indexes are not optimized. The query engine in SQL Server relies on the statistics kept for each index in your database in order to decide whether or not to use a particular index. These statistics are not updated automatically. You should schedule a job to run the UPDATE STATISTICS command on a regular basis. If you do not want to do this, then run the Index Wizard. It will take care of the statistics for you.

The Index Wizard may also look at the FreeSpacePageFetches/sec and the FreeSpaceScans/sec to determine whether or not the fillfactor for your index is set appropriately. If you have high values for these items, that means that many new records are being inserted into your table and are looking for free space in the index to be added. To alleviate this type of situation, you should make your fillfactor setting lower than what it is currently. This will allow more free space on each data page. For example, if your fillfactor is currently set to 75 percent. This means that 25 percent of the page is free space. If you decrease the counter to 50 percent, then half of the page is free space and can be used by these new records that you are adding.

## Important Profiler Events

SQL Profiler has many events with which you can work, but only a few are important for the exam.

**Tracking Stored Procedures**   When working with stored procedures, the ODBC/OLE-DB drivers have the option to run a real stored procedure that is saved on the SQL Server or send an SQL statement that will be prepared on the SQL Server. These prepared statements are stored in Tempdb and in SQL Server RAM. You can find out which of these procedures are truly *ad hoc* queries and which ones are truly stored procedures by monitoring the stored procedure cache. The specific events you want to filter are SP: Cache Hit and SP: Cache Insert. The Cache Hit tells you which stored queries were found in RAM, and the Insert shows you which queries are sent to the server and then prepared and placed into cache.

**Tracking Security**   For security reasons, you may want to create and audit various databases, tables, views, and other objects that are used in your SQL Server. To accomplish this task, you should create filters on the Object events. You can track the following information about Objects:

**Object:Opened**   This tells you when an object has been accessed through a SELECT, INSERT, UPDATE, or DELETE statement.

**Object:Closed**   This tells you when an object is closed. This occurs when the SELECT, INSERT, UPDATE, or DELETE statement has finished running.

**Object:Created**   This tells you when a CREATE statement has been run.

**Object:Deleted**   This tells you when an object has been dropped from a database using the DROP statement.

If you combine these events with the tracking of the SQL User Name and/or the NT User Name, then you can determine which users have operated on which database objects.

# Tune and Optimize SQL Server

In this section, we will focus on the different tools available to optimize various activities in SQL Server. This includes the use of RAID and working with SQL Server memory.

# RAID

RAID (Redundant Array of Inexpensive Disks) is used to protect your data and speed up your system. In a system without RAID, data that is written to disk is written to that one disk. In a system with RAID, that same data would be written across multiple disks, providing fault tolerance and improved I/O. Some forms of RAID can be implemented inexpensively in Windows NT, but this uses system resources like processor time and memory. If you have the budget for it, you might consider getting a separate RAID controller that will take the processing burden off Windows.

One thing to keep in mind when dealing with RAID and SQL Server is how SQL Server sends data to disk. SQL Server will generate one thread per disk. If you have a RAID array configured so that SQL Server sees it as only a single disk drive, then only one thread will be generated. RAID can be used for redundancy. If you split up your RAID array and add more logical disk drives, then SQL Server can create additional threads.

## Working with SQL Server Memory

SQL Server, like most BackOffice products, needs significant amounts of RAM. The more you put in, the happier SQL will be. However, there is one caveat about adding RAM: check your Level 2 cache. This is much faster (and more expensive) than standard RAM and is used by the processor for storing frequently used data. If you don't have enough Level 2 cache to support the amount of RAM in your system, your server may actually slow down rather than speed up. For the amount of memory that SQL requires, you should have at least 1MB of Level 2 cache on your system.

When you are working with SQL Server, you can modify two memory options: the Min Server Memory and the Max Server Memory. The options configure the amount of memory to be allocated to the buffer pool. The buffer pool is a small part of the total SQL Server memory.

By default, SQL Server modifies these options dynamically based on how much memory it needs. The default values are 0 for the minimum and 2.14 billion for the maximum (these are in megabytes). This buffer is used to keep Windows NT from paging SQL Server memory in and out of a swapfile.

If you set these options to the same value, then you have allocated a fixed amount of memory to SQL Server. This is useful when only SQL Server is running on the computer. You should use a range of values if you want to leave memory for other applications like Exchange or IIS.

For performance reasons, it is nice to allow SQL Server to lock Windows NT virtual memory. This keeps NT from swapping that memory to and from disk. To lock or unlock memory, use the Set Working Set Size server option. This can be configured using the sp_configure stored procedure.

The Set Working Set Size option is either true (1) or false (0). If you want to turn on the Set Working Set Size configuration option, you should ensure that Min Server Memory and Max Server Memory are set to the same value.

# Limit Resources Used by Queries

If you have long or expensive queries, you will want to limit the resources that they use. To first find out whether or not you have expensive and unoptimized queries you can use the Query Analyzer to view data about the costs associated with your query. The other side of optimization involves limiting the amount of time a query can run. This can be done with the Query Governor.

## The Query Analyzer

If you used SQL Server in its previous versions, you are probably familiar with ISQL/W, a graphic tool used for entering queries as T-SQL code. In SQL Server 7, this tool has been reborn as Query Analyzer. Up to this point, you have been using this tool to enter queries and see results, but it can do more.

One clue to its enhanced capabilities comes from its name: Query *Analyzer*. It is used not only to enter queries but also to analyze them, to see how many resources they consume, and to see how fast they run. The Query Analyzer accomplishes this analysis by timing each step of the execution; this includes parsing the command you typed and checking for errors, loading the data into memory, performing the query on the data, and more. If you would like to see a graphic representation of everything SQL Server is doing with your query, you can tell it to display an execution plan. This will display a series of icons that lead you through the execution process.

Once the analysis is complete, you will have a better idea of how to build your queries and optimize them for speed, but you will not yet have the full picture. To get a full understanding of how your queries respond to everyday use, you need to monitor them under stress—that is why we have SQL Profiler.

## Query Governor

Right out of the box, SQL will run any query you tell it to—even if that query is poorly written. You can change that by using the Query Governor. This is not a separate tool. It is part of the database engine and is controlled by the Query Governor Cost Limit. This setting tells SQL not to run queries longer than $x$ (where $x$ is a value higher than zero). If, for example, Query Governor Cost Limit is set to 2, any query that is estimated to take longer than 2 seconds would not be allowed to run. SQL is able to estimate the running time of a query because it keeps statistics about the number and composition of records in tables and indexes. The Query Governor Cost Limit can be set by using the command

```
sp_configure 'query governor cost limit', '1'
```

(The 1 in this code can be higher.) It can also be set on the Server Settings tab of the Server Properties page in Enterprise Manager.

If the Query Governor Cost Limit is set to zero (the default), all queries will be allowed to run.

## Monitor SQL Server Performance

**1.** The Performance Monitor allows you to view data in four different formats. These include _____, _____, _____, and _____.

**2.** The _____ view in Performance Monitor displays a graph of system performance. As the values change, the graph will spike or dip accordingly.

**3.** When you use the _____ view in the Performance Monitor, the Performance Monitor can generate a message and place it in the Windows NT Application Log.

**4.** To determine how often data is read from SQL Server RAM (cache) rather than from disk, you can monitor the _____ counter in the Performance Monitor.

**5.** You can use the _____ utility in SQL Server to create a Performance Monitor alert that will generate an alert to the NT Application Log that SQL Server can see.

**6.** The SQL Profiler monitors your SQL Server. When monitoring, you can create a _____, which is a record of events that have been captured.

**7.** By default, the Profiler captures an overwhelming amount of data. You can create _____ to delineate specific items of interest.

**8.** To create quick traces, you can use the _____, which can generate up to six different trace files.

## STUDY QUESTIONS

**9.** You want to track queries that are performing the slowest. You decide to do this by grouping your output according to the duration of each query. You can use the _____ _____ to quickly create this trace. Once this tool starts, you should choose the _____ option.

**10.** Using the Trace Wizard, you can track which users are performing which activities in which databases. To do this, you should select the _____ _____ option.

**11.** To problem solve, you can save your trace files and _____ them at a later time.

**12.** True or False. You can replay your trace against the local server or another server at any time.

_____

**13.** In order to replay a trace, you must capture some very specific events. List five of these events.

_____

_____

_____

_____

**14.** True or False. To replay a trace on another computer, all login IDs and database users in the trace must exist on the target computer.

_____

**15.** True or False. To replay a trace on another computer, the login IDs and database users on the target computer do not have to have all of the same permissions.

_____

**16.** True or False. To replay a trace on another computer, the password used for the Login IDs and database users must be the same as the source computers.

_____

**17.** You are trying to replay a trace on another computer. All of the SQL logins work; however, none of the NT logins work. Is this a bug in the trace file? Please explain.

_____

**18.** True or False. You can replay a trace on another computer that contains replication activity in the transaction log.

_____

**19.** Trace files can be initiated through the use of _____ stored procedures.

**20.** You can have up to 10 stored procedures marked as auto-starting procedures. This means that these procedures fire when the SQL Server begins running. Can one of the procedures start a trace? (Yes or No.)

_____

**21.** Trace files can be stored locally in a database _____ or to a _____ on disk.

**22.** True or False. You can place trace files into a table on another computer.

_____

**23.** You can use the _____ to create and tune your indexes. This is useful if you don't know a lot about the structure of your database or the workload on your server.

**24.** To get the most accurate picture for your Index Tuning Wizard, you should create a _____ during times of _____ database activity.

**25.** The query optimizer in SQL Server uses _____ to determine whether or not to use a particular index.

**26.** Index statistics are not automatically kept up to date. You should schedule a job to run occasionally that issues the _____ command to ensure that the index statistics are accurate.

**27.** You can run the command listed in the last question on an individual _____ or on all indexes in a _____.

**28.** If you have added a lot of information to your table and your table has multiple indexes, should you run an UPDATE STATISTICS on the table or on each index? Please explain.

_____

**29.** To determine what fillfactor to use, the Index Wizard may look at the _____ and the _____ trace events.

**30.** If the values of the events in the last question are too high, should you increase or decrease the value of your fillfactor setting? Please explain.

_____

**31.** When you work with client applications, you can use two types of stored procedures. These are known as stored procedures and _____ queries.

**32.** The _____ queries come to SQL Server and are "prepared" on the server and stored in the _____ database.

**33.** To determine the difference between the _____ queries and the real stored procedures, you can trace the following two events: _____ and _____.

**34.** The _____ corresponds to the stored procedures, and the _____ corresponds to the prepared statements.

**35.** The _____ event is what you will want to design traces on to track security.

**36.** To determine when an object has been accessed through a SELECT, INSERT, UPDATE, or DELETE statement, you should track the Object:_____ event.

**37.** If you want to determine which user has worked with one of these objects, you should also trace the _____ and the _____.

**38.** To determine how often data is read from SQL Server RAM (cache) rather than from disk, you can monitor the _____ counter in the Performance Monitor.

---

| STUDY QUESTIONS |
|---|

## Tune and Optimize SQL Server

**39.** You can improve performance and fault tolerance by using a _____ array.

**40.** SQL Server generates a single _____ for each logical disk drive.

**41.** True or False. If you have 10 logical disk drives, then SQL Server will generate 10 threads for disk I/O.

_____

**42.** True or False. If you have a RAID array that has five physical disks but is represented as a single logical drive, you can increase read/write performance for SQL Server by splitting it into multiple logical drives.

_____

**43.** Microchips can take advantage of RAM located on the processor itself. This processor-owned RAM is known as the _____.

**44.** The processor-owned RAM from the previous question should be at least _____ for SQL Server.

**45.** SQL Server dynamically allocates RAM to itself depending on its changing needs. You can configure a range of RAM that SQL Server will use by configuring the _____ and _____ options.

**46.**  True or False. If you set the configuration options mentioned in the last question to the same value, then SQL Server will not dynamically allocate memory for itself. This memory will not be swapped by Windows NT.

_____

**47.**  To ensure that Windows NT does not swap SQL Server owned RAM, you should set the _____ configuration option to _____. In addition to this, you must also set the _____ and the _____ to the same value.

**48.**  True or False. If you have other applications running on your SQL Server that are running slowly because SQL Server is using all of the RAM, you should set the Set Working Set Value to 0 to ensure that SQL Server does not take more RAM than is configured for it. Please explain.

_____

## Limit Resources Used by Queries

**49.**  The _____ times each step of a query execution.

**50.**  True or False. You can view a query plan in a graphical format using the Query Analyzer tool.

_____

**51.**  Which queries can you run in the Query Analyzer?

    **A.** T-SQL

    **B.** ANSI SQL

    **C.** T-SQL and ANSI

_____

**52.** True or False. You can view the indexes a query will use by reviewing the execution plan created in the Query Analyzer.

_____

**53.** True or False. You can force a query to use a particular index on a table by supplying "optimizer hints."

_____

**54.** True or False. You can run stored procedures from the Query Analyzer, but you cannot run extended stored procedures.

_____

**55.** You should use the Query Analyzer in conjunction with the _____ to get a full picture of how to optimize your queries.

**56.** You can use the _____ to set a cost limit on your queries.

**57.** The configuration option Cost Limit for the utility specified in the last question is set to the number _____ by default.

**58.** A Cost Limit of 3 indicates that no queries estimated to run longer than _____ should be allowed.

**59.** The Query Governor estimates query timing by reading the _____, which store information about the composition of records and indexes for a table.

**5-1** Your system has 64MB of RAM; you upgrade that to 512MB and find that your system has actually slowed down. What caused this?

    **A.** One of the SIMMs you purchased is defective.

    **B.** You need to add more Level 2 cache to the system.

    **C.** You need to configure SQL server to use the new RAM by adjusting the Memory setting in the advanced options of the Server properties.

    **D.** You need to configure the Max Server Memory setting to a higher value.

**5-2** You are writing a complex new query that joins columns from several tables and you are concerned about how it might affect system performance. Which tool could you use to see what this query will do to your system before implementing it?

    **A.** Profiler

    **B.** Query Governor

    **C.** Query Analyzer

    **D.** Performance Monitor

**5-3** Your SQL Server is running slowly and you suspect the disk subsystem. You monitor the Physical Disk Average Disk Queue length counter in Performance Monitor and find that it is within the acceptable range. What could you do to speed up the disk subsystem?

    **A.** Increase the value of the LazyWriter.

    **B.** Add another physical disk to the system.

    **C.** Implement RAID 1.

    **D.** Increase the Max Async I/O setting.

**5-4** You recently hired a developer to update your queries so that they would encompass some newly created tables. Your users are now complaining that the system seems slow. What can you do?

   **A.** Analyze the new queries with Query Analyzer.

   **B.** Monitor the Physical Disk: Average Disk Queue counter in Performance Monitor during a period of peak activity to see if the disk subsystem can handle the new queries.

   **C.** Create a trace with Profiler and use the trace file with the Index Wizard to improve the indexes.

   **D.** Increase the size of Tempdb.

**5-5** You need to know what kinds of queries each of your users is performing against SQL Server. What is the best way to accomplish this?

   **A.** Ask them via e-mail.

   **B.** Create a trace in Profiler that gathers information on all the available events.

   **C.** Create a trace using the Trace Wizard that will sort the data by user.

   **D.** Use Query Analyzer to analyze which users are using your queries.

**5-6** After using a trace in Profiler to monitor database activity, what should you do with the trace file?

   **A.** Delete it, as it is useless.

   **B.** Save it to disk so you can use it later for trend tracking.

   **C.** Archive it to tape (or another backup medium) and keep it for trend tracking.

   **D.** Print out the trace summary, put it in a binder, and then delete the trace file.

**5-7**  While reading a trace performed with Profiler, you notice that it is capturing system information. How can you keep this system information out of the trace?

**A.** In Enterprise Manager, go to System Properties and clear the Show Trace Information check box on the Server Settings tab.

**B.** In Profiler, in the Trace Properties, clear the Show System Information check box on the Server Settings tab.

**C.** In the Trace Properties dialog box in Profiler, on the Filters tab, select the Object ID event and check Exclude System Objects.

**D.** Execute `sp_showsysteminfo=0`.

**5-8**  You are using IIS on the same computer as your SQL Server. You have noticed that during high activity on SQL Server, IIS slows considerably. What can you do to improve response time for IIS?

**A.** Increase the Min Server Memory option.

**B.** Increase the Max Server Memory option.

**C.** Decrease the Min Server Memory option.

**D.** Decrease the Max Server Memory option.

**5-9**   You have just loaded 100,000 new rows of data to a table in your database, which has doubled its size. Which of the following should you do to ensure that queries run well against this table?

    **A.** Run an UPDATE STATISTICS on the table.

    **B.** Run a separate UPDATE STATISTICS on the indexes.

    **C.** Drop all affected indexes.

    **D.** Reconfigure the auto-statistics settings.

**5-10**   Your query has been running for nearly 10 minutes on your server and is locking everyone else out. What can you do to stop this query and return your system to a known point of consistency?

    **A.** Set the Query Governor to 10.

    **B.** Set the Query Governor to 600.

    **C.** Run the KILL statement to kill the process and let it rollback on its own.

    **D.** Let the process complete. Run a Transaction Log backup, restore the backup to the point in time right before the offending query began.

**5-11**   You are using Profiler to monitor and audit security. You want to track security information for a particular table in a database. Which of the following events should you trace?

    **A.** Object:Opened

    **B.** Security:Table

    **C.** SQL User Name

    **D.** NT User Name

## SAMPLE TEST

**5-12** You have a table that gets updated frequently. You decide to optimize the indexes. You run a trace on the FreeSpaceScans/sec and the FreeSpacePageFetches/sec and find the values to be very high. What should you do to your indexes to alleviate this problem?

**A.** Drop and re-create your indexes using the same settings.

**B.** Increase the fillfactor setting.

**C.** Decrease the fillfactor setting.

**D.** Nothing, this is not a problem at all.

**5-13** You want to lock physical RAM for SQL Server and prevent Windows NT from swapping that RAM. You have set the Min Server Memory value equal to the Max Server Memory value. What else do you need to do?

**A.** Set the Set Working Set value to 0.

**B.** Set the Set Working Set value to 1.

**C.** Add more RAM to SQL Server.

**D.** Set Min and Max Server Memory to 0.

**5-14** You have created a trace file that monitors replication activity. Where can you replay this trace file?

**A.** On the local server only

**B.** On a local server or on another server without modification

**C.** Only on another server

**D.** Only on the local server with modification

**5-15** You are monitoring activity on two SQL Servers using Profile and want to forward that trace information to another SQL Server. You also want the Profiler to start automatically when the SQL Servers start up. Which of the following should you do to implement this solution? (Choose all that apply.)

    **A.** Add auto-start stored procedures on the source servers and have those stored procedures call the appropriate Profiler extended stored procedures.

    **B.** The extended stored procedures called in Answer A should specify a table or file on the destination server where the trace files will be stored.

    **C.** Create an NT command that will fire automatically when NT restarts. The NT command will call the SQL Profiler and specify the default trace files to use.

    **D.** Use the Performance Monitor to track the activity and log it to a file.

# UNIT

# 6

Troubleshooting

# Test Objectives: Troubleshooting

- Diagnose and resolve problems in upgrading from SQL Server 6.*x*.

- Diagnose and resolve problems in backup and restore operations.

- Diagnose and resolve replication problems.

- Diagnose and resolve job or alert failures.

- Diagnose and resolve distributed query problems.

- Diagnose and resolve client connectivity problems.

- Diagnose and resolve problems in accessing SQL Server, databases, and database objects.

Exam objectives are subject to change at any time without prior notice and at Microsoft's sole discretion. Please visit Microsoft's Training & Certification Web site (www.microsoft.com/Train_Cert) for the most current exam objectives listing.

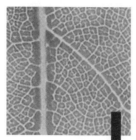

In this unit, we will cover various troubleshooting issues you may encounter on the exam. We will begin with a look at some basic trouble-shooting techniques. We will explore the issues regarding upgrading your database from a SQL Server 6.5 database to a SQL Server 7 database. Then we will look at some problems you may encounter when you perform backups and restorations in SQL Server 7. The next section will focus on potential problems regarding replication. Then we will move on to problems you may encounter when you attempt to run distributed queries. The inability of clients to connect to SQL Server is one of the most common problems encountered in SQL Server, so will look at connectivity issues. We will finish the chapter by discussing problems you may encounter when trying to access databases and database objects.

Troubleshooting is not only what you know, but how you choose to implement your knowledge in a given situation. Troubleshooting is an art form and, like any artist, you need to practice. You should take as much as possible from this book about what to do in a given situation, but there is nothing like practice. Work with the products as much as you can before you take the exams.

# Problems with Upgrading from SQL Server 6.x

When you upgrade SQL Server 6.x to version 7, you can use the SQL Server Upgrade Wizard. The upgrade checks the *syscomments* tables to look for inconsistencies, and it validates permissions on users and their SQL Server logins. The database schema, objects, and data are then transformed from the 6.x server to the 7.0 server.

When the Upgrade Wizard finds problems with the upgrade process, an error message will be displayed that says "One or more warnings have been logged. Please read the next screen carefully before you begin your upgrade." The Summary of Warnings screen is then displayed with the inconsistencies that the Upgrade Wizard found. As the administrator, you should attempt to resolve these problems. You can also find these problems stored in a log file with an "err.out" extension. The error files will be located in the following folder:

\MSSQL7\Upgrade\*<servername>_<date>_<time>*.

The error files themselves have a naming convention of:

"check65-*<dbid><dbname>*_err.out.

For example, if the SQL Server was named *Sybex* and you did the upgrade on February 27, 1999 at 12:22:23 P.M. on the MySample database, the full path and filename for this output file would be:

\MSSQL7\Upgrade\Sybex_02-27-99_12:22:23\check65-
019MySample_err.out

Here is a list of potential problems that may occur during an upgrade from SQL Server 6.5:

- Tempdb is too small. You should resize the Tempdb database to at least 10MB.

- Ensure that the database users have valid SQL Server logins in the syslogins table on the Master database.

- SQL Server stops and restarts the SQL Server during the upgrade process. To ensure that there are no problems, you should disable any stored procedures set to execute at startup.

- If you have databases with dependencies in other databases, you should upgrade all of the interdependent databases at the same time.

- SQL Server 6.5 login accounts that have a default database other than Master when upgraded to SQL Server 7 will not be upgraded if that default database does not exist in SQL Server 7.

- If you are using two computers to perform your upgrade, you cannot use the local system account because it has no network capabilities. The user account that you do use should have administrative capabilities on both computers.

- Disable replication and clear the associated transaction logs.

Although this checklist is not complete, it does cover almost every problem that you will encounter during an upgrade process.

# Problems in Backup and Restore Operations

**W**hen you back up and restore databases and transaction logs, you may encounter several different problems in several different areas.

The most common backup error is Error 3023. This means that you were attempting to do a backup during some type of database activity that is not allowed during a backup operation. You may not do any of the following during a backup:

- bcp
- CREATE INDEX
- Data file movement or resizing
- DBCC CHECKALLOC
- DBCC SHRINKDATABASE
- DBCC SHRINKFILE
- SELECT INTO

To fix this error, wait until the illegal process has completed and then reissue your BACKUP commands.

If you receive errors 3120 or 3149, you may be attempting to restore a backup with a different character set or sort order than what SQL Server is currently configured to use. SQL Server can restore only databases that have the same character set and sort order as the backup. If you encounter this error, there are several things that you can do. The best solution is to install another copy of SQL Server 7 on another computer with the proper character set and sort order and then do your recovery. Once your database has been recovered, you can use the Transfer Manager (which is part of Data Transformation Services) to move your schema, objects, and data from the temporarily restored database to your permanent database.

If you encounter error 3143, it means that you are attempting to restore a non-SQL Server backup into SQL Server. This is possible in SQL Server 7 because SQL Server 7 uses the same Microsoft Tape Format that is used for by Windows NT for backups. You should use the RESTORE HEADER– ONLY command to determine if the backup you are looking at is in fact a SQL Server backup.

Other errors that you may encounter involve attempting to back up a transaction log when you have the Truncate Log on Checkpoint database option enabled. There is no log to back up. You may also encounter errors when restoring your transaction logs. Remember that the transaction logs must be restored in order with no gaps.

# Replication Problems

**A**lthough replication is a fairly complex topic, replication troubleshooting is fairly straightforward. The architecture of the replication model that Microsoft implements in SQL Server 7 minimizes the areas of potential replication problems. You need to be concerned with three major areas and one minor area. The three major areas are security, the Log Reader Agent, and the Distribution Agent. A minor area is in the actual data definition on the tables that are to be replicated. As far as handling troubleshooting problems with the data definition issues, you must follow the rules laid out for the different data types and their replication properties.

For example, IDENTITY properties do not replicate; however, the value stored in the IDENTITY column will be replicated. Timestamps are replicated as binary 8 data types. In the following sections, we will take a closer look at security issues, the Log Reader Agent, and the Distribution Agent.

## Troubleshooting Security in Replication

For replication to work, the SQLServerAgent must have both administrator privileges on all computers involved in the replication scenario and the account must have network access. LocalSystem accounts cannot be used with replication.

Replication agents call the xp_loginfo stored procedure when they start up. The xp_loginfo stored procedure verifies that the SQLServeAgent has the appropriate permissions on the various servers.

This error can be a bit tricky to find. Because the agent never actually starts running, there is no error logged in the history associated with the agent. Instead, you must check the Jobs folder to check errors of this type. To fix this problem, ensure that your SQLServerAgent account is using an administrator account that has network capabilities.

You may encounter errors of this type if the various SQL Servers are not using a central domain account for the SQLServerAgent. If you insist on setting up different accounts for the various SQLServerAgents, you might try using standard security rather than NT security for your replication needs.

## Replication Will Not Run

Before replication can begin, an initial snapshot of the data must be copied to each Subscriber. If the snapshot is not applied, then replication cannot begin. This problem usually manifests itself in the Snapshot Agent or in the replication schedule.

You should check that the Snapshot Agent is running and that a snapshot has been applied to the Subscribers. You can view the Snapshot Agent's history through the Replication Monitor in the Enterprise Manager.

If the Snapshot Agent is not applying data to the Subscriber, then you might have problems with security between the Snapshot Agent and the publishing database.

If your Snapshot Agent is not doing anything at all, you should verify that your distribution server is online and available and that you have the appropriate permissions on the distribution working folder at the Distributor.

If the Snapshot Agent appears to be working properly, then it's time to start looking at other possibilities.

## No Subscribers Are Working

If none of your Subscribers are getting replicated data, but the Snapshot Agent appears to be working, then the problem is most likely with the Log Reader Agent. If the Log Reader Agent is not moving data from the transaction log of the publishing database to the distribution database, then the Distribution Agent cannot move those records to Subscribers. Because none of the Subscribers are getting data, it is far more likely that the Log Reader is not performing rather than the Distribution Agent.

Take a look at the Log Reader Agent in the Replication Monitor. Verify that jobs are running as scheduled and that data is moving. Verify that your distribution database is large enough to hold the replicated transactions. Verify that all servers involved in replication have enough user connections configured for the replication tasks to work.

Every publication will require a user connection from the distribution server. The distribution server in turn will require at least one user connection per subscription.

The last thing you want to verify is that the distribution database's transaction log is not full. If all of these things check out, then you might try modifying the schedule of your replication a little bit. Although many jobs can run in parallel, SQL Server will not allow the same job to run more than one version of itself at a time.

## Several Subscribers of Many Are Not Working

When several of your Subscribers of many are not working, it is almost definitely a problem with the distribution process. Because other Subscribers are receiving replicated data, you know that the Log Reader process is working properly. You should check for the following problems as part of your troubleshooting duties:

- Check the Distribution Agent histories for the failing servers.

- Ensure that the subscription server is online and has connectivity.

- Ensure that the subscription database is available, not marked for dbo-use only, and not set to read-only.

- Ensure that the SQLServerAgent security credentials are set properly for the subscription servers.

- Ensure that the Distribution Agent is not waiting to perform a manual synchronization.

With the potential problems with the agents out of the way, you need to focus your attention on one other area for troubleshooting replication. That is the recovery process. You should know what happens when various servers in the replication model are offline and what the potential problems of being offline are.

In most cases, replication will automatically recover itself and continue replicating where it left off when the server in question crashed. Keep the following in mind when dealing with replication recovery.

## Recovering the Publishing Server

When the publishing server goes down, the Subscribers won't get replicated data. This may be an inconvenience, but SQL Server is very good about recovering from this type of problem.

The Log Reader Agent uses pointers in the transaction logs of published databases. These pointers keep track of which transactions the Log Reader is currently working with. If the publishing server is down, the Log Reader Agent will continue from where it left off, once the publishing server is back online.

If you need to restore the publishing databases for some reason, then the pointers and your Subscribers will be out of synchronization. You should run a snapshot to resynchronize the Publisher and the affected Subscribers. Replication should then proceed normally.

## Recovering the Distribution Server

When your distribution server is down, replication halts. The Distribution Agent, however, keeps track of which transactions have been applied to which Subscribers. When the distribution server is brought back online, replication should continue from where it left off.

There are some potential problems with the replication if the distribution server has been down for an extended period of time. The Distribution Agent will hold transactions for a configurable amount of time (known as the retention period). The default retention period is 24 hours. After 24 hours, these transactions will age out of the distribution database and will not be applied to your Subscribers. If this happens, resynchronize your Subscribers by running a new snapshot.

If you know ahead of time that you are going to be down for an extended period of time, you can modify the time allotted for the transactions in the Distribution Agent.

Another potential issue with a downed distribution server is the synchronicity with the Publishers. As you know, the Log Reader Agent uses pointers in the transaction logs of published databases. If for some reason the transactions are not being applied to the distribution server, and the Log Reader Agent is still online, then the publishing server will not allow a transaction log backup. (This is why you should always maintain your distribution database's transaction log.) If, however, the distribution server is offline, the Log Reader Agent does not have any pointers in the Publisher's logs and those logs can be backed up and truncated. When the distribution server comes back online, you will be forced to resynchronize your Subscribers so that replication can begin again.

To avoid this problem, you should back up your distribution server (and recover your distribution server) when you make backups to your publishing servers.

This allows the distribution database to be in synch with the publishing databases.

## Recovering the Subscription Server

When your subscription servers go down, you simply need to bring the server back online. Replicated transactions on the distribution server will automatically be applied and the Subscriber will start running again normally.

If your Subscriber is down for an extended period of time, your stored transactions of the distribution server may age out. You can change the retention period or simply resynchronize the affected Subscribers.

# Job or Alert Failures

As an administrator, you can use jobs and alerts to proactively administrate your database. Alerts can fire off jobs that can take corrective actions. If the corrective actions fail, those jobs can then fire off additional alerts. This activity can lower your total cost of ownership by freeing you from routine maintenance duties to work on other parts of SQL Server.

When troubleshooting jobs, you should keep the following suggestions in mind:

- Ensure that the SQL Server Agent service is running.

- Ensure that the job is enabled.

- Ensure that the T-SQL or stored procedures in the job steps work.

- Ensure that the job owner has the appropriate permissions on all affected objects.

- Ensure that the steps fire appropriately. For example, step two fires when On Success from step one.

- If you are using e-mail or pager operators, ensure that SQL Mail is enabled and set up properly

- Check the job history to see if the jobs are firing.

- Verify that the job is scheduled properly. SQL Server allows only one instance of a particular job to run at a time.

When you are troubleshooting alerts, many of the same items from the previous list apply. In addition to these, you should verify the following:

- Ensure that the alerts are being generated in the Windows NT Application Log. If the message is not sent to the Application Log, then the Alerts Manager cannot see it.

- If you have alerts based on performance thresholds, ensure that the polling interval is set properly. SQL Server will poll the Performance Monitor every 20 seconds by default.

- If e-mail, pager, or net send notifications are not timely, check that the Delay between responses is not set too high.

# Distributed Query Problems

**W**hen working with distributed queries, you need to worry about two main problems: connectivity and security.

You should ensure that you have properly set up and configured the linked servers. Once you are connected, you may have problems running certain queries. If the query problem isn't syntactical, then it is most likely a permission problem. Ensure that you have the appropriate permissions on the various database objects on both the linked server and the local servers. Ensure that your login ID is on the SQL Server and mapped to a login ID on the target server. Keep in mind that you can have multiple SQL Server Login IDs mapped to a single remote login ID.

# Client Connectivity Problems

 $\mathbf{S}$ QL Server listens for connection requests on whatever protocols you have installed on the server. Clients can then communicate over any of those protocols with the SQL Server. Your clients will need to have the appropriate Net-Library installed as well as the appropriate DB-Library.

The default connection is over named pipes. In most cases, named pipes is the fastest method of communication with SQL Server. You can also use TCP/IP or Multi-Protocol, which are server side libraries installed by default. The Multi-Protocol library has the advantage of supporting encryption of data as it moves through the Tabular Data Stream to and from the SQL Server.

If you want to use a protocol other than named pipes at the client, then you need to use the Client Network utility. With this utility, you can set the default client Net-Library as well as the DB-Library options.

Changing the Net-Library on the client only affects that client's communications with SQL Server. It does not affect any other aspect of networking for the client.

The first step to handling network problems is to isolate where the problem is occurring. The errors could be coming from the SQL Server, the network, the front-end application, or any combination of these three items. Try the following to troubleshoot the problem.

Check your local connection to the SQL Server first. From the server machine, go to a command prompt and run the Osql utility. This will verify that you do have access to SQL Server and that named pipes is working on the local machine. The next step is to check your remote connection to SQL Server over named pipes. You can use the Makepipe and Readpipe command line utilities to check this.

Keep the following in mind when dealing with Windows 9x and connectivity. As a client, Windows 9x can use trusted connections over named pipes to work with a SQL Server installed on an NT computer. As a server, Windows 9x does not support trusted connections over named pipes.

If this completes successfully, then you know that named pipes is working. If it doesn't work, you may need to look for other problems. For example, verify network connectivity by running a NET VIEW statement from a command prompt or by double-clicking on the Entire Network icon in the Network Neighborhood. If something shows up other than your computer's name, then you know that you can see the rest of the network.

If named pipes comes up successfully, but you still cannot connect, you probably have a DB-Lib problem. You should verify that you have the same network library and DB-Libraries on both the Server and the client computer. This can be done with the Setup program or with the Client Configuration utility.

# Problems in Accessing SQL Server, Databases, and Database Objects

**W**hen you cannot access the objects in your database and permissions are not the problem, then you may need to verify the integrity of your database and its objects.

You can check the integrity of database objects by using the DBCC statements. There are several that you should know for the exam and several more that you should know to be a good administrator. This section will give you a quick overview of some of the most common DBCC statements.

**DBCC CHECKTABLE**  You can run this command to verify that index and data pages are correctly linked and that your indexes are sorted properly. It will also verify that the data stored on each page is reasonable and that the page offsets are reasonable.

**DBCC CHECKDB**  This command does the same thing as the CHECKTABLE command, but it does it for every table in a database.

**DBCC CHECKCATALOG**  This command will check for consistency in and between system tables. For example, if there is an entry in the sysobjects table, there should be a matching entry in the syscolumns table.

**DBCC CHECKALLOC** This command verifies that extents are being used properly and that there is no overlap between objects that live in their own separate extents.

**DBCC MEMUSAGE** This command provides a detailed report of how the server's memory is allocated at startup and how much memory is being used by the 20 largest in objects in both the procedure and data caches.

**DBCC TEXTALLOC / TEXTALL** This command checks the allocation of text and image columns in a table or a database. There is a FULL and a FAST option. FULL will generate a report, whereas FAST does not.

If these statements generate errors, you can try to recover data, or you can drop and rebuild the individual database objects in question.

If other problems occur, your database may be marked as suspect. Knowing what causes a suspect database will aid in your troubleshooting efforts.

If a database file is missing, or has been renamed or moved, then your database will be marked suspect. To resolve this problem, find out why the file is offline or otherwise missing and bring it back online. Stop and restart the SQL Server. The automatic recovery should unmark the suspect databases.

If a database device has been moved, renamed, or doesn't exist, you can bet that the error log will contain Error 822. If the database has been renamed, you should name it back to the original name and stop and restart the SQL Server. If the database is missing, you should start your recovery procedures.

The last thing that might cause a database to be suspect is a lack of permissions. This can happen only if you are using NTFS and the database files are on the NTFS partition. You can fix this problem by making the Administrator the owner of the database files and making sure that the MSSQL-Server service has read/write permissions on the file as well.

## STUDY QUESTIONS

## Problems with Upgrading from SQL Server 6.x

**1.** During the upgrade process, SQL Server reads the _____ table in the SQL
Server 6.5 database and looks for inconsistencies and also validates permissions for database
users and SQL _____.

**2.** An upgrade may fail if the Tempdb database is too small. By default, the Tempdb database
should be at least _____MB in size to attempt an upgrade.

**3.** SQL Server may be stopped and restarted several times during the upgrade process. To
ensure that the database starts properly, you should disable any _____
stored procedures.

**4.** When you attempt to upgrade from 6.5 to 7.0, the upgrade process fails. Upon further
inspection, you find that some of your SQL Server logins have a default database of Account-
ing. What should you do to successfully upgrade?

_____

_____

## Problems in Backup and Restore Operations

**5.** You are trying to perform a backup of your SQL Server and you receive error 3023 during
the upgrade process. After looking at the database, you notice that a CREATE INDEX statement is running while you are performing your backup operation. Could this be the culprit?
(Yes or No.) Please explain.

_____

_____

**6.**   True or False. SQL Server 7 allows you to restore a backup with a different character set or sort order.

_____

**7.**   True or False. SQL Server backups now use the Microsoft Tape Format. This means that SQL Server backups can exist on the same tapes that NT backups exist on.

_____

**8.**   You are attempting to perform a backup of a SQL Server transaction log and the backup is failing. What is the most likely cause of this problem?

_____

**9.**   You decide to restore your database and transaction logs. After restoring the database, you attempt to apply the first transaction log and the restoration fails. You need to supply the _____ keyword to the database restoration in order to apply your transaction log. When you restore the last transaction log, you should specify the _____ option to ensure that all committed transactions are rolled forward and that all uncommitted transactions are rolled back.

**10.**   True or False. You can restore transaction logs out of sequence as long as you specify the NO RECOVERY option.

_____

**11.**   You are performing a recovery of a filegroup. You have successfully restored the filegroup. What else should you do to ensure consistency?

_____

**12.** To ensure that no data is lost, you should always back up the _____ before rebuilding or restoring a database.

**13.** You are attempting to back up a database and transaction log. You are given an error message that indicates that you do not have the appropriate permissions. What fixed database role(s) must you be a member of in order to perform database backups?

_____

**14.** You are performing a recovery of your database and have restored roughly 6GB of a 10GB recovery when the recovery process halts due to an NT problem. To speed the recovery process, you decide to use the RESTART option. Is this a good solution, or should you restart the entire recovery process?

_____

## Replication Problems

**15.** True or False. Replication in SQL Server 7 has been improved to minimize replication problems.

_____

**16.** The IDENTITY column values will replicate as _____; however, the IDENTITY _____ will not.

**17.** The _____ account cannot be used for replication.

**18.** The _____ extended stored procedure verifies that the _____ account has appropriate permissions.

**19.** The SQLServerAgent account must have _____ privileges on all computers involved with replication.

**20.** Before replication can begin, a _____ of your data must be applied at each Subscriber.

**21.** You can verify that a snapshot of your data has been applied and that snapshot was applied by viewing the _____ in the Replication Monitor folder.

**22.** Your snapshot is not being applied to your Subscribers. Your Subscribers are all using their own Administrator account for the SQLServerAgent because they are all out of town and are not continually connected. What can you do to fix this problem?

_____

_____

_____

**23.** To ensure that snapshot replication works, you must verify that the other SQL Servers involved have the appropriate permissions to the _____ folder.

**24.** None of your Subscribers are receiving updates. This usually indicates a problem with the _____ agent.

**25.** You are monitoring the transactional replication tasks and a batch of transactions has just been downloaded to a Subscriber. You check the ms_replcommands folder on the distribution server and find it empty. You surmise that the cleanup task on the _____ has just cleared the applied transactions.

    **A.** Distributor
    **B.** Subscriber
    **C.** Publisher

**26.** For publishing and subscribing to work, the distribution database requires _____ user connection(s) per Subscriber or Publisher.

**27.** Every Subscriber will have at least _____ cleanup tasks on the distribution server.

**28.** You have several Subscribers that don't seem to be receiving their replicated transactions. You check the SQLServerAgent security credentials and find them properly set up. You verify that the subscription server is online and has connectivity. You have verified that the subscription database is not marked as read-only. You look at the Distribution Agent histories and find that it is empty for your Subscriber. What else could be the problem? Explain.

_____

_____

**29.** True or False. In most cases, replication will automatically recover itself from a server crash.

_____

**30.** If you suspect that your Log Reader Agent is not working, you can verify this by checking the Log Reader Agent _____ in the Replication Monitor.

**31.**   It appears that some servers are receiving replicated transactions, while others are not. This is most likely a problem with the _____ and not a problem with the Log Reader Agent.

**32.**   You are attempting to make a backup of the transaction log of a database that is used in publishing. The transaction log will not back up. What is the most likely cause?

_____

_____

**33.**   One of your Subscribers has been offline for about a week. When you bring it back online, replication will not start. What is the most likely cause?

_____

_____

**34.**   Given the scenario in the last question, you should run a new _____ to resynchronize and then restart replication.

**35.**   You want to perform a backup of your replication scenario. Which databases should you back up and in which order to guarantee 100 percent consistency with the least amount of recovery time?

_____

_____

**36.**   You want to back up your replication scenario. The recovery time is not an issue. What databases should you back up to ensure recovery of your replication scenario?

_____

_____

## Job or Alert Failures

**37.**  No jobs, alerts, or e-mail operators appear to be working. You should ensure that the
_____ is running.

**38.**  You have a particular job that you have created. When you run the job manually, everything
works correctly. When you schedule the job, nothing happens. You should ensure that the
job is _____.

**39.**  You can view the _____ to ensure that jobs are firing.

**40.**  For an alert to fire, an error must be generated in the Windows NT
_____.

**41.**  True or False. You can have the same job running in multiple schedules at the same time.

_____

**42.**  True or False. You can have the same job running in multiple schedules as long as the job is
not running more than once at a time.

_____

## Distributed Query Problems

**43.**  The two administrative issues that you need to worry about when working with distributed
queries are _____ and _____.

**44.** When you are running a distributed query on a linked server, your SQL Server login ID that has been mapped to the linked server must have the correct _____ in order to work with those remote objects.

**45.** You can currently execute remote stored procedures on two SQL Server 7 computers in your enterprise. This means that you have login capabilities on both computers. You want to run distributed queries on these two computers. To do this, you must first _____ the remote server from the Enterprise Manager and then reconfigure it as a _____ _____.

**46.** You are attempting to create a link to an Access database in order to run distributed queries. To link successfully you must specify the appropriate data source. The data source would be the _____ and _____ where the access database was contained.

**47.** You are attempting to link to an Oracle database. It appears that you have linked successfully. This was accomplished by installing the _____ software.

**48.** SQL Server must map a local login ID to the remote database in order for your SQL Server users to run distributed queries in that remote database. To accomplish this, you must specify the correct security credentials for the Remote _____ and Remote _____ parameters.

## Client Connectivity Problems

**49.** SQL Server will listen for connection requests on the various _____ that have been installed on it. For clients to talk to SQL Server, they must be running at least one of the same _____.

**50.** In addition to these protocols, your clients must have the appropriate _____ and _____ installed as well.

**51.** The _____ network library supports data encryption.

**52.** To configure protocols, Net-Libraries, or DB-Libraries on your client computers, you must use the _____.

**53.** SQL Server has been set up with TCP/IP and is using a nonstandard port. What must you do to the client in order to connect to SQL Server?

_____

_____

**54.** To verify that named pipes are working, you can run the _____ and _____ programs.

## Problems in Accessing SQL Server, Databases, and Database Objects

**55.** To verify the integrity of all of the tables in your database, you can run the DBCC _____ command.

**56.** To verify the integrity of your system tables, you can run the DBCC _____ command.

**57.** If a database file has been renamed or is otherwise missing, your database will most likely be marked _____.

**58.** True or False. If you resolve the problem of a missing file, the automatic recovery process in SQL Server should unmark the database.

_____

**59.** True or False. Your database may be inaccessible if the MSSQLServer does not have the appropriate permission on the NTFS drive.

_____

**60.** Julie owns a table and creates a view based on her table and then gives Suzanne access to that view. Suzanne then creates a view based on Julie's view and gives Lance access. Can Lance run Suzanne's view? (Yes or No.) Please explain.

_____

_____

**6-1** What commands can you use to verify that you have local access to SQL Server over a named pipe? (Select all that apply.)

    **A.** NET START MSSQLServer

    **B.** NET USE MSSQLServer

    **C.** MAKEPIPE and READPIPE

    **D.** osql /Usa /P

**6-2** Which of the following can cause a database to be marked suspect? (Select all that apply.)

    **A.** The database device is offline.

    **B.** The database device is in dbo use only.

    **C.** The database device is on an NTFS partition to which the SQL Server does not have rights.

    **D.** The database device has been renamed.

**6-3** If no Subscribers are receiving replicated transactions, what is most likely the problem?

    **A.** The log-reader process is dead.

    **B.** The distribution process is dead.

    **C.** The subscription process is dead.

    **D.** The problem is internal to SQL Server and has nothing to do with replication.

**6-4** If only one Subscriber of many isn't receiving replicated transactions, what is the most likely problem?

    **A.** The log-reader process

    **B.** The distribution process

    **C.** The subscription process

    **D.** The problem is internal to SQL Server and has nothing to do with replication.

## SAMPLE TEST

**6-5** What is the default folder for error logs for SQL Server 7?

    **A.** \MSSQL\Errors

    **B.** \MSSQL\Log

    **C.** \MSSQL7\Errors

    **D.** \MSSQL7\Log

**6-6** You have a SQL 6.5 Server with Service Pack 2 for SQL with 4GB of user databases on a Windows NT 3.51 Server with Service Pack 5. You have 2GB of free space. You want to upgrade the computer in place into a SQL 7 Server. Which of the following will happen when you attempt to upgrade?

    **A.** The upgrade will work correctly.

    **B.** The upgrade will not work because of a single problem.

    **C.** The upgrade will not work because of two problems.

    **D.** The upgrade will not work because of three problems.

**6-7** You have just created several new databases on your system and are worried about recovery. You decide to make backups of each of these databases. What other database should you back up?

    **A.** Master

    **B.** Model

    **C.** Msdb

    **D.** Tempdb

# UNIT

# 7

The Exam

These questions are not in any particular order.

# Sample Test

**7-1** On Monday, you made a full database backup. Throughout the week, you made three transaction log backups per day and everyday at 5 P.M. you made a differential backup. Your database crashes on Friday morning. Which of the following is the quickest recovery process?

    **A.** Restore the last differential database and apply the orphaned transaction log if it exists.

    **B.** Restore the full database backup and then apply all of the transaction logs (in order) and the differential backups. Apply the orphaned transaction log last if it exists.

    **C.** Restore the full database backup and then apply the transactions logs. Apply the orphaned transaction log if it exists.

    **D.** Restore the full database backup, then apply the last differential backup. Apply any transactions logs (in order) since the differential backup. Apply the orphaned transaction log, if it exists.

**7-2** You are attempting to make a backup of your transaction log for the MotorSports database. The MotorSports database is used as a publishing database with nearly 30 Subscribers. The transaction log is full and you cannot back it up. What is the most likely cause?

    **A.** All of the Subscribers are attempting to update the Publisher at the same time.

    **B.** The distribution service is not running.

    **C.** The Log Reader service is not running.

    **D.** The subscription service is not running.

**7-3**    You are attempting to upgrade your SQL Server from a 6.5 database to SQL Server 7. During the upgrade process, you notice that several stored procedures are not being upgraded. What is the most likely problem?

    **A.** There are no entries in the syscomments table for these stored procedures.

    **B.** The stored procedures refer to tables that do not exist in the current database.

    **C.** The stored procedures refer to tables in another database.

    **D.** You cannot upgrade stored procedures.

**7-4**    You have just purchased a new computer and taken it out of the box. You install Windows 98 and get ready to install SQL Server 7. You decide not to hook up a modem, and you don't have a network card in your computer. The installation of SQL Server 7 fails. What is the most probable cause of the failure?

    **A.** You must install a network card in order for SQL Server to install.

    **B.** You must install a network client like Client for MS Networks in order to install SQL Server.

    **C.** Windows 98 cannot be used with SQL Server 7.

    **D.** Your hard drive is FAT32 and SQL Server cannot run on FAT32 volumes.

**7-5**   You have added another 256MB of RAM to your Windows NT computer, giving it a total of 512MB of RAM. You decide to configure more RAM for SQL Server. After making the modifications and then stopping your SQL Server services, you find that you cannot restart SQL Server. It appears that you have incorrectly configured your SQL Server settings. How can you gain access to SQL Server to alleviate this problem?

   **A.** Use a command prompt and start the services using minimal configuration mode (the –f switch). Connect to the server and then use the sp_configure stored procedure to fix your problems.

   **B.** Use the Enterprise Manager to connect to SQL Server in minimal configuration mode, and use the –m switch to change your memory configuration options.

   **C.** You should use the command prompt to connect using the –m switch, and then run your sp_configure stored procedures.

   **D.** You should use the Enterprise Manager and start the services using the –f switch to connect. Once connected, run your sp_configure stored procedures.

**7-6**   You have just made a backup of your database and applied that backup to your standby server. You now want to run some DBCC commands on the standby server to check the validity of your database. Which of the following DBCC commands would verify and restore the structural integrity of your entire database?

   **A.** DBCC CHECKALLOC

   **B.** DBCC CHECKCATALOG

   **C.** DBCC CHECKTABLE

   **D.** DBCC CHECKDB

**7-7**  You are attempting to perform a bulk copy into a local temporary table called *#NewData*. The bcp operation is failing. What could be causing this?

  **A.** Temporary tables are available only for the connection that created them; therefore, bcp cannot see this table.

  **B.** You can only use bcp to move data into permanent tables.

  **C.** Bcp is not used to move data. You should use a SELECT INTO command.

  **D.** You do not have the appropriate permissions to run bcp.

**7-8**  You are using Microsoft Exchange on the same computer as your SQL Server. You have noticed that during high activity on SQL Server, Exchange slows considerably. What can you do to improve response time for Exchange?

  **A.** Increase the Min Server Memory option.

  **B.** Increase the Max Server Memory option.

  **C.** Decrease the Min Server Memory option.

  **D.** Decrease the Max Server Memory option.

**7-9**  Which roles (server or database) provide the ability to perform database backups? Choose three.

  **A.** sysadmin server role

  **B.** diskadmin server role

  **C.** db_owner database role

  **D.** db_backupoperator database role

**7-10**   You just loaded 300,000 new rows of data to a table in your database, thereby doubling its size. Which of the following should do to ensure that queries run well against this table?

    **A.** Run an UPDATE STATISTICS on the table.

    **B.** Run a separate UPDATE STATISTICS on the indexes.

    **C.** Drop all affected indexes.

    **D.** Reconfigure the auto-statistics settings.

**7-11**   You have a query that has been running for more than 7 minutes on your server and is locking everyone else out. What can you do to stop this query and return your system to a known point of consistency?

    **A.** Set the Query Governor to 7.

    **B.** Set the Query Governor to 420.

    **C.** Run the KILL statement to kill the process, and let it roll back on its own.

    **D.** Let the process complete. Run a transaction log backup, and restore the backup to the point in time right before the offending query began.

**7-12**   You are using Profiles to monitor and audit security. You want to track security information for a particular stored procedure in a database. Which of the following events should you trace?

    **A.** Object: Opened

    **B.** Security: Table

    **C.** SQL User Name

    **D.** NT User Name

**7-13**   You have a table that gets updated frequently. You decide to optimize the indexes. You run a trace on the FreeSpaceScans/sec and the FreeSpacePageFetches/sec and find the values to be very high. What should you do to your indexes to alleviate this problem?

**A.** Drop and re-create your indexes using the same settings.

**B.** Increase the fillfactor setting.

**C.** Decrease the fillfactor setting.

**D.** Nothing, this is not a problem at all.

**7-14**   To lock RAM for your SQL Server and prevent Windows NT from swapping that RAM, you set the "set working set" value to 1. What else do you need to do?

**A.** Set the Min Server Memory to 0.

**B.** Set the Max Server Memory to 0.

**C.** Set the Min Server Memory equal to the Max Server Memory.

**D.** Set the Min and Max Server Memory to 0.

**7-15**   You have created a trace file that monitors replication activity. Where can you replay this trace file?

**A.** On the local server only

**B.** On a local server or on another server without modification

**C.** Only on another server

**D.** Only on the local server with modification.

## SAMPLE TEST

**7-16** You are monitoring activity on two SQL Servers using SQL Profiler and now you want to forward that trace information to another SQL Server. You also want the Profiler to start automatically when the SQL Servers start up. Which of the following should you do to implement this solution?

    **A.** Add autostart stored procedures on the source servers and have those stored procedures call the appropriate profiler extended stored procedures.

    **B.** The extended stored procedures called in answer A should specify a table or file on the destination server where the trace files will be stored.

    **C.** Create an NT command that will fire automatically when NT restarts. The NT command from above will call the SQL Profiler and specify the default trace files to use.

    **D.** Use the Performance Monitor to track the activity and log it to a file.

**7-17** You have had problems in the past with hackers gaining access to your systems through unprotected TCP/IP ports. You decide to install TCP/IP on SQL Server and the SQL Server client computers. To improve your security, you decide not to use port 1433, which is the SQL Server default TCP/IP port. Now that you have enabled this non-standard port, what else must you do to enable your clients to access SQL Server?

    **A.** You must run the Client Network Utility on the clients and change the TCP/IP settings for each client to the new port.

    **B.** You don't need to do anything. SQL Server will automatically move calls to port 1433 to the newly configured port.

    **C.** You must reinstall all of the client utilities on the client computers.

    **D.** You must run the Client Network Utility on the SQL Server itself.

**7-18** You are currently working with an Oracle database and have recently installed SQL Server 7. You want to set up Oracle as a linked server in SQL Server 7. You install all of the necessary drivers and successfully register Oracle as a linked server. You now need to manage user accounts on the linked Oracle server. What fixed SQL Server 7 role allows you to do this?

    **A.** Setupadmin

    **B.** Accessadmin

    **C.** Linkedaccessadmin

    **D.** Securityadmin

**7-19** You are using snapshot replication in your replication scenario. Not all of your Subscribers are connected 100 percent of the time. Where are the snapshots stored until a Subscriber connects and then synchronizes?

    **A.** On the Distribution server in the ms_replcommands table

    **B.** On the Distribution server in the Msdb database

    **C.** On the Publishing server in the sysarticles table

    **D.** On the Distribution server in the ReplData folder

**7-20** You have a database that grows from 10MB to about 200MB throughout the course of a month. At the end of the month, most of the data is archived to a data warehouse. You now have a 200MB database that is using only about 10MB. What can you do to shrink the entire database?

    **A.** Run DBCC SHRINKFILE.

    **B.** Run DBCC SHRINKDATABASE.

    **C.** Run ALTER DATABASE, and set the size back to the original 10MB.

    **D.** Drop and re-create your database.

**7-21**   You are running merge replication on your servers. You have 12 Subscribers and one central Publisher. All of the Subscribers have the same priority level. One of your Subscribers makes a change to some data. The Publisher makes changes to the same data. At the next synchronization, which version of the data will be converged?

   **A.** The Publisher's data will be applied, then the Subscriber's data will be applied. All other Subscribers will then receive this new data.

   **B.** The Subscriber's data will be converged first, then the Publisher's changes will be applied.

   **C.** This type of merge replication is not supported in SQL Server 7.

   **D.** Each Subscriber will receive the Publisher's changes and apply them, then they will apply their own changes and then send their records back to the Publisher.

**7-22**   You have been restoring your databases to a standby server. You decide to test your disaster recovery process and take down your production server and bring the standby server online. Everything appears to be working until your users begin connecting. It appears that several of your database users do not have login IDs on the standby server. (You probably forgot to restore a backup of the Master database to the standby server.) Because these users have IDs in the database, but not login IDs, what do you need to do in order to give them access to the database and their objects?

   **A.** Run the sp_addlogin to SQL Server and add their logins.

   **B.** Map their IDs in through NT Authentication.

   **C.** Run the sp_addlogin to SQL Server and add their logins and then use the sp_change_user stored procedure to map their new login IDs to their database user IDs.

   **D.** Use the sp_changeowner stored procedure in the database and give their objects to dbo.

**7-23**  Your company creates large catalogs of information that need to be sent to Subscribers on a quarterly basis. What is the best method to accomplish this task?

**A.** Run the sp_certify_removable stored procedures to create a new database. Move the data into the new database and then place the database onto CDs and mail them out.

**B.** Create your database and then use the sp_detachdb stored procedure and send the database out on CD-ROM.

**C.** Create your database and then make a backup of the database and send the backup on CD-ROM.

**D.** Have all of your Subscribers replicate the database to their servers over the Internet.

**7-24**  You want to import a bunch of data that is currently stored on a few static Web pages. You want to dump this data into preliminary tables to test your migration. Which of the following is the most efficient method of data transfer?

**A.** Use DTS to read directly from your HTML files and have the transformation services automatically create the new tables.

**B.** Create the tables by hand, and use bcp to move the data.

**C.** Create the tables by hand, and then use DTS to move the data.

**D.** Use snapshot replication, and move the html files directly into your SQL Server.

**7-25**     You want to make a backup of your database, but only if the DBCC CHECKDB command does not report any errors. How can you set this up as a regularly scheduled job with the least amount of effort on your part?

     **A.** Create a new job, and add the CHECKDB task. Add a second step to the job that runs when the first task completes successfully.

     **B.** You can use the Database Maintenance Plan Wizard to set up these tasks automatically.

     **C.** You should set the DBCC CHECKB command up on a schedule, and have the output of the command e-mailed to you using xp_sendmail. If the job is successful, then you can enable the scheduled backup.

     **D.** You cannot run a DBCC CHECKDB command until the database has been backed up first.

**7-26**     To optimize your database and indexes, you need to find out what kinds of queries each of your users is performing against SQL Server. What is the best way to accomplish this?

     **A.** Ask them via e-mail.

     **B.** Create a trace in Profiler that gathers information on all the available events.

     **C.** Create a trace using the Trace Wizard that will sort the data by user.

     **D.** Use Query Analyzer to analyze which users are using your queries.

**7-27**     While reading a trace performed with Profiler, you notice that it is capturing system information. How can you keep this system information out of the trace?

     **A.** In Enterprise Manager, go to System Properties and clear the Show Trace Information check box on the Server Settings tab.

     **B.** In Profiler, in the Trace Properties, clear the Show System Information check box on the Server Settings tab.

**C.** In the Trace Properties dialog box in Profiler, on the Filters tab, select the Object ID event and check Exclude System Objects.

**D.** Execute `sp_showsysteminfo=0`.

**7-28**  You are currently running SQL Server 6.5 and are thinking about upgrading to SQL Server 7. On your SQL Server 7 computer, you want to use a different character set and sort order. You decide to upgrade the SQL Server 6.5 computer to 7 using the current 6.5 sort order and character sets. You then install another version of SQL Server 7 on the network with the new sort orders and character set. Which of the following methods of data transfer is the best choice to move your data from the recently upgraded SQL Server?

**A.** Re-create the objects in the destination database and then use bcp to move your data.

**B.** Re-create the objects in the destination database and then use DTS to transfer your data.

**C.** Use the Transfer Manager to move all objects and data from the source database to the destination database.

**D.** You cannot transfer data with different character sets and sort orders.

**7-29**  You are currently running SQL Server 4.2 and are thinking about upgrading to SQL Server 7. What is the best method of upgrading to SQL Server 7?

**A.** You must first upgrade 4.2 to 6.5. Then you can upgrade 6.5 to 7.

**B.** You should install SQL Server 7 on another computer and then use the Transfer Manager to transfer data and objects.

**C.** Set up SQL Server 7 on the same computer, and use bcp to move your data.

**D.** Use the Upgrade Wizard in SQL Server 7 to upgrade from 4.2 to 7.

**7-30**  Your environment includes a SQL Server 7 computer and an AS-400 running DB2. Only six people in your organization have access to the AS-400, but nearly 150 need access to the data. The AS-400 currently dumps large ASCII flat files to your computer. Because you are the SQL Server administrator, it is up to you to make the data available to those 150 users. You decide that you want to use the BULK INSERT Transact-SQL command. You also want the transfer to be as fast as possible. Which of the following will accomplish this task?

> **A.** You must drop all indexes on the affected tables to avoid transaction logging.
>
> **B.** You must drop all data in the affected tables to avoid transaction logging.
>
> **C.** You must enable the SELECT INTO/bulk copy database option to avoid transaction logging.
>
> **D.** You must enable the Truncate Log on Checkpoint database option to avoid transaction logging.

**7-31**  Security at your site is a major issue. You want SQL Server to interact with an Exchange server and you also have replication occurring. How would you configure the service accounts?

> **A.** Create a domain administrative account, and assign it to both SQL services.
>
> **B.** Create a local administrative account, and assign it to both SQL services.
>
> **C.** Create separate accounts for the SQL Server and SQL Agent services. Assign the domain admin account to SQL Server and the local admin account to the SQL Agent.
>
> **D.** Create separate accounts for the SQL Server and SQL Agent services. Assign the domain admin account to SQL Agent and the local admin account to the SQL Server.

**7-32** You have a database called *PhoneNumbers* that everyone in your company needs to be able to run queries against. You create a user called *guest* in the database, and make it a member of Db_datareader. You then assign the Windows NT group "Domain Guests" to SQL Server. Can all of your Windows NT users access the database?

**A.** Yes, it works fine as is.

**B.** It will work after you make Domain Guests members of the database.

**C.** It will work after you make the guest user a member of the public role in the database.

**D.** It will not work.

**7-33** You have a payroll database that should be modified only by the payroll application. Which of these steps should you do to ensure that users can modify data only when using the payroll application?

**A.** Create an application role for the database.

**B.** Assign the appropriate rights to the application role.

**C.** Modify the application so that it triggers the application role when the application is started.

**D.** Put the appropriate users in the application role.

**7-34** Which of the following network libraries will allow a user to make a trusted connection?

**A.** TCP/IP

**B.** Banyan Vines

**C.** Named Pipes

**D.** IPX/SPX

**7-35**    You want to create a DTS package that can access and work with sensitive data. When you store the package, you want to give some people the ability to run the package and others the ability to edit it. For security reasons, you also want the package encrypted. Which of the following steps should you take to accomplish these goals?

    **A.** Supply an owner password for the package.

    **B.** Supply an operator password for the package.

    **C.** Select the encrypt option for the package.

    **D.** Do nothing. Only the sysadmin can work with packages.

**7-36**    You have four SQL Servers. Server1 is SQL 6.5 running on Windows NT Server, Server2 is SQL 7 running on Windows 98, Server3 is SQL 7 running on Windows NT Workstation, and Server4 is running on Windows NT Server. Which servers can be designated as Target servers in a multiserver environment?

    **A.** Server1

    **B.** Server2

    **C.** Server3

    **D.** Server4

**7-37**    Server1 is designated as a target server for multiserver jobs. Where will the status of the jobs it gets from the master server be recorded?

    **A.** Only at the master server

    **B.** Only at the target server

    **C.** At both the master and target server

    **D.** Nowhere

## SAMPLE TEST

**7-38** You want SQL Server to be able to send messages upon job completion using an Exchange operator. Which of these steps is required to create e-mail operators?

A. Create an Exchange account for the SQL Agent service account.

B. Assign the SQL Agent service to use a service account.

C. Create an operator.

D. Assign the job to notify the appropriate operator.

**7-39** You have created the user-defined message "Please call the help desk." It is numbered 50001 and is configured to post to the NT Application Log. Which command will display the SQL message number 50001 and post it to the Windows NT Application Log?

A. Print 50001

B. Print (50001, 10, 1)

C. Raiserror 50001

D. Raiserror (50001, 10, 1)

**7-40** You have developed a distributed application that uses business objects deployed through Microsoft Transaction Server to enforce all business rules and call stored procedures in your database. You only want users to be able to call these stored procedures when they are making calls through your business objects. Which security approach should you use?

A. Create database roles that give your users permissions to execute the stored procedures.

B. Use an application role that has been granted permissions to execute the stored procedures. Activate this application role from the client application.

C. Create roles in Microsoft Transaction Server that contain all NT users and groups that you want to have access to the stored procedures. Set the identity of the MTS packages to a single user, and grant execute permissions on the stored procedures to this user.

D. Assign execute permissions on the stored procedures directly to the NT user and group accounts.

**7-41**  Bruce is a member of a Windows NT group called *SQLUsers*. All members of this group need to have access to the Inventory database located on a SQL Server. The membership of this group changes regularly, and you want to be able to log the identity of every user that modifies data in the database. What is the most efficient way to accomplish this?

   **A.** Grant SQL Server access to the SQLUsers group, and assign permissions in the database directly to that group.

   **B.** Create a SQL Server account for each member of the group, and assign permissions to each user individually.

   **C.** Grant SQL Server access to each NT User account, and assign permissions individually.

   **D.** Create a SQL Server account for each member of the group. Create a database role and assign the necessary permissions to that role. Make each SQL Server account a member of that role.

**7-42**  You have a database that you expect to grow to over 500GB in size. This database is part of a data warehousing solution and, as such, is somewhat denormalized and heavily indexed. You want the database to perform as efficiently as possible, and you also want to be able to back up the database one table at a time on a rotating basis. Which of the following options would be the best way to structure the database files to accomplish these goals?

   **A.** Configure your hard disks into a volume set. Place your database on two files, one for the data segments and one for the transaction log.

   **B.** Create one file for each table and its indexes. Place each file on a separate physical disk. Create another file for the transaction log.

   **C.** Configure your disks into a RAID 5 array and create one file for the database and another for the transaction log.

   **D.** Create a filegroup for each table and its indexes. Within each filegroup, create a file to hold the data and another to hold the indexes. Place each file on separate physical disks. Create an additional file for the transaction log.

**7-43**  You are having trouble performing a typical installation on a computer with the following configuration:

AMD K6 166 processor
120MB hard drive space free
32MB RAM

Which of the following is probably causing the installation problem?

**A.** The processor must be faster than 166MHz.

**B.** AMD processors do not support SQL Server installations.

**C.** The computer has insufficient memory.

**D.** The computer has insufficient hard disk space free.

**7-44**  You have a SQL Server that is heavily accessed for a mission-critical application. It is imperative that downtime due to system failure be minimized or eliminated. You have implemented a RAID 5 solution to protect against hard disk failure. You would also like to be able to perform some load balancing to add performance to your application. Which of the following options would provide the best support for this scenario?

**A.** Standby Server

**B.** Disk Mirroring

**C.** NT Clustering

**D.** Periodic snapshot replication to another server.

## SAMPLE TEST

**7-45**   You need to migrate data from a FoxPro 2.5 database file into a SQL Server database. You have not yet created the table in SQL Server that will hold this data. Which of the following approaches will provide the easiest migration path?

    **A.** Use bcp to move the data directly from the FoxPro table.

    **B.** Migrate the FoxPro data to an Access database, and use an OLE DB link to connect to the Access database.

    **C.** Use the Data Transformation Services to migrate the data from the FoxPro table.

    **D.** Use snapshot replication to move the data from the FoxPro table.

**7-46**   Which of the following steps is not necessary before you can upgrade a SQL Server 6.5 installation to SQL Server 7?

    **A.** Ensure that the Tempdb database is at lease 10MB in size.

    **B.** Ensure that both the SQL Server 6.5 and 7 services are running.

    **C.** Install SQL Server 6.5 Service Pack 3 or higher.

    **D.** Disable and start up stored procedures.

**7-47**   You are installing Macintosh clients on your network, and you want these clients to be able to interact with your SQL Servers. Which of the following network libraries can be used on the server to communicate with Macintosh clients? Choose two.

    **A.** AppleTalk

    **B.** Named Pipes

    **C.** TCP/IP Sockets

    **D.** NWLink

**7-48**   Which of the following services must be running on a subscription server to perform a pull-based transactional replication. Choose two.

   **A.** MSDTC

   **B.** MSSQLServer

   **C.** SQLServerAgent

   **D.** MicrosoftSearch

**7-49**   You have two computers upon which you want to install identical SQL Server installations. You want to minimize the possibility that errors can occur, and you want to keep network activity to a minimum. Which of the following would be the best approach to accomplish this?

   **A.** Use an unattended setup (*.iss) file.

   **B.** Do a remote installation to both machines.

   **C.** Provide written installation instructions to the administrator performing the installation about the desired installation options.

   **D.** Use snapshot replication to mirror one installation on another machine.

**7-50**   Which of the following character sets would be the most appropriate for exchanging data between servers installed in a wide variety of locales?

   **A.** Multilingual (code page 850)

   **B.** U.S. English (code page 437)

   **C.** ISO Latin-1 (code Page 1252)

   **D.** Unicode

**7-51**  Which of the following sort orders will provide the fastest performance for sorting and character comparisons?

    **A.** Dictionary order, Case-sensitive

    **B.** Dictionary order, Case-insensitive

    **C.** Binary order

    **D.** Dictionary order, Case-insensitive, Uppercase preference

**7-52**  Which of the following conditions would result in a null return when a divide-by-zero error occurs?

    **A.** ANSI Warnings ON

    **B.** ANSI Padding ON

    **C.** ANSI Warnings OFF

    **D.** ANSI Padding OFF

**7-53**  You have created a Full-Text index on the Vendors table of your inventory database. The media that stores the Inventory database is lost, and you restore from a backup. Which additional step should you take to recover the Full-Text index?

    **A.** Repopulate the index.

    **B.** Rebuild the index.

    **C.** Reconfigure Full-Text searching for the Vendors table.

    **D.** Do nothing. The Full-Text index is recovered with the database.

**SAMPLE TEST**

**7-54**  You have a table with 100,000 rows. Each row uses about 4,500 bytes per row. How much disk space is needed to store this table?

A. 5GB

B. 100MB

C. 500MB

D. 800MB

**7-55**  Mike is the owner of a database called *Orders*. The Orders database has very limited transaction log space, so he wants to be notified via e-mail when the transaction log is about 90 percent full. Which of the following options will allow Mike to accomplish this with the least configuration possible?

A. Create an alert in Performance Monitor. Have this alert call the xp_sendmail stored procedure when the desired threshold has been reached.

B. Write a program in Visual Basic that uses a timer to check the size of the log file every minute. Have this application e-mail Mike when the file reaches a certain size.

C. Use the Performance Monitor alert type supported by the SQLServerAgent services, and have this alert e-mail Mike when the desired threshold is reached.

D. Move the transaction log for this database to another server so that there will not be a capacity problem for the transaction log.

**7-56** You have 10,000 rows in your Orders table. You plan to add another 20,000 rows within the next few weeks. This data will be distributed evenly throughout the table. You want to rebuild your indexes today using a configuration that will provide the most efficient support for the new data and prevent performance problems over the next few weeks. Which fill factor should you use for your indexes to provide this support?

    **A.** 0

    **B.** 30

    **C.** 80

    **D.** 100

**7-57** You have set up a linked server environment from your Microsoft SQL Server to an Access database. This allows you to use the SQL Server data services to access information in the Microsoft Access database. Which technology is being implemented to make this possible?

    **A.** ODBC

    **B.** OLE–DB

    **C.** Remote Data Objects (RDO)

    **D.** Data Access Objects (DAO)

**7-58** You have created two filegroups in your database, each on a separate physical disk. One filegroup contains all of your tables, and the other contains all of your indexes. You are attempting to back up each filegroup separately, but the backup is failing. What is most likely the cause of the failure?

    **A.** You cannot back up filegroups. You must back up the files individually.

    **B.** The filegroups must be on the same physical media to be backed up as a single unit.

    **C.** Tables must always be backed up in the same unit as their corresponding indexes.

    **D.** You must first perform a differential backup before you can perform a filegroup backup.

**7-59**   Which of the following services is not installed when a typical installation is performed?

   **A.** MSSQLServer

   **B.** SQLServerAgent

   **C.** MSDTC

   **D.** MicrosoftSearch

**7-60**   Which of the following commands should you use to find and repair object allocation problems in a SQL Server database?

   **A.** DBCC NewAlloc

   **B.** DBCC CheckAlloc

   **C.** DBCC CheckDB

   **D.** DBCC DBRepair

**7-61**   Which SQL Server command line switch will start the service in single-user mode?

   **A.** −f

   **B.** −m

   **C.** −s

   **D.** −u

**7-62**   When are SQL Server index statistics updated?

   **A.** Dynamically in the background

   **B.** When you issue an UPDATE STATISTICS statement

   **C.** When you drop and re-create an index

   **D.** All of the above

**7-63**   You decide to bring your standby server online for read-only access. You apply the last transaction log to the standby server using the WITH RECOVERY option, allowing your users access to the server. When you attempt to apply subsequent transaction log backups, the process fails. What is causing the problem?

  **A.** You must apply each transaction log "with recovery."

  **B.** You should have applied the previous transaction log backup using the Standby option, indicating an undo file.

  **C.** You should have specified "NoRecovery" for the previous log.

  **D.** You cannot use a standby server for read-only activity.

**7-64**   You want to recover a database to a specific point in time, which is halfway through the time period covered by your last transaction log. Which of the following restore options should you use to accomplish this? Choose two.

  **A.** stopat

  **B.** NoRecovery

  **C.** Recovery

  **D.** Standby

**7-65**   You execute a query that will update information and inadvertently forget to include a restriction clause. The query is only 50 percent complete and has been running for a long time. What is the fastest way to return the database to a point of data integrity?

  **A.** Kill the process and allow the transaction to roll back.

  **B.** Stop and restart the SQL Server.

  **C.** Let the query complete and roll the query back.

  **D.** Let the query complete and apply backups to restore data integrity.

**7-66** You want to optimize your database index structure using the Index Tuning Wizard. Which of the following can be used as an input file for the Tuning Wizard to evaluate? Choose two.

**A.** SQL Script File

**B.** Profiler Trace File

**C.** Perfmon Counter

**D.** SQL Agent job

**7-67** What is the smallest unit of replication to which a server can subscribe?

**A.** Table

**B.** Column

**C.** Publication

**D.** Article

**7-68** You are attempting to make a connection to your SQL Server from a Linux workstation. Which of the following authentication processes should you use?

**A.** Authenticate using an NT User account.

**B.** Authenticate using an NT group account.

**C.** Authenticate using a Linux user account.

**D.** Authenticate using a Standard SQL Server account.

**7-69** Which of the following files is needed to perform an unattended installation of SQL Server?

**A.** SQL script file (.sql)

**B.** Install script file (.iss)

**C.** Batch File (.bat)

**D.** Command file (.cmd)

# APPENDIX

Study Question and
Sample Test Answers

# Unit 1

## Study Questions

### Develop a Security Strategy

1. Windows NT Only; SQL Server and Windows NT

2. Mixed authentication provides support for clients that cannot use Windows NT authentication.

3. Windows NT authentication

4. Windows NT groups; SQL Server roles

5. SQL Server roles

6. fixed server; fixed database; user-defined database

7. fixed database

8. user-defined database

9. MSSQLServer; SQLAgent

10. MSDTC (Microsoft Distributed Transaction Coordinator)

11. local system; user

12. user; administrators

13. guest

14. Microsoft Transaction Server

15. True

16. False

17. fixed server

18. True

19. True

20. False

21. SQL Server and Windows NT authentication (mixed)

22. Jon

## Develop a SQL Server Capacity Plan

23. primary data; transaction log

24. disk striping with parity

25. False

26. Use disk striping with parity for the data files of the database and disk mirroring for the transaction log files.

27. primary

28. disk striping with parity

29. Intel Pentium 166MHz or Alpha

30. memory

31. ALTER DATABASE

32. None

    **Explanation:** The expansion is automatic as long as the database has not grown to its maximum size.

33. CPU

## Develop a Data Availability Solution

34. database; transaction log; differential, file/filegroup

35. False

36. full database backups only

37. full database and transaction log backups

38. True

39. False

40. very large databases (VLDB)

41. orphaned transaction log

42. filegroups; filegroup

43. full database

44. standby server

45. load balancing; fault tolerance

46. load balancing; fault tolerance

47. False

**48.** True

**49.** standby server

**50.** cluster

**51.** Enterprise; Enterprise

## Develop a Migration Plan

**52.** True

**53.** SQL Server 6.5 Service Pack 3 or higher; 10

**54.** named pipes; tape

**55.** export server

**56.** import server

**57.** Data Transformation Services (DTS)

**58.** False

**59.** True

**60.** replication

**61.** False

## Develop a Replication Strategy

**62.** remote distributor

**63.** single Publisher with a local Distributor

64. multiple Publisher, single Subscriber

65. multiple Publisher, multiple Subscriber

66. snapshot replication

67. per-seat

68. Install a SQL Server to act as a dedicated Distributor. Configure each Publisher to use the dedicated server as its distribution server.

69. merge replication

70. transactional replication

71. merge replication

72. transactional replication

73. multiple Publisher, single Subscriber (central Subscriber)

74. No

    **Explanation:** Replication is a low consistency model, and there is no guarantee that the two servers will look alike at any given time.

75. distributed transactions

76. Microsoft Distributed Transaction Coordinator (MSDTC)

## Sample Test

1-1    C

       **Explanation:** The MSDTC service is required when issuing distributed transactions or using immediate updating subscribers in a replication environment.

1-2    C

       **Explanation:** SQL Server requires a Pentium 166 or higher with at least 32MB RAM and 180MB hard drive space for a complete installation.

**1-3**  D

**Explanation:** Only domain administrator accounts will have the necessary rights and permissions to communicate with services on other computers.

**1-4**  A

**Explanation:** The central server is a reporting server, so there is no need for merge replication. Also, because the data is being gathered from all over the company, shapshot replication might be a very high overhead solution.

**1-5**  D

**Explanation:** Allowing your five Publishers to replicate to a remote Distributor sends all of the activity through a single distribution source. This is the most network-efficient approach.

**1-6**  B

**1-7**  A

**Explanation:** When using Windows NT security, the NT user name is also the SQL Server user name for the purposes of logging and ownership.

**1-8**  C

**Explanation:** Backing up each filegroup separately allows you to back up the whole database on a rotating basis.

**1-9**  B, D

**1-10**  D

**Explanation:** Clustering provides no protection against media failure. Volume sets provide no protection and also provide no performance advantages.

**1-11**  A

**Explanation:** Because the concern is OLAP, usually a processor-intensive activity, clustering servers together can provide the needed load balancing.

**1-12**  D

**1-13**   C

Explanation:  Because it is a small table with occasional updates, snapshot replication is appropriate.

**1-14**   D

Explanation:  Macintosh clients cannot operate in a trusted security environment.

**1-15**   B

Explanation:  Clustering uses a single set of hard drives for all clustered servers, and as such provides no protection against media failure.

---

# Unit 2

## Study Questions

### Install SQL Server 7

1. character set; sort order

2. The character set maps a numerical value from 0 to 255 stored in the database to a character representation used in the application.

3. CP 1252

4. True

5. CP 850 (multilingual)

6. CP 1252

7. binary

8. Case-sensitive. The SQL Server doesn't have to consider that uppercase and lowercase versions of the same character sort and compare the same way. To a case-insensitive sort order, there is no difference between an uppercase "A" and a lowercase "a." Therefore, additional processing is required to identify both ASCII 65 and 97 as the letter "a" and sort them the same way. Case-sensitive sort orders do not need to take this extra step, resulting in a different sort for uppercase and lowercase. To take this one step further, binary is the fastest possible sort order.

9. the performance of sorts and comparisons; the requirements of the client application

10. 2

11. when you have to store characters from many different languages that are not available in a single ANSI character set

12. general, case-sensitive

13. general, case-insensitive

14. Network libraries provide a layer of software that sits between the data services and the network, organizing data into the network packets. This abstracts the developer from the network and provides communication between client and server.

15. named pipes, multiprotocol, and TCP/IP sockets.

16. TCP/IP sockets, AppleTalk

17. NWLink; NWLink

18. multiprotocol

19. local system; domain user

20. No

    **Explanation:** Because the services are confined to the local server, you can use both local system and domain user accounts.

21. domain user

22. Microsoft Distributed Transaction Coordinator (MSDTC)

23. SQLAgent

24. Microsoft Search (Full-Text Search)

25. Desktop

26. batch, response

27. Sql70ins.iss

28. False

29. 10MB

30. named pipe

31. export; import

## Configure SQL Server

32. MAPI

33. You must first log into the NT Server using the account created for the SQL Services.

34. False

35. ANSI warning

36. True

37. If the switch is engaged and you create a table without explicitly defining whether its columns will allow nulls, nulls will be allowed.

**38.** The application is more likely to be compliant with applications that require ANSI compatibility. They are also more likely to be portable to other server platforms that support ANSI standards.

**39.** the Connection tab of the Server Properties dialog

**40.** Change the server registration properties in the Enterprise Manager to show system objects and databases.

## Implement Full-Text Searching

**41.** Standard indexes are stored in the database while full-text indexes are stored in a catalog in the file system. Standard indexes are dynamically maintained while full-text indexes are static. Standard indexes can use only high sort elements for searching, while full-text indexes list all non-noise words for searching.

**42.** `sp_fulltext_column`

**43.** Run the SQL Server setup program and perform a custom installation. Select the Full-Text Search from the list of server components.

**44.** False

**45.** uniquely constrained column

## Sample Test

**2-1**    C

Explanation: Only the Enterprise Edition of SQL Server can take advantage of these Windows NT Enterprise benefits such as clustering and 4GB tuning.

**2-2**    D

Explanation: Unicode contains characters for all of the world's most common languages. If you use Unicode data types for all character data in your tables, you don't need to worry about the differences.

**2-3** B

**Explanation:** If only a moderate amount of data has been modified, there is no need to do a rebuild or a full repopulation.

**2-4** C

**2-5** B

**2-6** A

**2-7** B

**Explanation:** The preferred path is to upgrade to 6.5, and then to 7. You cannot upgrade directly from 4.2 to 7.

**2-8** C

**2-9** D

**2-10** C

**Explanation:** Because binary order is machine native, SQL Server does not need to perform any additional processing to perform the sort.

**2-11** A

**2-12** D

---

# Unit 3

## Study Questions

### Secure Server Access

1. mixed, Windows NT–only

2. sp_addlogin

3. True

4. False

5. sp_grantlogin

6. sp_denylogin

7. False

8. sa

9. Builtin\Administrators

10. False

## Configure Database Access

11. False

12. sa

13. sp_grantdbaccess

14. sp_changedbowner

15. sp_change_users_login

## Manage Roles

16. fixed server, fixed database, custom database, application

17. sysadmin, serveradmin, securityadmin, setupadmin, processadmin, diskadmin, dbcreator

18. sp_addsrvrolemember

19. diskadmin

20. sysadmin, processadmin

21. sysadmin, serveradmin

22. public

23. public, db_owner

24. db_accessadmin, db_securityadmin

25. db_denydatareader, db_denydatawriter

26. False

27. True

28. sp_droprolemember

29. sp_addrole

30. role name, owner name

31. application

32. only for the duration of the connection

33. True

34. Server roles cannot be dropped.

35. sysadmin server role, db_owner database role, db_backupoperator database role

## Manage Permissions

**36.** Stored Procedure

**37.** Table, View

**38.** statement, object

**39.** GRANT, REVOKE, DENY

**40.** DENY

**41.** REVOKE

**42.** WITH GRANT OPTION

**43.** True

**44.** sysadmin

**45.** Public

**46.** No

**47.** False

**Explanation:** The DENY keyword will always prevent a user from accessing an object unless that user is associated with an administrative role.

**48.** GRANT, DENY

**49.** True

**50.** standard SQL Server

## Auditing Activity with SQL Profiler

**51.** file, SQL Server table

**52.** file

**53.** True

**54.** Index Tuning Wizard

**55.** An Exclude allows you to configure a trace filter to include general events but exclude activity coming from specific sources.

# Sample Test

**3-1**   C

**3-2**   B

Explanation: The DENY associated with the *localusers* group is preventing you from accessing the server. Remove your membership to the group, and you should be able to access the server.

**3-3**   C

Explanation: Although admittedly not the best solution, granting sysadmin role membership is the only one of the stated solutions that will allow the account to read from the table because of the DENY on SELECT permissions.

**3-4**   D

Explanation: Use REVOKE to remove security qualifications assigned through either a GRANT or DENY.

**3-5**   B

**3-6**   B

**3-7**   A

Explanation: As long as you have CREATE VIEW permissions, you can create any view you want; however, unless you have SELECT permissions on the underlying objects, you may not be able to select from your own views.

**3-8**   B

**3-9**   D

**3-10**   B

Explanation:  Because Sue's NT account would be visible from within SQL Server, you need only assign Sue's NT account to the db_owner role.

**3-11**   C

Explanation:  The rights assigned to application roles replace the user rights for the duration of that database connection.

**3-12**   B

---

# Unit 4

## Study Questions

### Create and Manage Databases

1.  NDF, LDF

2.  Model

3.  Yes

4.  CREATE DATABASE. Either db_creator or sysadmin is correct for the second blank.

5.  MAXSIZE

6.  SHRINKDATABASE, SHRINKFILE

7.  30MB

## Loading Data Using Various Methods

8. True

9. INSERT

10. True

11. SELECT INTO

12. #, ##

13. False

 **Explanation:** only the connection that created the temporary table can access it.

14. Select Into/bulk copy

15. False

16. CREATE TABLE

17. True

18. False

19. False

20. INSERT

21. SELECT

22. False

23. SELECT INTO/bulk copy, indexes

24. defaults, datatypes, rules, triggers, constraints

**25.** True

**26.** BULK INSERT

**27.** True

**28.** Data Transformation Services

**29.** VBScript, Jscript, C++, PerlScript, Delphi, and many more.

**30.** package

**31.** `dtswiz, dtsrun`

**32.** True

**33.** True

**34.** True

**35.** step

**36.** step objects

**37.** False

**Explanation:** Tasks can be associated with multiple step objects, but the same task cannot be executing more than once at a time.

**38.** Run step when a prior step completes successfully, when a prior step fails to complete, or run regardless of success or failure.

**39.** data file, data source

**40.** data source

**41.** data file

**42.** data pump

**43.** Truncate Log on Checkpoint, TRUE

**44.** True

**45.** owner, operator

**46.** COM, Microsoft Repository

**47.** Transfer Manager

**48.** True.

**Explanation:** This is one of the most important features of the Transfer Manager.

**49.** SELECT, dbo or member of the db_owners role.

**50.** True

**Explanation:** Even though collation sequences may be different, you can use any of these tools to move your Unicode data around.

## SQL Backups and SQL Recovery

**51.** transaction log, differential, filegroup, individual file.

**52.** backup device, sp_addumpdevice

**53.** Full, Differential, Filegroup and File. You cannot perform a transaction log backup as there is no transaction log to make a backup of.

**54.** False

**Explanation:** SQL Server 7 can restore only 7.0 backups.

**55.** False

**Explanation:** The character set and sort order must match for a restoration to be successful.

**56.** True

   **Explanation:** Unicode data can be recovered no matter what its designation or collation sequence. Keep in mind that the regular character set and sort orders must match.

**57.** Transaction Log

**58.** Yes

   **Explanation:** this is an excellent solution. You may have non-logged transactions in your transaction log, so making a full database backup is probably the best choice in this situation.

**59.** TRUNCATE_ONLY

**60.** NO_LOG

**61.** full database backup.

**62.** RECOVERY, NO RECOVERY

**63.** RECOVERY, NO RECOVERY

**64.** No, No

**65.** Yes, No

   **Explanation:** The transactions that were successfully completed will be rolled forward by the recovery command. Those that were in process will be rolled back.

**66.** Transaction Log backups

## Manage Replication

**67.** MSSQL7\ReplData, snapshot

**68.** True

69. Publisher

    **Explanation:** If all defaults are used and data is changed at both the Subscriber and the Publisher, the changes at the Publisher will overwrite the changes from the Subscriber.

70. snapshot

71. True

72. True

73. In SQL Server 7, you cannot subscribe to an individual article in a publication as you could in SQL 6.*x*. To enable this type of feature, you should create a publication with a single article in it.

74. Distribution cleanup jobs, of which there should be one for every subscription

## Automate Administrative Tasks

75. Msdb, SQLAgentMail

76. CMDExec jobs, replication jobs, active script jobs.

77. True

    **Explanation:** These are known as multiserver jobs.

78. True

79. Windows NT Application Log

80. True

81. True

82. error number, severity level

83. True

**84.** fail-safe

**85.** linked

**86.** You should drop the server from the Enterprise Manager and then reconfigure it as a linked server. In addition to this, you must ensure that you have login rights on the other server.

**87.** data source, SQL Server

**88.** SQL*NET

## Enable Access to Remote Data

**89.** Login ID, Password

**90.** useself

# Sample Test

**4-1**    A, B

Explanation: The account needs the Log On as a Service right, as well as membership in the Administrators group.

**4-2**    D

Explanation: MAPI (Messaging Application Programming Interface) is the set of functions that allows SQL Server to interact with Exchange and other e-mail systems.

**4-3**    C

Explanation: The Msdb database holds alert, job, and operator information.

**4-4**    B

Explanation: Rebuilding the Master database automatically rebuilds the Msdb database, which means that all of your previous alerts, jobs, and operators have to be restored from a backup.

**4-5** A

**Explanation:** The alert engine checks the NT Application log for errors.

**4-6** A, B, C, D

**Explanation:** T-SQL, command prompt, replication, and active script jobs can be built.

**4-7** A

**Explanation:** You can disable alerts, which is the best way to turn them off temporarily.

**4-8** D

**Explanation:** A fail-safe operator can be set up that gets notified if all other operators are off duty.

**4-9** A, B, C, D

**Explanation:** To have a job notify an operator via e-mail, you must create an Exchange account for the SQL service account, make sure the SQL Agent is using the NT service account, create an operator, and assign the job to notify the operator.

**4-10** B, C, D

**Explanation:** Integrated Security (analogous to NT Authentication in SQL Server 7) will not be supported until Windows 2000 when security account delegation is implemented.

**4-11** C

**Explanation:** If you are using the data source parameter, then the name you chose for the server name parameter is not the actual remote server name and Microsoft SQL Server is performing much of the communication setup during the first run of the query, thereby timing out over the slow link. If you use the actual name for the server name parameter, most of the communication setup is done when you configure the link.

**4-12** D

**Explanation:** If your users are connecting via nontrusted connections, then they are being authenticated by Microsoft SQL Server and their NT credentials are ignored. Answer A is invalid because you cannot create server roles. Answer B is invalid because you can only map SQL login IDs.

**4-13**   D

> **Explanation:** Answer A is invalid because you cannot create server roles. Answer B is invalid because you can only map SQL login ids. Answer C is invalid because workgroups do not have the global group "Domain Users".

**4-14**   C

> **Explanation:** Domain Users is an NT global group that all domains have defined by default and all users logging into the domain are members of this global group. Answer A is invalid because you cannot create server roles. Choice B is invalid because you can only map SQL login IDs.

**4-15**   C

> **Explanation:** Authorized Subscribers can subscribe only to an entire publication. You may not subscribe to a Publisher.

**4-16**   D

> **Explanation:** Because the price list at each salesperson's database is not being changed by the salesperson, transactional replication would be the best. Because a salesperson might look at another salesperson's quote and modify it by adding or removing specific items, merge replication is probably the best choice here.

**4-17**   C

> **Explanation:** To minimize the cost of a slow and expensive telephone line, you can use a publishing Subscriber model. Essentially, the Sacramento office would publish to one of the German offices, say Köln. Köln would then take the subscribed data and republish it to its more local offices in München and Hamburg.

**4-18**   B

> **Explanation:** The central Subscriber model is fantastic for rollup reporting, local customer order processing, or local inventory management. In order to maintain transactional consistency, you really should use a RegionCode or LocationID as part of the primary key in the replicated tables.

**4-19**   A

**Explanation:** The replication monitor is only on the distribution server. You then want to look at the snapshot history. The distribution agent history is used for moving transactions, not snapshots.

**4-20**   D

**Explanation:** Typically there is at least one cleanup job for each Subscriber and each subscription. Cleanup jobs don't run on the Publisher.

**4-21**   D

**Explanation:** When Publishers and Subscribers make changes to a record which are then merged at the Publisher, the Subscribers' changes will be applied first and then the Publishers' changes. When multiple Subscribers have made changes to the same record, the converge process looks at the priorities assigned to each Subscriber. The highest priority modification will take precedence. Remember that by default, the Publisher has the highest priority.

**4-22**   A, C

**Explanation:** A and C describe exactly how transactions are handled by the Distributor.

**4-23**   A, D

**Explanation:** You must have the Select Into/Bulk Copy database option enabled. SELECT INTO statements are, by nature, non-logged transactions and as such, you should back up your database after running them. You must have CREATE TABLE permissions in the database. This can be accomplished if you have the permission, are a member of the sysadmin server role, or are a member of the db_owner or the db_ddladmin database role.

**4-24**   A, B

**Explanation:** Both the Bulk Copy utility and the BULK INSERT statement can be used to move the data into SQL Server 7. SELECT INTO and INSERT by themselves cannot gather the data from a flat file.

**4-25**  A, C

**Explanation:**  To perform a fast bulk copy, you must drop indexes on affected tables and set the Select Into/Bulk Copy database option. By doing this, INSERTs are not logged.

**4-26**  B, C

**Explanation:**  When you perform a bulk copy operation, default and datatypes are always enforced, but rules, triggers, and constraints are always ignored. You should run some SQL statements to verify the integrity of your data.

**4-27**  A, B, C

**Explanation:**  There is no such thing as SELECT INTO permissions. You must have INSERT permissions on the affected tables when copying data in to SQL Server, and you must have SELECT permissions to copy data out of SQL Server.

**4-28**  B, D

**Explanation:**  The BULK INSERT statement is a T-SQL version of the bcp command. It has advantages over bcp in that it can read an entire file as if it were an OLE-DB recordset. Bcp reads only one record at a time.

**4-29**  A

**Explanation:**  DTS can move only data from one OLE-DB– or ODBC-compliant data source to another OLE-DB– or ODBC-compliant data destination.

**4-30**  D

**Explanation:**  The Transfer Manager is capable of moving data, schema, and database objects (like views and stored procedures) from one SQL Server 7 computer to another SQL Server 7 computer.

**4-31**  A, B, C, D, and E

**Explanation:**  All answers are correct. The task object can also gather results from another running DTS package and send e-mail using the SQLMail interface.

**4-32** A, B, C and D

**Explanation:** All answers are correct. These are the four precedence constraints. On Success will run a particular step when the previous step completes successfully. On Failure will run when the previous step failed. The Unconditional constraint will run a step when the previous step completes regardless of that prior step's success or failure. The Return Codes constraint allows a step to make return codes available to other steps.

**4-33** A, B

**Explanation:** When you set the owner password, anyone who knows the owner password can work with the internals of the package. The operator password allows users who know the password to execute the package. Any password supplied for a package automatically encrypts the package contents.

**4-34** C

**Explanation:** This is an excellent solution. The Transfer Manager can move data from one SQL Server 7 computer to another SQL Server 7 computer regardless of character set, sort order, or platform.

---

# Unit 5

## Study Questions

### Monitor SQL Server Performance

1. Chart, Report, Alert, Log

2. Chart

3. Alert

4. Buffer Cache Hit Ratio. This value should be as high as possible.

5. SQLALRTR

6. trace

7. filters

8. Trace Wizard

9. Trace Wizard, Find the Worst Performing Queries

10. Trace Transact-SQL Activity by User.

11. replay

12. True

13. Application Name, Binary Data, Connect, Connection ID or SPID, Database ID, Disconnect, Event Sub Class, ExistingConnection, Host Name, Integer Data, RPC:Starting, Server Name, SQL:BatchStarting, SQL User Name, Start Time, Text.

14. True

15. False
    **Explanation:** They must be the same.

16. True

17. No
    **Explanation:** Users connected to SQL Server using NT Authentication cannot be replayed on another computer. They can be replayed on the source computer however.

18. False

19. extended

20. Yes

21. table, file

22. True

23. Index Tuning Wizard

24. trace, peak

25. statistics

26. UPDATE STATISTICS

27. index, table

28. If you run it on the table, all indexes in the table will be updated. This will be less work for you than running the UPDATE STATISTICS on each individual index.

29. FreeSpacePageFetches/sec, FreeSpaceScans/sec

30. Decrease

    **Explanation:** The inserted row is looking for space in the index to insert itself. By lowering the fillfactor setting, you are increasing the amount of free space. Therefore, SQL Server does not have to go looking for additional free space.

31. ad hoc

32. ad hoc, Tempdb

33. ad hoc, SP: Cache Hit, SP: Cache Insert

34. SP: Cache Hit, SP: Cache Insert

35. Object

36. Opened

**37.** SQL User Name, NT User Name

**38.** Buffer Cache Hit Ratio. This value should be as high as possible.

## Tune and Optimize SQL Server

**39.** RAID

**40.** thread

**41.** True

**42.** True

**43.** Level 2 Cache

**44.** 1MB

**45.** Min Server Memory, Max Server Memory

**46.** False

   **Explanation:** Windows NT may still swap that RAM in and out of a paging file.

**47.** Set Working Set, 1 or True, Min Server Memory, Max Server Memory

**48.** False

   **Explanation:** Setting the set working set to 0 tells SQL Server to dynamically allocate RAM between the values of Min Server Memory and Max Server Memory.

## Limit Resources Used by Queries

**49.** Query Analyzer

**50.** True

**51.** C

52. True

53. True

    **Explanation:** Use the (INDEX = n) statement in your query.

54. False

    **Explanation:** You can run extended stored procedures in the Query Analyzer. These generally begin with an 'xp_' prefix.

55. SQL Profiler

56. Query Governor

57. zero

58. 3 seconds

59. statistics

# Sample Test

5-1  B

    **Explanation:** If your system does not have enough Level 2 cache, adding more RAM can actually slow it down. You need to have 1MB of Level 2 cache for a 512MB RAM system.

5-2  C

    **Explanation:** Query Analyzer is used to estimate what a query will do to your system before putting that query into production.

5-3  D

    **Explanation:** Increasing Max Async I/O will allow SQL to handle more outstanding read and write requests, thereby using the disks to their full capacity.

5-4  C

    **Explanation:** Because the tables and queries are new, any indexes involved have probably not been stress tested. The Index Wizard will find and correct the problem indexes.

**5-5**    C

**Explanation:** Using the Trace Wizard to create the Trace Transact-SQL Activity by User is the easiest way.

**5-6**    C

**Explanation:** Archive the files to tape and keep them for as long as you can. They will prove very valuable when you need to track trends later on. Incidentally, there is no trace summary to print out.

**5-7**    C

**Explanation:** You will need to filter out the information using the Filters tab in the Trace Properties dialog box. Note that the other options do not even exist.

**5-8**    D

**Explanation:** By doing this, you will slow down your SQL Server somewhat, but this will allow more RAM to be used by IIS.

**5-9**    A

**Explanation:** You should update your statistics so that SQL Server has a better idea of how the table and indexes are comprised. Another option to speed the insertion of this much data is to drop affected indexes and re-create them after the import has finished.

**5-10**    C

**Explanation:** This is probably the best choice. By setting the Query Governor to 10, you are specifying that no queries longer than 10 seconds should be run. B is also incorrect because it would not allow the 10 minutes and longer query to run at all.

**5-11**    A, C, and D

**Explanation:** There is no Security:Table event in the SQL Profiler.

**5-12**    C

**Explanation:** The records being added to the index are searching for a place to live. When this value is high, it indicates that it is spending a lot of time looking. By decreasing the value of fillfactor, you are increasing the amount of free space available in the index.

**5-13**  B

> **Explanation:** The Set Working Set value along with the Max And Min Server Memory settings (set to the same value) indicate that SQL Server wants to prevent NT from paging those blocks of memory.

**5-14**  A

> **Explanation:** Replication information cannot be played back on a remote server. If you exclude replication activity from the trace, then you can replay the trace on any server.

**5-15**  A, B

> **Explanation:** This solution also has a minimal impact on the source servers.

# Unit 6

## Study Questions

### Problems with Upgrading from SQL Server 6.x

1. Syscomments, logins

2. 25

3. startup

4. You can do two things. You can set the default database of your SQL logins to the Master database, or you can upgrade the particular database that the SQL logins are defaulted to first and then upgrade the other databases.

## Problems in Backup and Restore Operations

**5.** Yes

   **Explanation:** CREATE INDEX is one of the few things that you cannot do when you are making a backup of your database.

**6.** False

   **Explanation:** You will encounter error 3120 or 3149 if you attempt this.

**7.** True

   **Explanation:** You need to be careful when you restore. You should ensure that you are restoring a SQL Server backup and not an NT backup.

**8.** The Truncate Log on Checkpoint database option is set.

**9.** NO RECOVERY, RECOVERY

**10.** False

   **Explanation:** Logs must be recovered in order.

**11.** Apply the transaction log for that filegroup backup.

**12.** Orphaned Transaction Log

**13.** dbo or dbo_owner or db_backupoperator are allowed to perform database backups.

**14.** Yes, this is an excellent solution.

## Replication Problems

**15.** True

**16.** binary 8, property

**17.** LocalSystem.

18. xp_loginfo, SQLServerAgent

19. administrator

20. snapshot

21. Snapshot Agent history

22. This is a security issue. Instead of registering each server using NT Authentication, you should register your servers using the sa account. You should also ensure that the SQLServerAgent accounts on all of the SQL Servers have administrator permissions.

23. distribution working

24. Log Reader

25. A

26. one

27. one

28. The most likely solution at this point is that the Distribution Agent hasn't performed a synchronization. You should manually synchronize your servers and then begin replication.

29. True

30. history

31. Distribution Agent.

32. The most likely cause is that there is a problem with the Log Reader Agent. If the Log Reader Agent is not moving transactions from the Publisher to the Distributor, then the Publisher cannot perform backups of the log. The Distributor may be full or offline.

33. The transactions in the distribution server have aged out.

**34.** snapshot

**35.** Back up the Publishers, then the distribution database, and then the Subscribers.

**36.** The publishing databases and the distribution databases. You can always resynchronize your Subscribers, but the distribution database is what drives everything.

## Job or Alert Failures

**37.** SQLServerAgent Service

**38.** enabled

**39.** job history

**40.** Application Log or Event Viewer

**41.** False

**42.** True

## Distributed Query Problems

**43.** connectivity, security

**44.** permissions

**45.** drop or remove, linked server.

**46.** share name, folder

**47.** SQL*NET

**48.** Login ID, Password

## Client Connectivity Problems

**49.** protocols, protocols

**50.** Net-Library, DB-Library

**51.** Multi-Protocol

**52.** Client Network Utility

**53.** Run the Client Network Utility and change to the correct port number.

**54.** Makepipe, Readpipe

## Problems in Accessing SQL Server, Databases, and Database Objects

**55.** CHECKDB

**56.** CHECKCATALOG

**57.** suspect

**58.** True

**59.** True

**60.** No

Explanation: Lance will not be able to use the view unless he also has permission on Julie's view.

# Sample Test

**6-1**   C, D

**Explanation:** You can use the MAKEPIPE and READPIPE commands to verify a named pipe on a local server or across a network. Osql also can be used to test named-pipe connectivity over a local connection.

**6-2**   Answer C, D

**Explanation:** Both of these can cause a database to be marked suspect.

**6-3**   Answer A

**Explanation:** Because no subscribers are receiving information, it is not likely that the distribution process is broken as distributions operate on a subscription-by-subscription basis. It is far more likely that the subscription and distribution process is working normally, but the Log Reader is not sending any data to be replicated.

**6-4**   Answer B

**Explanation:** We know the Log Reader works correctly because some Subscribers are working.

**6-5**   D

**Explanation:** The default folder for log files is the \MSSQL7\Log folder.

**6-6**   D

**Explanation:** There are several reasons why the upgrade will not work. First, Windows NT 4 (with SP 4) is required. Second, Service Pack 3 or higher is required for SQL 6.5, and third, you should have at least 1.5 times the size of the current databases (in this case 6GB) to upgrade them.

**6-7**   A

**Explanation:** You should make a backup of the Master database after making any modifications to your SQL Server that affect the Master database. This includes adding, altering, or dropping databases and transaction logs, new or modified SQL Server logins, and SQL Server options like memory and user connections.

# Unit 7

## Sample Test

**7-1**    D

Explanation: Option A would not work. You must have a baseline to begin your recovery process. Option B would work, but it would take a while. Option C would be quicker than Option B, but option D is the quickest recovery given this scenario.

**7-2**    C

Explanation:  The Log Reader service is not running and, therefore, marked transactions in the publishing database are not allowed to be truncated by the backup process.

**7-3**    A

Explanation:  If theT-SQL used to generate the stored procedures is not found in the syscomments table, then the upgrade process cannot upgrade that stored procedure.

**7-4**    B

Explanation:  As part of the installation process, SQL Server attempts to connect to itself. In order to do this, it must have a loopback of some type over a network client.

**7-5**    A

Explanation:  You cannot use Enterprise Manager to connect to SQL Server in minimal configuration mode. The -m switch starts SQL Server in single-user mode, while the -f switch starts SQL Server in minimal configuration mode.

**7-6**    D

Explanation:  CHECKALLOC verifies that data is stored properly on the data pages and that extents don't overlap etc. The CHECKCATALOG verifies that your system tables are in good shape. The CHECKTABLE does the same thing as CHECKDB, except it only applies to a single table.

**7-7**   A

**Explanation:** You can use bcp to move data into a global temporary table like ##MyGlobalTable

**7-8**   D

**Explanation:** By doing this, you will slow down your SQL Server somewhat, but this will allow more RAM to be used by Exchange.

**7-9**   A, C, D

**Explanation:** The diskadmin server role can manipulate database files, but it cannot work with the Backup utility.

**7-10**   A

**Explanation:** You should update your statistics so that SQL Server has a better idea of how the table and indexes are comprised. Another option to speed the insertion of this much data is to drop affected indexes and re-create them after the import has finished.

**7-11**   C

**Explanation:** This is probably the best choice. By setting the Query Governor to 7, you are specifying that no queries longer than 7 seconds should run. B is incorrect also, because it would not allow queries that are 7 minutes long or longer to run at all.

**7-12**   A, C, and D

**Explanation:** There is no Security: Table event in the SQL Profiler. You do, however, need to know which SQL and/or NT users are in your system and what objects they are working with.

**7-13**   C

**Explanation:** The records being added to the index are searching for a place to live. When this value is high, it indicates that it is spending a lot of time looking. By decreasing the value of fillfactor, you are increasing the amount of free space available in the index.

**7-14** C

**Explanation:** The "set working set" value along with the Max and Min Server Memory settings (set to the same value) indicate that SQL Server wants to prevent NT from paging those blocks of memory.

**7-15** A

**Explanation:** Replication information cannot be played back on a remote server. If you exclude replication activity from the trace, then you can replay the trace on any server.

**7-16** A, B

**Explanation:** This solution also has a minimal impact on the source servers.

**7-17** A

**Explanation:** This is the best method of changing Net-Library and DB-Library options on your client computers.

**7-18** A

**Explanation:** The setupadmin allows you to manage security on linked and remote servers.

**7-19** D

**Explanation:** Snapshots are stored in the working folder on the Distributor. This folder has a default extension of \MSSQL7\ReplData. You should ensure that your Subscribers have file permissions on this folder.

**7-20** B

**Explanation:** DBCC SHRINKFILE will shrink individual files in the database. The SHRINKDATABASE command will shrink all files in the database to a size that you specify.

**7-21** B

**Explanation:** In merge replication, each Subscriber can be given a priority level. The Subscriber with the lowest priority level will have its changes applied first and so on. The Publisher, by default, always has the highest priority level and will, therefore, overwrite changes made by Subscribers.

**7-22**   C

**Explanation:** Answer A will create new security credentials for these login IDs. Because the credentials will be different from the ones that own the objects in the database, you must also run the sp_change_user stored procedure to map those new credentials to the database user names. This is not a problem with NT Authentication because the credentials are stored on the NT Server and not in SQL Server.

**7-23**   A

**Explanation:** This is an interesting problem. The idea of using sp_detachdb is a good one; however, it has certain problems—mainly security. The Subscriber will receive an entire copy of the database complete with objects, users, and permissions. If you use the sp_certify_removable, all users are removed from the database, all objects are owned by dbo, and the transaction log is truncated. This gives the Subscriber the cleanest version of the data.

**7-24**   A

**Explanation:** This is the most efficient method to create new tables and move data. It works great with Excel, Access, and other flat files.

**7-25**   B

**Explanation:** The Database Maintenance Plan Wizard can ease the day-to-day maintenance tasks (as well as their creation) from you as the DBA.

**7-26**   C

**Explanation:** Using the Trace Wizard to create the Trace Transact-SQL Activity by User is the easiest way.

**7-27**   C

**Explanation:** You will need to filter out the information using the Filters tab in the Trace Properties dialog box. Note that the other options do not even exist.

**7-28** C

**Explanation:** This is an excellent solution. The Transfer Manager can move data from one SQL Server 7 computer to another SQL Server 7 computer regardless of character set, sort order, or platform.

**7-29** A

**Explanation:** SQL Server 7 does not allow upgrades from SQL Server 4.2x. The recommended method is to first upgrade your 4.2x system to SQL Server 6.5 and then use the install SQL Server 7 on the same computer. The Upgrade Wizard will recognize the 6.5 installation and automatically upgrade it to 7.

**7-30** A, C

**Explanation:** To perform a fast bulk copy, you must drop indexes on affected tables and set the Select Into/Bulk Copy database option. By doing this, INSERTs are not logged.

**7-31** D

**Explanation:** If security is an issue you may want to create and assign different accounts to the SQL services. While the SQL Agent requires a domain account with admin rights, the SQL Server service mainly needs a user account with rights to the \MSSQL7 folder.

**7-32** D

**Explanation:** Although creating the guest account is on the right track, you should have brought over the Windows NT group called *Domain Users* instead of *Domain Guests*. Domain Users automatically contains all of your NT user accounts, while Domain Guests only contains accounts that are configured as guest accounts.

**7-33** A, B, C

**Explanation:** By creating an application role and having an application trigger the role, you can ensure that users get their rights only when the application is run. You do not have to assign users to the role to make it work.

**7-34**   A, C

**Explanation:** Neither IPX/SPX nor Banyan Vines protocols are supported for trusted connections.

**7-35**   A, B

**Explanation:** When you set the owner password, anyone who knows the owner password can work with the internals of the package. The operator password allows users who know the password to execute the package. Any password supplied for a package automatically encrypts the package contents.

**7-36**   C, D

**Explanation:** To participate in a multiserver environment, you must be running SQL Server 7 on Windows NT.

**7-37**   C

**Explanation:** You can check the history and status of target jobs at the target server and at the master server.

**7-38**   A, B, C, D

**Explanation:** To have a job notify an operator via e-mail, you must create an Exchange account for the SQL service account, make sure the SQL Agent is using the NT service account, create an operator, and assign the job to notify the operator.

**7-39**   D

**Explanation:** The Raiserror T-SQL command will display a SQL error message and post it to the NT Application Log, while the print command only shows it to the client application. The message number, its severity, and state need to be enclosed in parentheses.

**7-40**   C

**Explanation:** Because MTS supports connection pooling, you cannot use an application role that will be specific to a user connection. MTS packages can assume the identity of a single NT user. This user can then be given permission to the SQL Server objects.

**7-41**  A

**Explanation:** Windows NT groups can be assigned permissions directly, while still allowing the individual NT accounts to be tracked within SQL Server.

**7-42**  D

**Explanation:** Placing each table/index set in a filegroup allows them to be backed up separately, while spreading the physical files across multiple disks promotes asynchronous disk I/O.

**7-43**  D

**Explanation:** Typical installations require more than 120MB of disk space. All of the other specifications are adequate.

**7-44**  C

**Explanation:** Clustering is the only option that provides true load balancing to a single set of hard drives.

**7-45**  C

**Explanation:** You cannot bcp directly from a FoxPro file. The other options are available, but they are less efficient than DTS.

**7-46**  B

**Explanation:** You cannot have the SQL 6.5 and 7 services running on the same computer. Use the Switch utility to move between the services.

**7-47**  A,C

**Explanation:** Macintosh clients can communicate in a Windows network by using either AppleTalk or TCP/IP.

**7-48**  B, C

**Explanation:** The SQLServerAgent controls replication automation, while the MSSQLServer service is needed to execute the transactions.

**7-49**   A

**Explanation:** Unattended setup scripts ensure identical installations on multiple computers.

**7-50**   D

**Explanation:** Unicode contains 64K characters, representing most of the common characters in use in the world today. Using Unicode data types (nchar, nvarchar, etc.) allows you to store information in this format.

**7-51**   C

**Explanation:** Binary order required no additional processing to determine proper order. Everything is arranged in logical binary order.

**7-52**   C

**Explanation:** ANSI Warnings allow warnings to be issued for overflow, divide-by-zero, and other types of errors. Unless this is set on, nulls will be returned when the errors occur.

**7-53**   B

**Explanation:** Full-Text indexes are stored in the file system, not the database, and are, therefore, not recovered with the database. The recovered database will already be configured to use the Full-Text indexes, but they will have to be rebuilt first.

**7-54**   D

**Explanation:** Each SQL page is 8K in size, and rows cannot cross pages. Because you cannot fit two rows on a page, this table will require 100,000 pages. Because each page is 8K in size, this will use 800MB of disk space.

**7-55**   C

**Explanation:** SQL Server 7 allows the administrator to tie a SQL Agent alert directly to a Performance Monitor counter. This is the easiest approach.

**7-56** B

**Explanation:** The data currently in the table represents only about 30 to 35 percent of the data that will be in the table in the coming weeks. Setting a fill factor to 30 will leave enough empty room in each index leaf page to accommodate the data while minimizing the likelihood of page splitting.

**7-57** B

**Explanation:** SQL Server uses OLE–DB to connect to other data sources. Because there is a native OLE DB service provider for Jet databases, ODBC is not needed.

**7-58** C

**Explanation:** Tables cannot be backed up without their indexes, and the reverse is also true. To correct the problem, place each table and its indexes in the same filegroup, putting different tables in different filegroups.

**7-59** D

**Explanation:** The MicrosoftSearch service, which supports Full-Text indexing, must be installed using a custom installation option.

**7-60** B

**Explanation:** DCBB NewAlloc has been eliminated from SQL Server 7, and its functionality has been rolled into DBCC CheckAlloc.

**7-61** B

**Explanation:** The –m switch is used to start SQL Server is single-user mode. The –f switch is used to start SQL Server with a minimal configuration. This is useful in situations where SQL Server will not restart due to some modifications that you had made.

**7-62** D

**Explanation:** All three of these events will cause statistics to be maintained.

**7-63** B

**Explanation:** The standby option saves the recovery information in an undo file, allowing the database to be access by users, but also allowing additional transaction logs to be restored.

**7-64**    A, C

**Explanation:** The stopat switch allows you to state the point in time when you want to end the application of further transactions. The Recovery switch makes this database available for user activity.

**7-65**    A

**Explanation:** If you allow the query to complete, the auto-commit mode will prevent you from being able to roll back the query. Killing the process is faster than stopping and restarting the SQL Server service.

**7-66**    A, B

**Explanation:** Either a script file or a Profiler trace is usable by the Index Tuning Wizard.

**7-67**    D

**Explanation:** A Subscriber cannot subscribe directly to a table or a column. These must be defined within an article.

**7-68**    D

**Explanation:** SQL Server does not support Linux account authentication or trusted authentication from a Linux workstation.

**7-69**    B

**Explanation:** The installation script files come in several different styles. There is a predefined script for the unattended client setup as well as an unattended typical server setup. You can create your own custom setup scripts.

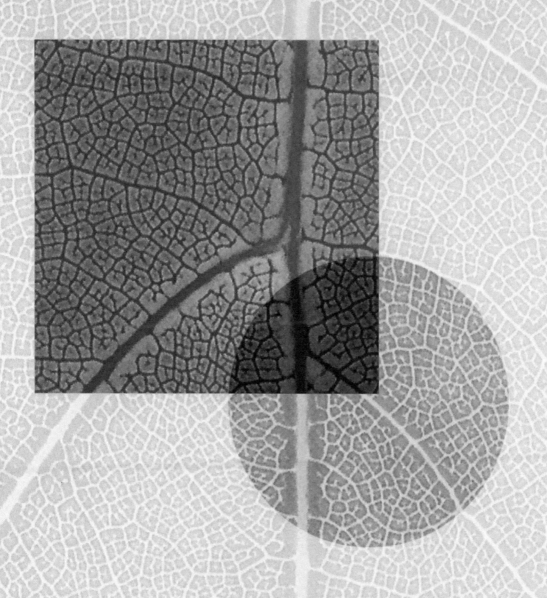

Glossary

**ActiveX Data Objects (ADO)**    A COM (Component Object Model) object set created by Microsoft intended to replace all other database access object models in future releases of Microsoft products. ADO is a very robust object model in that it defines a core set of functions and allows extensions to be built into the model to support the individual features of certain types of databases. It is specifically designed to access OLE-DB data sources.

**Alert**    A mechanism that tells SQL Server which error codes to look for in the Windows NT Application log, and tells it what action to take if an event is found. Alerts can be based on a severity level, an error code, and the database in which the error occurred. An alert can notify an operator and/or perform a task. Alerts are stored in the Msdb database.

**Alias**    A mechanism that allows a login to access a database under the user name assigned to another login. The alias is stored in the sysalternates system table of the database. Each login can have either a user name in a database or an alias, but not both. An alias can be used to consolidate permissions under special user accounts, such as dbo. These have been kept in SQL Server 7 for backward-compatibility. SQL 7 uses the concept of roles, which replaces the need for an alias.

**Allocation unit**    In SQL Server, a structure designed to provide a method of keeping track of which pages are allocated to which objects. When a database is created, it is divided into allocation units. When an allocation unit is created, it is built from 32 *extents*. The very first page of the first extent of the allocation unit is called the *allocation page*. The allocation page is responsible for keeping track of every extent in the allocation unit. Allocation units affect the size of the database. Databases must be created and maintained in full allocation-unit intervals, which are 8 extents, or 512KB in size.

**Article**    The basic unit of replication. An article is one or more columns and rows of a table.

**Automatic recovery**    A feature built into SQL Server that ensures that a database is brought up to date when the server is first started. Transactions completed since the last checkpoint process are rolled forward and put into the database, while partially completed transactions are rolled back or removed from the database. Every time SQL Server is restarted, SQL Server runs its automatic recovery feature.

**B-Tree format**   The format used for indexes in SQL Server. B-Tree is short for *balanced tree*. It is called this because every page of the index is exactly the same distance from the root as is every other page at the same level. A B-Tree resembles a pyramid.

**BackOffice**   Microsoft's line of client/server support applications that run on Windows NT Server. Some components of BackOffice are Microsoft SQL Server, Systems Management Server (SMS), Internet Information Server (IIS), Exchange Server, SNA Server, and Proxy Server.

**Backup device**   A file or tape to which SQL Server backs up a database. Also called a *dump device*. SQL has no built-in backup devices that point to files or tapes. You will need to create all your backup devices that point to files or tapes.

**Backup domain controller (BDC)**   A server that keeps a copy of the Authentication database from the primary domain controller (PDC). Users can log on to either the PDC or any of the BDCs. Domain controllers are used for network login validation.

**Bcp (Bulk Copy Program)**   A command-line utility used for transferring information into and out of SQL Server.

**Broken ownership chain**   See *ownership chain*.

**Browser**   See *Web browser*.

**Caching**   A speed optimization technique that keeps a copy of the most recently used data in a fast, high-cost, low-capacity storage device rather than in the device upon which the actual data resides. Caching assumes that recently used data is likely to be used again. Fetching data from the cache is faster than fetching data from the larger, slower storage device. Most caching algorithms also copy next-most-likely-to-be-used data and perform write-caching to further increase speed gains.

**Character set**   The set of characters that SQL Server will recognize and therefore store. Of the 256 characters contained in each character set, the first 128 are the same throughout the various code pages. The last 128 characters, also known as *extended characters*, differ according to the set.

**Checkpoint**   The mechanism by which SQL Server periodically writes modified data to a hard disk. The dbo of a database may also issue a checkpoint at any time by running the Checkpoint command in the appropriate database. By default, the checkpoint process wakes up once a minute and checks every transaction log for 5 minutes' worth of changes to the data pages in cache. If 5 minutes of changes or more are found, the data pages are written to disk. This establishes a known point of consistency between the data pages on hard disk and the transactions stored on hard disk. The 5-minute period is known as the *recovery interval* and can be modified.

**Client**   A computer on a network that subscribes to the services provided by a server.

**Client Network utility**   A utility used to configure SQL Server clients' Net-Libraries. It also reports on the DB-Libraries that are in use for a particular client.

**Client/server**   A network architecture that dedicates certain computers, called *servers,* to act as service providers to computers called *clients,* on which users perform work. Servers can be dedicated to providing one or more network services, such as file storage, shared printing, communications, e-mail, and Web response.

**Client/server application**   An application that is split into two components: computer-intensive processes that run on application servers, and user interfaces that run on clients. Client/server applications communicate over the network through interprocess communication mechanisms (IPCs).

**Column**   The component of a table that holds individual pieces of data. In a database, a row in a table is often referred to as an entity. The column would be an attribute of the entity and describes an aspect of the row. For example, a row of data might describe an individual. A column would describe the name of the individual or the eye color, etc.

**Commit**   The process whereby completed transactions are put into the database. SQL Server will automatically commit the data at regular intervals, or a manual commit can be initialized by the dbo or sa.

**Component Object Model (COM)**   COM is an object-oriented architecture for building reusable application components. COM provides a specification, or model, for what an object is, and it provides services for both the creation of objects and the communication between a client and the server objects. COM replaces OLE (Object Linking and Embedding) and has other advantages. COM's most notable advances are its binary compatibility and cross-platform development capabilities, code reusability, and version control.

**Computer name**   A 1-to-15-character NetBIOS name used to uniquely identify a computer on the network.

**Concurrency**   The ability of SQL Server to support multiple users at the same time, even if those users want the same data.

**Control Panel**   A Windows software utility that controls the function of specific operating system services by allowing users to change default settings for the service to match their preferences. The Windows Registry contains the Control Panel settings on a system and/or per-user basis.

**Data Access Objects (DAO)**   A set of programmable objects that Microsoft Access developers use to manipulate data through Jet, the data-access engine for Access and other Microsoft desktop products.

**Data cache**   SQL Server does its own caching of data to speed up access to databases. The size of the data cache can be indirectly manipulated by allocating more or less RAM to SQL Server.

**Data Source Name (DSN)**   A user-created identifier used by ODBC to negotiate connections to any ODBC-compliant data source. A DSN consists of a server location and a driver name and can optionally contain a database name and authentication information. See also *ODBC*.

**Data mart**   A database system concerned with live updates and new data, such as an online ordering system. See also *OLTP*, or *online transaction processing*.

**Data warehousing**   Storage and querying of historical data, also referred to as *decision-support systems*. The main focus of data warehousing is the ability to quickly query existing data and perform complex analyses, usually looking for patterns or other relationships that are difficult to locate during the day-to-day operations of a company.

**Database file**   In SQL Server 7, databases are stored on two types of database files. One file stores the actual data and indexes while the other file stores the transaction log. By default, the first data file has an .MDF extension. Additional data files have an .NDF extension. The transaction log files always have a default extension of .LDF.

**Database management system (DBMS)**   An environment created specifically for the purpose of working with databases. The term *database management system* usually refers to an electronic system or a computer program designed to work with databases. Microsoft Access and FoxPro are both examples of database management systems.

**Database Maintenance Plan Wizard**   A wizard (step-by-step utility) provided with SQL Server 7 that helps you schedule backups and perform database optimizations and consistency checking. This wizard can also automate and schedule these routine database maintenance tasks.

**Database user**   A SQL Server login ID that has been mapped into a particular database. Without a valid mapping, a login will not have access to a database.

**Datatype**   A component of a SQL Server database that determines what kinds of data, such as character data, numeric data, or date/time data, can be stored in a column. A column can hold data of only a single datatype.

**DB-Library**   A set of functions and connectivity programs that allow clients to communicate programmatically with database engines. A database engine is responsible for processing queries, maintaining data, ensuring data consistency, and providing a mechanism for backup and restoration.

**DBCC (Database Consistency Checker)**   SQL Server commands used to check the consistency of databases. These commands are generally used to gather information about the status of a database rather than to make changes to it.

**Dbo (database owner)**   In SQL Server, a user who has full permissions in a particular database. This includes the ability to back up and restore the database and transaction log. The sa is also considered the dbo of every database. The dbo is specified through the sp_changedbowner stored procedure.

**Dboo (database object owner)**   In SQL Server, a user who creates a particular database object. The dboo has all rights on that object, including the right to allow other database users to use the object.

**Default**   A SQL Server object assigned to a column or user-defined datatype in a table. If no data is entered, the default value will be used. This can also refer to the default database that is assigned to a SQL Server login ID. If the login attempts to run a query without specifying a database, the query will be applied to the default database.

**Desktop**   A directory represented by the background of the Windows Explorer shell. By default, the Desktop holds objects that contain the local storage devices and available network shares. Also a key operating part of the Windows GUI.

**Distributed Transaction Coordinator (DTC)**   The DTC helps coordinate queries that are run between two or more SQL Servers. The DTC ensures that the transaction is performed simultaneously on both servers, or not at all.

**Distribution Server**   For replication in SQL Server, the server that keeps track of replication. It copies the data from the publishing server, stores it, and then forwards it to all subscribing servers.

If you designate the SQL Server machine where you are installing publishing as the one that holds the Distribution database, you are installing a *local distribution server*. Designating a remote server rather than a local one as your distribution server may make better use of a WAN.

**Distributor**   See *distribution server*.

**Domain**   In Microsoft networks, an arrangement of client and server computers, referenced by a specific name, that share a single security permissions database. On the Internet, a domain is a named collection of hosts and subdomains, registered with a unique name by the InterNIC (the agency responsible for assigning IP addresses).

**Domain controller**   A server that authenticates workstation network login requests by comparing a user name and password against account information stored in the user accounts database. A user cannot access a domain without authentication from a domain controller. Windows NT employs a single primary domain controller (PDC) per domain. To help off-load some of the workload, backup domain controllers (BDCs) can be created and enabled within a domain.

**Dump device**   See *backup device*.

**Dynamic backup**   A type of backup that allows you to back up your SQL Server databases while they are in use. Users can stay connected to the server and run most queries while a dynamic backup is in progress.

**Dynamic Data Exchange (DDE)**   A method of interprocess communication within the Microsoft Windows operating systems.

**Dynamic Link Library (DLL)**   A set of modular functions that can be used by many programs simultaneously. There are hundreds of functions stored within DLLs.

**Electronic mail (e-mail)**   A type of client/server application that provides a routed, stored-message service between any two user e-mail accounts. E-mail accounts are not the same as user accounts, but a one-to-one relationship usually exists between them. Because all modern computers can attach to the Internet, users can send e-mail over the Internet to any location that has telephone or wireless digital service.

**Enterprise Manager**   See *SQL Enterprise Manager*.

**Enterprise network**   A complex network consisting of multiple servers and multiple domains; it can be contained within one or two buildings or encompass a wide geographic area.

**Exchange**   See *Microsoft Exchange*.

**Explorer**   The default shell for Windows 95/98 and Windows NT 4. Explorer implements the more flexible Desktop object paradigm rather than the Program Manager paradigm used in earlier versions of Windows. See also *Desktop*.

**Extent**   In SQL Server, the unit of allocation for tables and indexes. All SQL Server objects and data are stored in tables. Tables and indexes are organized into extents. Each extent consists of eight 8KB pages. When a table or an index requires additional storage space, a new extent is allocated.

**Extended stored procedure**   See *stored procedure*.

**Extranet**   A network between two or more companies that takes advantage of the low-cost Internet connection rather than privately held dedicated communication lines.

**Fast bcp**   A form of importing data with the bcp utility that takes place when there are no indexes on the table being imported to, and when the Select Into/Bulk Copy database option is set.

**File Allocation Table (FAT)**   The file system used by MS-DOS and available to other operating systems such as Windows (all variations), OS/2, and Windows NT. FAT has become something of a mass-storage compatibility standard because of its simplicity and wide availability. FAT has few fault-tolerance features and can become corrupted through normal use over time. In the new 32-bit Windows 95/98 platforms, FAT32 is also available. FAT32 has many new features including the ability to address more than 2GB of hard disk space.

**Flat-file database**   A database whose information is stored in files and is accessed sequentially. Examples of flat-file database programs include dBASE, Access, FoxPro, and other personal computer databases.

**Group**   A security entity to which users can be assigned membership for the purpose of granting a broad set of permissions. By managing permissions for groups and assigning users to groups, rather than assigning permissions to users, security administrators can more easily manage large security environments. SQL Server 6.5 differs from most network applications in that it allows a user to be a member of only one other group besides the Public group. SQL Server 7 allows users to be a member of as many groups as they please. Groups have also been renamed in SQL 7 to *database roles*.

**Guest user**   If a specific user doesn't exist in the database permissions list, but a user called *guest* does, then users in SQL Server will have the rights of the guest user in that particular database.

**Horizontal partitioning**   In SQL Server replication, a method by which you can publish only certain rows of a table. This is often referred to as *horizontal filtering*. See also *vertical partitioning*.

**HTML**   See *HyperText Markup Language*.

**HTTP**   See *HyperText Transfer Protocol*.

**Hyperlink**   A link in text or graphics files that has a Web address embedded within it. By clicking on the link, you jump to another Web address. You can identify a hyperlink because it is a different color from the rest of the Web page.

**HyperText Markup Language (HTML)**   A textual data format that identifies sections of a document as headers, lists, hypertext links, and so on. HTML is the data format used on the World Wide Web for the publication of Web pages.

**HyperText Transfer Protocol (HTTP)**   An Internet protocol that transfers HTML documents over the Internet and responds to context changes that happen when a user clicks on a hyperlink.

**IDE**   A simple mass-storage-device interconnection bus that operates at 5Mbps and can handle no more than two attached devices. IDE devices are similar to but less expensive than SCSI devices.

**IIS**   See *Internet Information Server*.

**Index**   A data structure that provides a mechanism for resolving queries more efficiently by working through a subset of the data rather than all of it. A full table scan can be avoided by using an index. In SQL Server, each table is allowed one *clustered* index. This index is the actual sort order for the data in the table. *Nonclustered* indexes consist of a list of ordered keys that contain pointers to the data in the data pages. Up to 249 nonclustered indexes can be created per table, but these occupy more space than clustered indexes do.

**Indexed Sequential Access Method (ISAM)**   A method of data access that uses file I/O routines with indexing and a few enhanced features. This type of data access is normally found when using flat-file databases like dBASE, FoxPro, and Access or DB2.

**Industry Standard Architecture (ISA)**   The design standard for 16-bit Intel-compatible motherboards and peripheral buses. The 32/64-bit PCI bus standard is replacing the ISA standard. Adapters and interface cards must conform to the bus standard(s) used by the motherboard in order to be used with a computer.

**Integrated security**   A SQL Server security mode in which SQL Server accepts, or trusts, the Windows NT validation of a user. The Windows NT account information is used to validate the user to SQL Server. These connections are referred to as *trusted connections*.

**Internet**   A voluntarily interconnected global network of computers based on the TCP/IP protocol suite. TCP/IP was originally developed by the U.S. Department of Defense's Advanced Research Projects Agency to facilitate the interconnection of military networks and was provided free to universities. The obvious utility of worldwide digital network connectivity and the availability of free complex networking software developed at universities doing military research attracted other universities, research institutions, private organizations, businesses, and finally the individual home user. The Internet is now available to all current commercial computing platforms.

**Internet Explorer**   A World Wide Web browser produced by Microsoft and included free with Windows 95/98 and Windows NT 4.

**Internet Information Server (IIS)**   A server produced by Microsoft that serves Internet higher-level protocols like HTTP and FTP (File Transfer Protocol) to clients using Web browsers.

**Internet Protocol (IP)**   The network-layer protocol upon which the Internet is based. IP provides a simple, connectionless packet exchange. Other protocols such as UDP or TCP use IP to perform their connection-oriented or guaranteed delivery services.

**Internet service provider (ISP)**   A company that provides dial-up or direct connections to the Internet.

**Internetwork Packet eXchange (IPX)**   The network protocol developed by Novell for its NetWare product. IPX is a routable protocol similar to IP but much easier to manage and with lower communication overhead. The term IPX can also refer to the family of protocols that includes the Synchronous Packet eXchange (SPX) transport layer protocol, a connection-oriented protocol that guarantees delivery in order, similar to the service provided by TCP.

**Interprocess communication channel (IPC)**   A generic term describing any manner of client/server communication protocols, specifically those operating in the session, presentation, and application layers. Interprocess communication mechanisms provide a method for the client and server to trade information.

**Intranet**   A privately owned network based on the TCP/IP protocol suite.

**I/O (input/output)**   The process of reading and writing data back and forth from cache to disk. The smallest unit of I/O in SQL Server is the 8KB page. All I/O happens in page increments. *Logical I/O* is defined as a data read or write operation that is made to cache or disk. *Physical I/O* is sub-classified as a data read or write that is made to disk only.

**IP**   See *Internet Protocol*.

**IP address**   A four-byte (32-bit) number that uniquely identifies a computer on an IP internetwork. InterNIC assigns the first bytes of Internet IP addresses and administers them in hierarchies. Huge organizations like the government or top-level ISPs have class A addresses, large organizations and most ISPs have class B addresses, and small companies have class C addresses. In a class A address, InterNIC assigns the first byte, and the owning organization assigns the remaining three bytes. In a class B address, InterNIC or the higher-level ISP assigns the first two bytes, and the organization assigns the remaining two bytes. In a class C address, InterNIC or the higher-level ISP assigns the first three bytes, and the organization assigns the remaining byte. Organizations not attached to the Internet are free to assign IP addresses as they please.

**IPC**   See *interprocess communication channel*

**IPX**   See *Internetwork Packet eXchange*.

**ISA**   See *Industry Standard Architecture*.

**ISP**   See *Internet service provider*.

**Jet**   The data engine for Microsoft Access and other Microsoft desktop products. Microsoft Access ships with Jet. Microsoft Visual Basic also uses Jet as its native database. Jet can also be accessed by Excel, Word, Project, SQL Server 7, and PowerPoint through VBA (Visual Basic for Applications).

**Job**   A task, such as a backup procedure, performed by a system. In SQL Server 7, you can schedule jobs to run at regular intervals or when an alert is triggered. A job can run a Transact-SQL command, a command-prompt utility, a Visual Basic or JavaScript script, or replication procedures.

**Kernel**   The core process of a preemptive operating system, consisting of a multitasking scheduler and the basic services that provide security. Depending on the operating system, other services such as virtual memory drivers may be built into the kernel. The kernel is responsible for managing the scheduling of threads and processes.

**LAN Manager**   The Microsoft brand of a network product jointly developed by IBM and Microsoft that provided an early client/server environment. LAN Manager/Server was the genesis of many important protocols and IPC mechanisms used today, such as NetBIOS, named pipes, and NetBEUI. Portions of this product exist today in OS/2 Warp Server and Windows NT.

**LAN Server**   The IBM brand of a network product jointly developed by IBM and Microsoft. See also *LAN Manager*.

**LazyWriter**   A system process responsible for physical I/O. The role of the LazyWriter is to flush pages from cache to disk as free buffers are needed by the system. The LazyWriter differs from the checkpoint in how it performs its work. The checkpoint process executes its work in spikes and then goes back to sleep. The LazyWriter may be continuously active, writing out pages from cache to disk as needed.

**Local group**   A group that exists in a Windows NT computer's local security database. Local groups can reside on NT Workstation or NT Server computers and can contain users or global groups.

**Lock**   A mechanism by which SQL Server manages concurrency. SQL Server places locks on data when it is being accessed by a client application. SQL Server locks are primarily *page* locks. This means that when a client accesses a single record on an 8KB page, SQL Server will lock the entire page until it is appropriate to release the lock. SQL Server also supports *table* locks for times when it would make more sense to lock the entire table rather than individual pages. Row-level locking is also supported automatically with SQL Server 7.

**Lock escalation**   The SQL Server process of increasing a lock from the page to the table level. When a transaction acquires a configured number of page locks, a table lock is set and the page locks are released. This behavior is configured through lock-escalation thresholds.

**Logging**   The process of recording information about activities and errors in the operating system.

**Logical I/O**   See *I/O*.

**Login**   A name that, when combined with a password, allows access to SQL Server resources. Logins are stored in the syslogins system table. (For easier queries, use the syslogins view.) This table is located in the Master database only, and there is only one per server.

**Long Filename (LFN)**   A filename longer than the eight characters plus three-character extension allowed by MS-DOS. In Windows NT and Windows 95/98, filenames can contain up to 255 characters.

**MAKEPIPE**   A command-line utility that can be used in conjunction with the READPIPE utility to verify that the named pipes protocol is working properly.

**MAPI**   See *Messaging Application Programming Interface*.

**Master database**   The system database that contains all the settings for the SQL Server engine, including configurations, user accounts, and links to user databases. This information is known collectively as the *system catalog*.

**Messaging Application Programming Interface (MAPI)**   Messaging application standard developed to allow for interaction between an application and various message service providers. It is essentially a set of ANSI-standard DLLs. SQL Server 7 has the ability to generate e-mail to any MAPI-compliant message service provider (post office).

**Microsoft Exchange**   Microsoft's messaging application. Exchange implements MAPI as well as other messaging protocols such as POP, SNMP, and fax services to provide a flexible message composition and reception service.

**Microsoft Query**   A utility used to graphically create SQL statements for any ODBC-compliant data source. Microsoft Query (also called MS Query) can link to Microsoft Office applications (such as Word and Excel) and other ODBC-compliant applications and databases.

**Mixed security**  A SQL Server security mode that combines the functionality of integrated security with the flexibility of having SQL Server manage its own login accounts. In mixed mode, Windows NT accounts can be linked into SQL Server (using trusted connections), but unique SQL Server login accounts can also be created and used if a trusted connection is not possible. This is sometimes referred to as SQL Authentication in SQL Server 7.

**MMC (Microsoft Management Console)**  The MMC is Microsoft's new framework utility for managing the various Windows NT services and functions. All Microsoft's new BackOffice applications use MMC, including SQL Server 7, SMS 2, and IIS 4. One of the advantages of the MMC is that different management *snap-ins* can be added to the utility at the same time, which means that management of servers is more standardized and can be done from one application.

**Model database**  The template database for SQL Server that is used when new databases are created. All users, groups, and security existing in this database are automatically part of any new databases, but changes made to the Model database will not affect existing databases.

**MS Query**  See *Microsoft Query*.

**Msdb database**  A SQL Server database that stores information about the alerts, tasks, events, and replication tasks created on that server by the SQLServerAgent service. The Msdb database also includes information about system operators.

**MSDTC**  See *Distributed Transaction Coordinator*.

**Multiprocessing**  Using two or more processors simultaneously to perform a computing task. Depending on the operating system, processing may be done asymmetrically, wherein certain processors are assigned certain threads independent of the load they create; or symmetrically, wherein threads are dynamically assigned to processors according to an equitable scheduling scheme. The term usually describes a multiprocessing capacity built into the computer at a hardware level in that the computer itself supports more than one processor. However, *multiprocessing* can also be applied to network computing applications achieved through interprocess communication mechanisms. Client/server applications are examples of multiprocessing.

**Multi-Protocol**    A network library available with SQL Server 6.5 and 7. Multi-Protocol allows SQL Server to communicate over any open interprocess communication (IPC) mechanism. It also provides support for integrated security and encryption. Multi-Protocol takes advantage of remote procedure calls (RPCs) to pass information between the client and server

**Multitasking**    The capacity of an operating system to switch rapidly among threads of execution. Multitasking allows processor time to be divided among threads as though each thread ran on its own slower processor. Multitasking operating systems allow two or more applications to run at the same time and can provide a greater degree of service to applications than single-tasking operating systems like MS-DOS can.

**Multithreaded**    Multithreaded programs have more than one chain of execution, thus relying on the services of a multitasking or multiprocessing operating system to operate. Multiple chains of execution allow programs to simultaneously perform more than one task. In multitasking computers, multithreading is merely a convenience used to make programs run more smoothly and to free the program from the burden of switching between tasks itself. When multithreaded applications run on a computer with multiple processors, the computing burden of the program can be spread across many processors. Programs that are not multithreaded cannot take advantage of multiple processors in a computer.

**Named pipes**    An interprocess communication (IPC) mechanism that is implemented as a file system service, allowing programs to be modified to run on it without using a proprietary API. Named pipes was developed to support more robust client/server communications than those allowed by the simpler NetBIOS. Named pipes is the default SQL Server protocol and is required for installation.

**Native API**    The methods of data access that are specific to certain database management systems. Also called the *proprietary interface*. (API stands for *application programming interface*.) These are generally implemented as a set of DLLs or COM-based objects.

**Network operating system**    A computer operating system specifically designed to optimize a computer's ability to respond to service requests. Servers run network operating systems. Windows NT Server is a network operating system.

**New Technology File System (NTFS)**   A secure, transaction-oriented file system developed for Windows NT that incorporates the Windows NT security model for assigning permissions and shares. NTFS is optimized for hard drives larger than 500MB and requires too much overhead to be used on hard-disk drives smaller than 50MB.

**Normalization of data**   The process of organizing data into tables, in a consistent and complete format, in order to create a relational database.

**NT Event Viewer**   A Windows NT utility used to view Windows NT events and errors. The Application Log records SQL Server events and errors as well as events from other applications running under Windows NT.

**NTFS**   See *New Technology File System.*

**Object permissions**   SQL Server permissions that generally allow users to manipulate data controlled by a database object. For example, to view the information in a table, you must first have the SELECT permission on that table. If you want to run a stored procedure, you must first have the Execute permission on that stored procedure. Object permissions can be granted by the sa, dbo, or dboo.

**ODBC (Open Database Connectivity)**   An API set that defines a method of common database access. Client applications can be written to the ODBC API. ODBC uses a Data Source Name (DSN) to make a connection to a database and to load an appropriate ODBC driver. This driver will translate client calls made to the ODBC API into calls to the native interface of the database. The goal of ODBC is to provide interoperability between client applications and data resources.

**OLE-DB**   A method of common database access that defines an interface based on the COM (Component Object Model) rather than a traditional API interface like ODBC. The goal is similar to ODBC, which is to provide interoperability between client applications and data resources.

**OLTP**   See *online transaction processing.*

**Online transaction processing (OLTP)**   A type of database activity that involves frequent changes to the data stored in your database. This is the opposite of online analytical processing (OLAP), which rarely changes data, but runs frequent ad hoc–type queries to generate MIS reports.

**Operator** A user who is notified about certain network events. In SQL Server, operators can be defined by name, along with their e-mail and pager addresses. Operator information is stored in the Msdb database. Operators are notified about the success and/or failure of scheduled jobs and alerts.

**Optimization** Any effort to reduce the workload on a hardware or software component by eliminating, obviating, or reducing the amount of work required of the component through any means. For instance, file caching is an optimization that reduces the workload of a hard disk drive.

**OSQL** A command-line utility that uses ODBC and provides a query interface to the SQL Server. You can run Transact-SQL statements as well as stored procedures and DBCC commands from OSQL; ISQL (which uses DB-Library) is also supported in SQL 7 for backward-compatibility.

**Ownership chain** In SQL Server, the result of a user who owns an object creating another object based on the original one, such as when a user creates a view based on a table. This ownership chain has only one object owner. If another user creates an object based on the original owner's object, this now becomes a *broken ownership chain,* because different users own objects within the permission chain. If a person who owns objects that are dependent on each other grants another person rights to the final object, then the ownership chain is unbroken. However, if the second person then grants rights to a third person, the ownership chain becomes broken, as the third person needs rights from the first person, not the second person.

**Page** The smallest unit of data storage in SQL Server. Every page is 8KB in size with a 32-byte header. Data rows are written to data pages, index rows to index pages, and so on.

**Parallel striped backup** A SQL Server backup created across two or more backup devices.

**PCI** See *Peripheral Connection Interface.*

**PDC** See *Primary Domain Controller.*

**Per-seat license** A type of SQL Server license that allows you to pay once for each seat (person) in your company, and then use any number of connections to any number of SQL servers.

**Per-server license**   A type of SQL Server license that allows you to pay for only a connection to a single server.

**Performance Monitor**   A Windows NT utility that tracks statistics on individual data items, called *counters*. You can get information about the performance of SQL Server through Performance Monitor. For example, you can monitor the log space used, the number of current connections, and memory use.

**Peripheral Connection Interface (PCI)**   A high-speed 32/64-bit bus interface developed by Intel and widely accepted as the successor to the 16-bit ISA interface. PCI devices support I/O throughput about 40 times faster than the ISA bus.

**Permissions**   SQL Server security constructs that regulate access to resources by user name or role affiliation. Administrators can assign permissions to allow any level of access, such as read-only, read/write, or delete, by controlling the ability of users to initiate object services. Security is implemented by checking the user's security identifier against each object's access control list.

**Physical I/O**   See *I/O*.

**Preemptive multitasking**   A multitasking implementation in which an interrupt routine in the kernel manages the scheduling of processor time among running threads. The threads themselves do not need to support multitasking in any way because the microprocessor will preempt the thread with an interrupt, save its state, update all thread priorities according to the operating system's scheduling algorithm, and pass control to the highest-priority thread awaiting execution. Because of the preemptive feature, a thread that crashes will not affect the operation of other executing threads.

**Primary Domain Controller (PDC)**   In a Microsoft network, the domain server that contains the master copy of the security, computer, and user accounts databases (often referred to as the SAM database) and that can authenticate workstations or users. The PDC can replicate its databases to one or more backup domain controllers (BDCs). The PDC is usually also the master browser for the domain.

**Procedure cache**    After SQL Server fulfills its requirements for RAM from the RAM assigned to it, the rest is assigned to cache. The cache is divided into a data cache and a procedure cache. The procedure cache contains stored procedures that have been run by users or the system. The ratio of procedure cache to data cache is now set automatically by SQL Server 7.

**Process**    A running program containing one or more threads. A process encapsulates the protected memory and environment for its threads.

**Program Developers' Kit (PDK)**    Extra SQL Server documentation and programming examples useful to developers who want to know which DLL (dynamic link library) functions are available and how they work in SQL Server.

**Public group**    See *Public role.*

**Public role**    A role that exists in every SQL Server database. Any rights granted to the Public role automatically apply to all users in the database, including the guest user (if present).

**Publication**    In SQL Server replication, a collection of *articles*. Subscribing servers can subscribe to an entire publication only. In earlier versions of SQL Server, it was possible to subscribe to an individual article in a publication.

**Publisher**    See *publishing server.*

**Publishing server**    In SQL Server replication, the server that has the original data and is making that data available to other replication servers.

**Pull page**    A model of Web-page creation in which a server-side process requests data dynamically from the database when the Web browser makes the request. No static page is created. The HTML response to the request is created dynamically by the server-side process.

**Push page**    A model of Web-page creation in which static Web pages are created by executing queries on a SQL Server and formatting the output in HTML. This HTML page is placed on a Web server and can be accessed by a Web browser. Although the pages can be updated frequently, they are still static pages.

**Query**    A request sent to SQL Server to manipulate or retrieve data. Queries can have many formats, but the most common are known as SELECT queries.

**Query Analyzer**   An interactive SQL interface for Windows, this utility allows you to run all the same commands that the OSQL command-line utility does. It has an added advantage of being a Windows interface. This allows you to run multiple queries and view the results of such queries in their own separate windows.

**Query Optimizer**   In SQL Server, a mechanism that determines which index (or no index) will result in the lowest amount of logical I/O. This is done by evaluating the data and the restrictions that the query is requesting. With this information, the Query Optimizer estimates how many pages will be read for each possible scenario and chooses the scenario with the lowest estimated page I/O.

**RAID 0**   RAID 0 writes data across multiple hard-disk partitions in what is called a *stripe set*. This can greatly improve speed as multiple hard disks are working at the same time. RAID 0 can be implemented through the use of Windows NT software or on third-party hardware.

**RAID 1**   RAID 1 uses disk mirroring, which writes information to disk twice—once to the primary file, and once to the mirror.

**RAID 5**   RAID 5 (*striped with parity*) writes data to hard disk in stripe sets. Parity checksums will be written across all disks in the stripe set; they can be used to re-create information lost if a single disk in the stripe set fails.

**RAID 10**   RAID 10 (sometimes referred to as *RAID 1 + 0*) implements striping as in RAID 1and then mirrors the stripe sets.

**Remote Data Objects (RDO)**   A COM (Component Object Model) encapsulation of the ODBC API. RDO is a very thin layer of software that provides an object model for calling the ODBC API.

**Read-ahead**   A SQL Server mechanism for retrieving data from disk into cache before the data is actually needed. Separate read-ahead threads pull the data into cache, thus freeing the query thread to process the data that it finds in cache.

**READPIPE**   A command-line utility that can be used in conjunction with the MAKEPIPE utility to verify that the named pipes protocol is working properly.

**Registry**   A database of settings required and maintained by Windows NT and its components. The Registry contains all the configuration information used by the computer. It is stored as a hierarchical structure and is made up of keys, hives, and value entries. You can use the Registry Editor (REGEDT32 or REGEDIT) to change these settings.

**Relational database**   A database composed of tables that contain related data and other objects such as views, stored procedures, rules, and defaults. Also, a database of related information that supports the SQL query language. SQL Server databases are stored on database devices.

**Relational Database Management System (RDBMS)**   A database management system that supports true data, transactional integrity, and a server-side relational database engine. SQL Server is an RDBMS.

**Remote procedure calls (RPC)**   A network interprocess communication mechanism that allows an application to be distributed among many computers on the same network.

**Removable media database**   A SQL Server 7 database created on a removable medium, such as a CD-ROM or floppy disk. Removable media databases can be sent to another location and used from that location.

**Replication**   For SQL Server systems, the ability to automatically copy data and changes made to data from one server to another server. The data may not be copied immediately, so replication is used when "real-enough-time" data replication is needed. In replication, the change is made to one server and then sent out to one or more servers. Another type of replication, called *two-phase commit*, is used in conjunction with the MS-DTC to provide 100 percent synchronization 100 percent of the time.

**Roll back**   To cancel an entire transaction if any part of the transaction fails and undo any changes made to data.

**Row**   In a SQL Server database, a complete set of columns within a single table; it represents a single entity in a table.

**RPC**   See *remote procedure calls*.

**Rule** In a SQL Server database, an object that is assigned to a column so that data being entered must conform to standards you set. Rules can enforce domain integrity (a valid range of values). You can create rules to enable pattern matching, enable a range of values, or force a selection from a list of values.

**SA, sa (system administrator)** The default login ID for SQL Server; the global administrator of the SQL Server system. This ID has no restrictions on what it can do within the SQL Server environment. By default, anyone who has logged in to SQL Server will be able to use the sa account unless you change this.

**SAM** See *Security Accounts Manager*.

**Scheduling** The automation of tasks in SQL Server. Tasks that can be automated include backups, transfers, index creation and reorganization, and other maintenance procedures.

**Script** A saved query that has an .SQL extension by default. Scripts can be loaded, edited, and run from Query Analyzer or OSQL. Scripts can also be created by Enterprise Manager for existing databases and objects. Scripts are saved as ASCII text and generally have an .SQL extension.

**SCSI** See *Small Computer Systems Interface*.

**Security** Measures taken to secure a system against accidental or intentional loss of data, usually in the form of accountability procedures and use restriction. SQL Server security is based on the server, database, and database objects.

**Security Accounts Manager (SAM)** The module of the Windows NT Executive that authenticates a user name and password against a database of accounts, generating an access token that includes the user's permissions. Also known as the *Directory database*.

**Security identifier (SID)** A unique code that identifies a specific user or group to the Windows NT security system. Security identifiers contain a complete set of permissions for that user or group.

**Server**  A computer dedicated to servicing requests for resources from other computers on a network. Servers typically run network operating systems such as Windows NT Server. The basic functionality of a server can be added to by installed programs such as SQL Server.

**Service**  A process dedicated to implementing a specific function for other processes. Most Windows NT components are services. SQL Server is composed of two main services: MSSQLServer, which is the main database engine, and SQLServerAgent, which is the helper service. Additional services that make up the SQL Server include the MSDTC (Microsoft Distributed Transaction Coordinator), used for two-phase commits; and the Index server, which can allow SQL Server to run queries that use Web page indexes.

**Service Pack**  A group of bug fixes and enhancements offered by Microsoft on a (semi) regular basis. There are various Service Packs for different applications. As of this writing, the current Service Packs include Windows NT 3.51 Service Pack 5 and NT 4 Service Pack 4.

**Severity level**  For a system error, a component of the error message that provides information about the error. Levels from 0 to 10 are informational, 11 to 16 are user errors, 17 and 18 are resource problems, and 19 to 25 are fatal errors.

**SID**  See *security identifier*.

**Small Computer Systems Interface (SCSI)**  A high-speed, parallel-bus interface that connects hard disk drives, CD-ROM drives, tape drives, and many other peripherals to a computer.

**Sort order**  In SQL Server, an option that determines how the system will collate, store, and present data. The sort-order options available depend on the character set chosen. The most important sort-order descriptions include dictionary order, binary order, case-sensitive, and case-insensitive.

**SPID (server process ID)**  In SQL Server, the number that identifies a connection currently accessing the SQL Server machine. It is most often found red procedure.

**SQLServerAgent**  A SQL Server service that can take care of automating tasks on your server. The service includes managers that can handle alerts processing, tasking, event processing, and replication. It works for local automation with the local system account, but for many activities that occur over the network, it will need to be assigned a separate logon account that has administrative rights to the computer, as well as the *Log on as a Service* right.

**SQL-DMO (SQL Server Distributed Management Objects)** An interface that exposes COM-based objects that other programs can take advantage of to manipulate the SQL Server Engine and the SQLServerAgent utilities.

**SQL Enterprise Manager** The main SQL Server administration program provided with SQL Server 7. Multiple servers can be monitored and maintained by SQL Enterprise Manager. The Enterprise Manager works with SQL Server through the SQL-DMO.

**SQL login** See *login*.

**SQL Server administrator** The individual usually responsible for the day-to-day administration of SQL Server databases. The administrator takes over where the programmer left off.

**SQL Server books online** All the books that normally ship with Microsoft SQL Server, in an electronic format.

**SQL Server developer** The individual responsible for designing, programming, and populating SQL Server databases.

**SQL Server engine** The core service (MSSQLServer) that performs all query-related activities of SQL Server as well as the data storage and management.

**SQL Server Web Assistant** A SQL Server 7 utility that facilitates the creation of push Web pages. It can use the SQL Executive service to schedule the creation of the static Web pages in order to keep them more current.

**SQL trace** A SQL Server file created by the SQL Profiler utility used to monitor who is running what on a SQL Server machine. It is used primarily to audit security in SQL Server and for optimization purposes.

**SQLMaint** A SQL Server utility that can be used to create tasks that will take care of day-to-day administration of SQL Server. This includes automating backups, updating statistics, and rebuilding indexes. SQLMaint is configured by the Database Maintenance Plan Wizard.

**SQL Profiler**   A SQL Server utility that can be used to create trace files. Trace files can track all connections to SQL Server and what those connections are doing. These are often used for security and for optimization.

**Statement permissions**   SQL Server permissions that allow database users and groups to perform tasks that are not specific to objects. These permissions are generally related to the creation of certain database objects.

**Stored procedure**   In SQL Server, a set of Transact-SQL statements combined together to perform a single task or set of tasks. This object is like a macro, in that SQL code can be written and stored under a name. Invoking the name actually runs the code. Because stored procedures are precompiled, they run much more quickly and efficiently than regular queries do. There are three types of stored procedures: *system, user-defined,* and *extended. System stored procedures* are shipped with SQL Server and are denoted with an *sp_* prefix. These are typically found in the Master database. *User-defined stored procedures* can be registered with the system by the sa. *Extended stored procedures* work outside the context of SQL Server and generally have an *xp_* prefix. These are actually calls to DLLs.

**System stored procedure**   See *stored procedure.*

**System table**   Tables in relational databases that are used for administrative purposes by SQL Server. For example, in the Master database, the syslogins table, which holds SQL logins and passwords, is a system table. The Master database has two sets of system tables. The first set, known as the system catalog, tracks information about the configuration of SQL Server as a whole. Every database also has a database catalog made up of system tables that track configuration information about that particular database. This would include the objects in the database as well as the permissions granted on those objects. System tables generally begin with the "sys" prefix.

**Subscriber**   See *subscribing server.*

**Subscribing server**   In SQL Server replication, the server that gets data originating on the publishing server and updates one or more tables with both new and changed data.

**Suspect database**   A database that SQL Server believes to be corrupt or otherwise unavailable. A database can be marked suspect for a number of reasons, such as when a database device is offline or has been removed or renamed.

**Table**   In a SQL Server database, the object that contains rows and columns of data.

**Taskbar**   The gray bar at the bottom of the screen; it replaces the Task Manager in previous versions of Windows. The Taskbar holds the Start menu button and buttons that represent running programs It is used to switch between running programs and to choose the Start menu.

**Task Manager**   An application that manually views and can close running processes in Windows NT. In Windows 95/98, the Task Manager is called the *Close Program window*. Task Manager can also be used to view CPU and memory statistics. Press Ctrl+Alt+Del to launch the Task Manager.

**TCP**   See *Transmission Control Protocol*.

**TCP/IP**   See *Transmission Control Protocol/Internet Protocol*.

**TechNet**   Microsoft's monthly CD-ROM set that contains patches to existing programs, technical notes about issues (bugs), and white papers describing technologies in more detail. Most of the information in TechNet can also be found on Microsoft's Web site.

**Tempdb Database**   A SQL Server database reserved for storing temporary objects. These may be tables or stored procedures and can be created implicitly by SQL Server or explicitly by the user. The Tempdb database is also used to store server-side cursors.

**Thread**   A list of instructions running on a computer to perform a certain task. Each thread runs in the context of a process, which embodies the protected memory space and the environment of the threads. Multithreaded processes can perform more than one task at the same time.

**T-SQL**   See *Transact-SQL*.

**Transact-SQL (T-SQL)**   SQL is a database language, originally designed by IBM, that can be used not only for queries but also to build databases and manage security of the database engine. Microsoft SQL Server uses Transact-SQL (T-SQL), an enhanced version of the SQL language, as its native database language.

**Transaction**   A logical set of one or more commands that need to be processed as a whole in order to make a complete unit of work.

**Transaction SQL**   See *Transact-SQL*.

**Transaction log**   In SQL Server, a reserved area in the database that stores all changes made to the database. All modifications are written to the transaction log before writing to the database. The transaction log provides a durable record of database activity and can be used for recovery purposes.

**Transmission Control Protocol (TCP)**   A transport layer protocol that implements guaranteed packet delivery using the Internet Protocol (IP). See also *TCP/IP, Internet Protocol*.

**Transmission Control Protocol/Internet Protocol (TCP/IP)**   A suite of network protocols upon which the global Internet is based. TCP/IP is a general term that can refer either to the TCP and IP protocols used together or to the complete set of Internet protocols. TCP/IP is the default protocol for Windows NT.

**Trigger**   A SQL Server object that is a stored procedure. A trigger activates when data is added, updated, or deleted from a table. Triggers are used to ensure that tables linked by keys stay internally consistent with each other.

**Trusted connection**   See *integrated security*.

**Two-phase commit**   A type of data replication for SQL Server. With two-phase commit, two or more SQL Server computers either complete a transaction simultaneously or not at all. The Distributed Transaction Coordinator (MSDTC service) is designed to help manage these types of transactions.

**UNC**   See *Universal Naming Convention*.

**Uniform Resource Locator (URL)**   An Internet standard naming convention for identifying resources available via various TCP/IP application protocols. For example, `http://www.microsoft.com` is the URL for Microsoft's World Wide Web server site, and `ftp://ftp.microsoft.com` is a popular FTP site. A URL allows easy hypertext references to a particular resource from within a document or mail message.

**Universal Naming Convention (UNC)**   A multivendor, multiplatform convention for identifying shared resources on a network.

**User**   In SQL Server, a database-specific identifier that maps to a login and allows access to database resources. If a user is mapped to a login entry in the sysxlogins system table of the server, that login is allowed access to the database and database objects. Users are stored in the sysusers system table of each database.

**User name**   A user's account name in a login-authenticated system (such as Windows NT and SQL Server).

**VBSQL**   One of the interfaces provided with the native API of SQL Server. VBSQL is designed for use from Visual Basic and Visual Basic for Applications (VBA) applications.

**Vertical Partitioning**   In SQL Server replication, a method by which you can publish only certain columns of a table. This is often referred to as a *vertical filter*. See also *horizontal partitioning*.

**View**   In SQL Server, an object that is usually created to exclude certain columns from a table or to link two or more tables together. A view appears very much like a table to most users.

**Web browser**   An application that makes HTTP requests and formats the resultant HTML documents for the users.

**Web page**   Any HTML document on an HTTP server.

**Win16**   The set of application services provided by the 16-bit versions of Microsoft Windows: Windows 3.1 and Windows for Workgroups 3.11.

**Win32**   The set of application services provided by the 32-bit versions of Microsoft Windows: Windows 95/98 and Windows NT.

**Windows 3.11 for Workgroups**   The current 16-bit version of Windows for less-powerful, Intel-based personal computers; this system includes peer-networking services.

**Windows 95/98**   The current 32-bit version of Microsoft Windows for medium-range, Intel-based personal computers; this system includes peer-networking services, Internet support, and strong support for older DOS applications and peripherals. SQL Server 7 (Desktop version) can run on Windows 95/98.

**Windows NT**   The current 32-bit version of Microsoft Windows for powerful Intel, Alpha, PowerPC, or MIPS-based computers. The system includes peer-networking services, server-networking services, Internet client and server services, and a broad range of utilities. Windows NT Workstation is a version of Windows NT that is primarily used on desktop and laptop computers, but it can act as a server for up to 10 simultaneous connections.

Windows NT Server is a version of Windows NT that is primarily used as a file/application server that can theoretically have thousands of simultaneous users connected to it. Windows NT Server Enterprise Edition is designed for large corporations and supports more powerful hardware.

SQL Server 7 (Desktop or regular version) runs on either version of Windows NT. SQL Server 7 Enterprise Edition requires Windows NT Enterprise Edition.

**Workgroup**   In Microsoft networks, a collection of related computers, such as a department, that don't require the uniform security and coordination of a domain. Workgroups are characterized by decentralized management as opposed to the centralized management that domains use. See also *domain*.

**World Wide Web (WWW)**   A collection of Internet servers providing hypertext-formatted documents for Internet clients running Web browsers. The World Wide Web provided the first easy-to-use graphical interface for the Internet and is largely responsible for the Internet's explosive growth.

**WWW**   See *World Wide Web*.

# Index

**Note to the Reader:** Page numbers in **bold** indicate the principal discussion of a topic or the definition of a term. Page numbers in *italic* indicate illustrations.

## B

# E

## R

# SYBEX BOOKS ON THE WEB

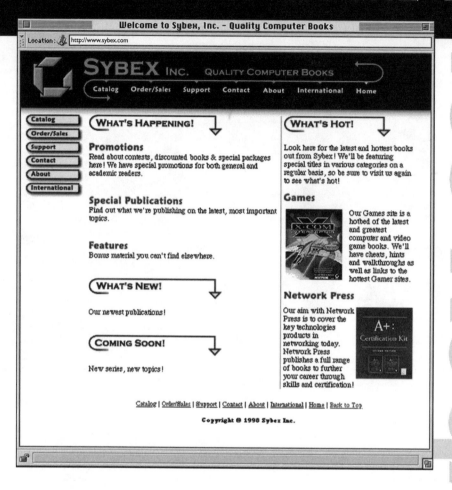

At the dynamic and informative Sybex Web site, you can:

- view our complete online catalog
- preview a book you're interested in
- access special book content
- order books online at special discount prices
- learn about Sybex

## www.sybex.com

# MCSE CORE REQUIREMENT STUDY GUIDES FROM NETWORK PRESS

Sybex's Network Press presents updated and expanded second editions
of the definitive study guides for MCSE candidates.

ISBN: 0-7821-2220-5
704pp; 7¹/₂" x 9"; Hardcover
$49.99

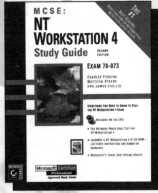

ISBN: 0-7821-2223-X
784pp; 7¹/₂" x 9"; Hardcover
$49.99

ISBN: 0-7821-2222-1
832pp; 7¹/₂" x 9"; Hardcover
$49.99

ISBN: 0-7821-2221-3
704pp; 7¹/₂" x 9"; Hardcover
$49.99

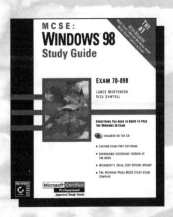

ISBN: 0-7821-2373-2
800pp; 7¹/₂" x 9"; Hardcover
$49.99

A $50.00 SAVINGS!

MCSE Core Requirements
Box Set
ISBN: 0-7821-2245-0
4 hardcover books;
3,024pp total; $149.96

Microsoft Certified
Professional
*Approved Study Guide*

NETWORK PRESS
SYBEX ®

## STUDY GUIDES FOR THE MICROSOFT CERTIFIED SYSTEMS ENGINEER EXAMS

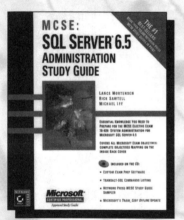